D0374220

North with Franklin
The Lost Journals of James Fitzjames

"A suspenseful and enjoyable read."—Booklist

"*Wilson's fictional account has an authentic ring...I grew increasingly fond of Fitzjames, a decent and brave man. As the ghastly end to the adventure approaches, Fitzjames' composure cracks: I suddenly found my heart as well as my head engaged by this story.*"—Charlotte Gray, The National Post

"*...a richly re-imagined fable which goes far beyond anything the historical record alone might suggest, though it is carefully researched and never discordant with the glimmers history has left us...We do not so much hear as overhear [Fitzjames's] voice, and like some future explorer coming upon a frozen cache of letters, we bring our own sense of elegy to a correspondence that we know in advance cannot have ended happily...For readers of historical fiction who yearn to sojourn in those 'regions of thick-ribb'd ice' there could be few better companions than Wilson's James Fitzjames.*"—Russell A. Potter, The Arctic Book Review

"*Wilson has managed to make his invented journal seem authentic and his account of the ill-fated adventures seem plausible...one reads on, fascinated, to the bitter end.*"—The Globe and Mail

"*North With Franklin is as close an account of the expedition's fate as we are likely to have, at least until Captain Fitzjames's real journals are found under some Arctic cairn.*"—Crawford Kilian, author of The Fall of the Republic and Icequake

"*Meticulously researched...North With Franklin is both entertaining and thought-provoking for readers of historical fiction. Highly recommended.*"—Canadian Book Review Annual

"*I am helpless before this compelling story. Knowing what happened never makes the story dull or predictable, unless it is the predictability of high tragedy brought on by human error and hubris. You may not be such an incurable romantic as I, but I am prepared to wager that you too will be captivated by Wilson's narrative and find yourself, as I was, reading eagerly to find out when James will record what we know is coming next.*" - Sherrill Grace, Canadian Literature

Also by John Wilson

NOVELS

Heretic: The Heretic's Secret book I

Quest: The Heretic's Secret book II

Rebirth: The Heretic's Secret book III

The Heretic's Secret (single volume edition)

The Alchemist's Dream

The Third Act

The Ruined City

Graves of Ice

Shot at Dawn

Where Soldiers Lie

And in the Morning

Germania

Flames of the Tiger

Four Steps to Death

Lost Cause

Lost in Spain

NON-FICTION

Lands of Lost Content: A Memoir

Ghost Mountains and Vanished Oceans: North America from Birth to Middle Age

John Franklin: Traveller on Undiscovered Seas

Norman Bethune: A Life of Passionate Conviction

A Soldier's Sketchbook: The Illustrated First World War Diary of R.H Rabjohn

North with Franklin

The Lost Journals of James Fitzjames

John Wilson

North with Franklin: TheLost Journals of James Fitzjames

Copyright © 1999 and 2020 by John Wilson.

All rights reserved. No part of this publication may be reproduced or transmitted in any form or by any means, electronic or mechanical, including photocopying, recording or by any information storage and retrieval system now known or to be invented, without permission in writing from the publisher except in the case of brief quotations embodied in critical articles and reviews.

This book is a work of fiction. References to historical places, events and persons are used fictitiously. All other places, events and characters are the products of the author's imagination and any resemblance to actual places, events or persons is coincidental.

Library and Archives Canada Cataloguing in Publication

Wilson, John (John Alexander), 1951 -
North with Franklin: The Lost Journals of James Fitzjames/John Wilson

ISBN (paperback) 978-0-9877065-7-7

Cover photography and design by John Wilson

Originally published in 1999 by Fitzhenry and Whiteside

For Elizabeth and Jenifer, who both had to wait behind while Fitzjames and I took this journey.

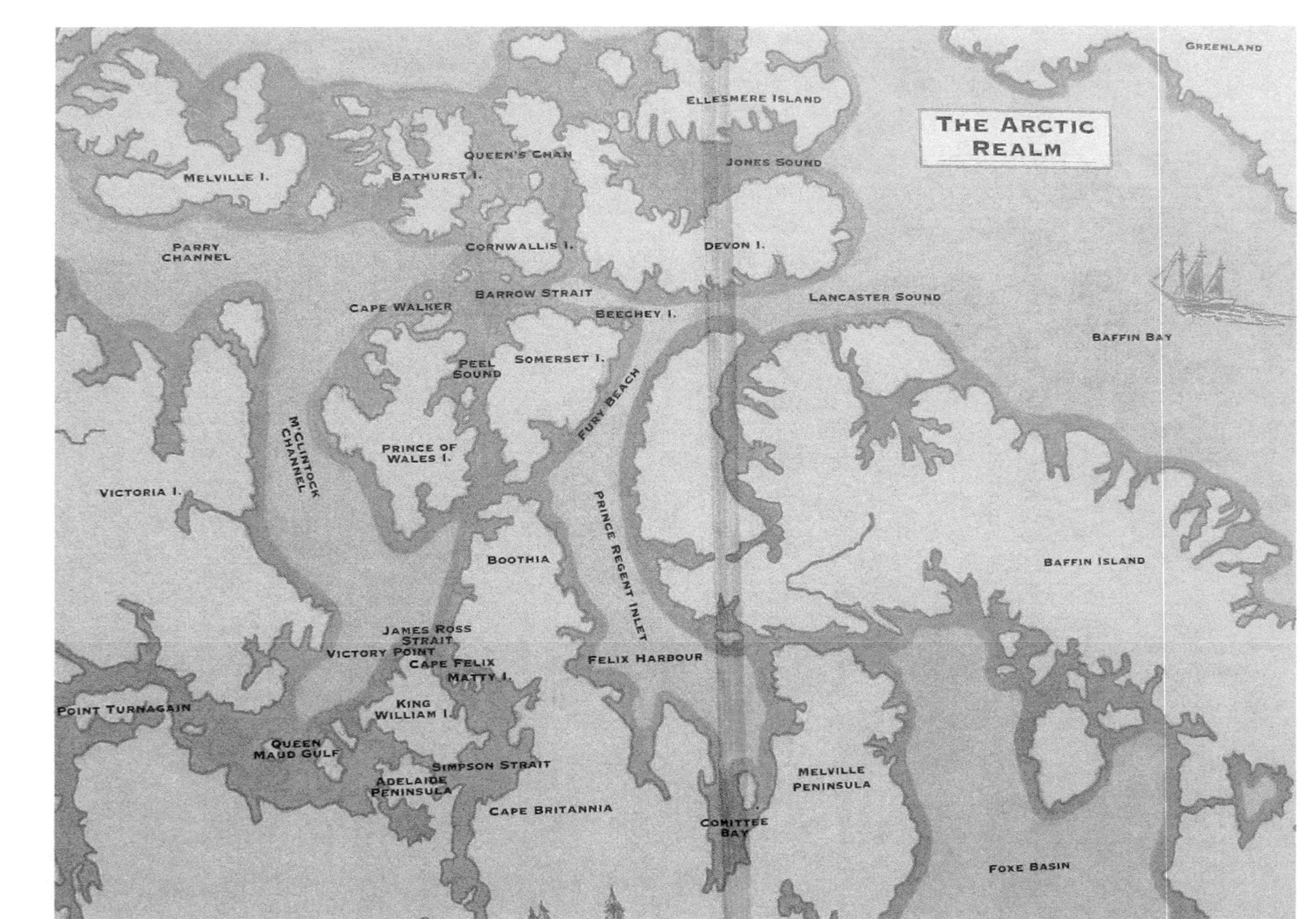
THE ARCTIC REALM
Greenland
Ellesmere Island
Jones Sound
Queen's Chan
Melville I.
Bathurst I.
Parry Channel
Cornwallis I.
Devon I.
Barrow Strait
Lancaster Sound
Cape Walker
Beechey I.
Baffin Bay
Peel Sound
Somerset I.
Fury Beach
M'Clintock Channel
Prince of Wales I.
Victoria I.
Prince Regent Inlet
Boothia
Baffin Island
James Ross Strait
Victory Point
Cape Felix
Matty I.
Felix Harbour
Point Turnagain
King William I.
Queen Maud Gulf
Simpson Strait
Adelaide Peninsula
Melville Peninsula
Cape Britannia
Comittee Bay
Foxe Basin

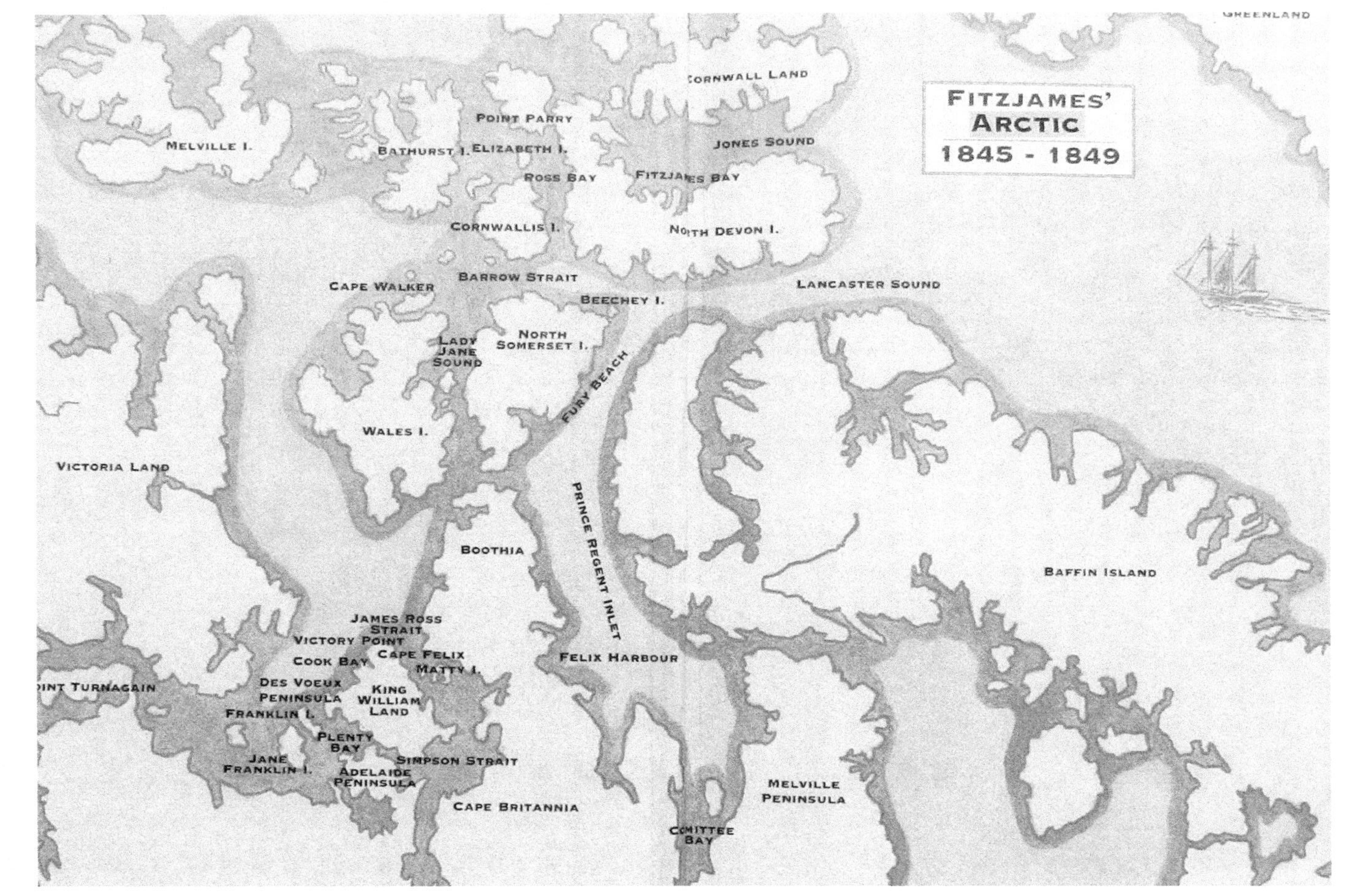

FITZJAMES' ARCTIC
1845 - 1849
GREENLAND
CORNWALL LAND
MELVILLE I.
POINT PARRY
BATHURST I.
ELIZABETH I.
JONES SOUND
ROSS BAY
FITZJAMES BAY
CORNWALLIS I.
NORTH DEVON I.
BARROW STRAIT
CAPE WALKER
BEECHEY I.
LANCASTER SOUND
LADY JANE SOUND
NORTH SOMERSET I.
FURY BEACH
WALES I.
VICTORIA LAND
PRINCE REGENT INLET
BOOTHIA
BAFFIN ISLAND
JAMES ROSS STRAIT
VICTORY POINT
CAPE FELIX
COOK BAY
MATTY I.
FELIX HARBOUR
POINT TURNAGAIN
DES VOEUX PENINSULA
KING WILLIAM LAND
FRANKLIN I.
PLENTY BAY
JANE FRANKLIN I.
SIMPSON STRAIT
ADELAIDE PENINSULA
CAPE BRITANNIA
MELVILLE PENINSULA
COMITTEE BAY

Prologue

The Historical Background

On April 25, 1848, three men huddled in a wind-blown tent in one of the coldest, most remote places on earth. They were composing a message. One had just trekked four miles to get the paper; another dictated; the third laboriously thawed the ink and wrote the words. Outside, as an incessant wind blew mournfully between piles of clothing and supplies, 102 British officers, sailors and marines made final preparations for a desperate escape. Many were sick. Not one would live to see his home again.

The man writing the message was James Fitzjames, Captain of Her Majesty's Ship *Erebus* and second in command of what was left of Sir John Franklin's once vaunted Arctic Expedition. What was going through his mind? Certainly, the irony of the situation, as the men struggled to survive at a place called Victory Point, would not have been lost on him. Perhaps he also recalled the hope and joy which had surrounded the expedition's departure from England almost three years earlier.

The date was May 19, 1845. At 10:30 a.m., the *Erebus* and her sister ship, *Terror*, slipped from the dock at Greenhithe on the Thames River. Amongst their supplies the two ships carried 136,656 pounds of flour, 32,224 pounds of beef, 3,684 gallons of concentrated spirits—enough for three winters' survival in the High Arctic. Also on board were the aspirations and expectations of an entire nation.

* * *

Eighteen-forty-five was a heady time to be alive. Queen Victoria had been on the throne only eight years. England was on the verge of controlling the greatest empire the world had ever seen. It already included Upper and Lower Canada, Cape Colony, New Zealand and coastal strips of Australia. India was but a conglomeration of conquered areas and princely states run as a vast commercial enterprise by the East India Company. Within 50 years, Victoria would be declared Empress of India; and the dominion of Canada, Australia and vast areas of Africa, as well as Malaysia, Singapore and a host of smaller colonies would be added to her Empire.

British ships ruled the trade routes, bringing raw materials to factories in the teeming cities and carrying manufactured goods back to the colonies for sale. Great inventions were announced almost daily. Steam ships and trains carried people and goods farther and faster in more comfort and safety than ever before. The telegraph would soon allow near instant communication between distant points. Every change appeared geared for the better. Surely, the industrial revolution would lead to a perfect world in, at most, a generation or two.

Britain stood supreme. Its military forces had remained unchallenged on land and sea since Waterloo and Trafalgar. Anything must have seemed possible for a man of Fitzjames' class and background. Only two years earlier, Charles Napier arrived in India with only £2 in his pocket and conquered the entire nation of Sind. Social relations, although rigid by today's standards, were not yet as fossilized as they would be at century's end. There was still room enough in the world for an idealistic young adventurer to make his mark.

Of course, most of the men on the *Erebus* were not of Fitzjames' class, and must have maintained quite a different outlook on that bright May morning in 1845. The Chartist revolt had only recently pushed Britain to the brink of revolution, its failure only serving to entrench class divisions and delay democracy. Major cholera and typhus epidemics still swept through the filthy, overcrowded streets of major industrial cities. Medical practices, where available, were brutal. Labour was both grindingly monotonous and dangerous. For many, escape meant the even less pleasant system of workhouses and debtors' prisons or the acceptance of the equally harsh conditions then prevalent aboard the ships of Her Majesty's Navy.

In 1845, the Industrial Revolution was at its height. Though it supplied advantages to a few, it brought virtual enslavement to most. The great movement from farm to factory was well underway and hundreds of thousands of new workers in London, Manchester and Liverpool saw little of the promise that Fitzjames did. What they did see was an incredible burst of exploration. Many in Britain felt it their nation's God-given duty to explore and civilize the remote corners of the world, and they supported this goal with enthusiasm. If the working classes could not escape their dark slums and indentured lives, they could at least glimpse a different world through the adventures recounted in newspapers and exhibitions.

Every new geographic and scientific discovery was greeted with wild enthusiasm, and people from all walks of life flocked to see the latest wonders demonstrated and the most recently discovered animal or "savage" displayed. In an era when distant travel took months, even years, the remote corners of the globe were the early Victorians' equivalent of the moon.

* * *

John Ross made the first voyage around Baffin Bay in 1818, and his reports encouraged a steady stream of explorers to head north by sea and land. Parry, Back, John Ross and his nephew James, Simpson, and Franklin himself, had all contributed greatly to the knowledge of the north polar lands, and James Ross had spent four years on an epic voyage circumnavigating Antarctica. Much had been achieved by many remarkable men. But one great goal eluded them all—the Northwest Passage. Frobisher, Drake, Hudson, and Cook had all searched, but none had found it.

By 1845, few believed there was a commercially viable route to the Orient through the Arctic waters north of Canada. Only some sixty miles (100 kilometres) of the Northwest Passage actually remained unexplored and sailors' stories of the harshness of the Arctic climate discouraged most from venturing there for commercial gain. Nonetheless, the lure remained. The completion of the Northwest Passage became a goal in itself, much as the attainment of the south pole would become for Robert Falcon Scott sixty years later. The search captured the public's imagination, but the discovery itself, would be pointless.

Yet, despite the lure of the Northwest Passage, it was science that really drove Franklin's 1845 expedition. Magnetism was a relatively poorly understood phenomena which both fascinated and baffled the scientific community. Both the north and south magnetic poles had been located by James Ross in 1831 and 1841 respectively, and Britain, with her sweeping empire, was in an ideal position to complete a network of global readings in an effort to understand magnetism's planetary significance. A comprehensive suite of accurate readings taken throughout the Arctic would provide a significant piece of this network. Crozier had taken readings with Ross in the Antarctic. Fitzjames would do it with Franklin in the Arctic. A vast collection of botanical, geological, and zoological specimens and astronomical, meteorological, and oceanographic readings could also be collected by an expedition of this size. The potential to dramatically increase scientific knowledge in a large number of fields was therefore very real.

The Franklin expedition that sailed north in 1845 was the greatest and most thoroughly prepared Arctic expedition ever. It would fill in a huge blank spot on the map. But perhaps more important, Franklin and his men were a symbol of escape to those working classes struggling to survive in smoke-blackened factories and squalid, filthy tenements. The vast icy wastes of the north were pure, clean and filled with exotic animals and people.

What better place for the Dickensian imagination to sail?

So, in addition to the 129 men and three years' worth of supplies, the *Erebus* and *Terror* carried the vicarious hopes of thousands. This was the ultimate voyage of discovery, the final proof that anything was possible. A tiny bit of Franklin's success would belong to every Briton who cheered him on. What a shock then, when great expectations began to crumble in the face of the inescapable fact that something had gone horribly wrong.

What did go wrong? What led Fitzjames and the others to desperately abandon their ships which had been their homes for three years, scrawl a hasty note and disappear into the mists of controversy?

The possibility of complete disaster must have been unimaginable to the people back home. No polar expedition before or after Franklin had departed England with such high expectations. Failure was not considered. It would be a great adventure and the dangers only served to heighten the excitement. Franklin's officers universally expressed naive, almost boyish enthusiasm in their letters sent home from Greenland. They believed the voyage would take only one or at most two seasons. The ships left Disco, on the coast of Greenland, on July 12, 1845, and were last seen late that month by the crews of two whaling ships as they lay anchored to an iceberg, awaiting a fair wind to carry them across Baffin Bay and into Lancaster Sound and the beginning of the Northwest Passage proper. They were never seen by European eyes again.

As no word of Franklin had been received in Britain by the autumn of 1847, the government made plans to mount relief expeditions the following summer. Concern reached a peak in 1849 when not one of these expeditions returned with any news of Franklin's whereabouts. Public prayers were said. Twenty-thousand pounds were offered to anyone who rescued the missing officers and men. In 1850, five separate expeditions comprising thirteen vessels were engaged in the search. The effort led to the discovery of Franklin's first wintering site at Beechey Island. This site was important but, oddly, gave no clue as to the subsequent route taken by the original expedition. Thus, the searchers fanned out through the Arctic and, although they added much to the Admiralty Chart, discovered little of Franklin.

The next piece in the puzzle was provided in October of 1854 by Dr. John Rae on his return from an overland expedition to Boothia Peninsula. Although Rae was not specifically searching for Franklin, he collected much telling information including artifacts and stories from local Inuit. The artifacts included the medal Franklin was wearing in the daguerreotype taken of him shortly before he sailed. The stories Rae collected told of disaster, starvation and, least acceptable to Victorian sensibilities, cannibalism. Rae was shouted down by leading contemporaries for supporting the tales told by Arctic "savages." Charles Dickens asserted on more than one occasion that no British sailor could ever sink to such depths —merely to stay alive. However, Franklin's ultimate fate was not questioned. The Admiralty declared the explorers dead. The case was closed in January, 1856.

Not so willing to give up the search was Franklin's widow, Lady Jane, a strong personality who had been badgering the navy for years to increase its rescue efforts. Using her own money, she outfitted a small expedition led by Francis McClintock. It sailed from Aberdeen in the yacht Fox on July 2, 1857, but was beset in ice and drifted the full length of Baffin Bay during the winter of 1857-8. After a second summer, the party settled into winter quarters in the ice off the eastern end of Bellot Strait (referred to by Fitzjames as Crozier Strait).

In the spring of 1859, McClintock led a sledging party to King William Island, the area indicated in Rae's stories as the scene of disaster. Here, McClintock collected many artifacts and Inuit stories. Along the western shore of the island he discovered the first *in-situ* evidence of Franklin's fate after 1846: abandoned boats, discarded equipment, and weathered bones. At Victory Point, the farthest west attained by James Ross in 1830, McClintock's men found a huge cache of supplies: piles of clothes four feet high, complete medical chests, and lightning rods. They also found Fitzjames' note, sealed in a tin can and buried in a cairn of stones.

The note was actually two separate messages. The first had been written in May of 1847 and had been deposited by Lieutenant Graham Gore as he led Mate Charles Frederick Des Voeux and six men on a sledging expedition to complete the last sixty miles of the Northwest Passage. It ended with the cheery declaration, "All Well."

The second message, written around the margins of the first, had been composed in the wind-blown tent in April, 1848. *All was not well.* Franklin was dead, a bare three weeks after Gore built his cairn. So were eight other officers, including Gore and probably Des Voeux, and fifteen men. Crozier was in command and both ships had been abandoned in the ice. The 105 survivors were ashore and, as Crozier added—apparently as an afterthought below his own signature—his men were striking out to the south for Back's Fish River the following day.

The second message was written in appalling conditions by desperate men. For almost a century and a half, people have examined it in detail hoping to discover the real intentions of Crozier and Fitzjames. Why were the ships abandoned so early in the year? Had they been crushed? Why did the crew bring such an assortment of apparently useless things with them? Why were they heading to Back's Fish River and, presumably, on across the vast Barren Lands to some distant fur-trading post?

Everyone had their own answers to these questions: the officers were inflexible, hidebound martinets incapable of adjusting to circumstance; the canned food was bad and the men were starving; scurvy was rampant; and most recently, the canned food was contaminated with lead, the ingestion of which caused dementia and impaired the officers' judgment. Despite all the speculation, no-one seriously challenged McClintock's original interpretation. He held that the crews abandoned useless equipment as they struggled south, weakening and dying as they went. This explained the abandoned supplies, scattered bodies and boats. Later discoveries of more bones and abandoned boats at Starvation Cove on the Adelaide Peninsula merely indicated the farthest reach of the desperate men. McClintock's arguments were neat and tidy.

Except things were not so clear cut. Why was the boat sled that McClintock discovered pointing back to the ships and not, more logically, the other way? How did Lieutenant Irving come to be buried at Victory Point when he was obviously alive when the crews set off to the south? (Irving was the officer in the tent who had trekked four miles to fetch the piece of writing paper.) Why did so many of the Inuit stories collected by Charles Francis Hall in the 1860's not fit the common belief that all the sailors died on King William Island in 1848?

It was a terrible, mysterious tragedy that fired the Victorian imagination. The hopes that had gone with Franklin were lost with his ships. How was such a thing possible? The nation's best had been found wanting. Courage combined with the latest technology had not been enough. Perhaps the future was not so easily tamed. Not until the sinking of the *Titanic* six decades later would England's confidence in technology's control over nature again be so shaken.

But what of the personal tragedies? There were, after all, 129 men and 129 losses. Of Sir John Franklin, we know a great deal. He was already famous in 1845. But of Fitzjames, we know less.

* * *

James Fitzjames was born on July 27, 1813 in Rio de Janeiro. Many conflicting tales surround his mysterious background, but he may well have been the illegitimate son of Sir James Gambier, a minor diplomat in Brazil. As an infant, Fitzjames was given into the care of the Reverend Robert Coningham and his wife, who accepted the boy and provided for him as if he were one of his own. Coningham was moderately well-off and well connected to the ruling class of his day. In fact, it was Coningham who secured James his first navy posting in 1825 and whose connections hastened his nephew's early advancement. James developed a close relationship with Coningham's son, William, whom he regarded as a brother and with whom he corresponded throughout his life. It is to William's young wife Elizabeth, "the wife of him I love best," that the Fitzjames journal is addressed.

Fitzjames joined the navy as a ship's boy where he served unremarkably for nine years on various vessels and progressively rose in rank from midshipman to mate. (A young man destined for a commission learned the ropes as a Ship's Boy. This was different from a Cabin Boy who was essentially an officer's servant and could rise no higher than a senior crew member.) In 1834, he was selected to join the Chesney expedition to the Euphrates to ascertain whether the river was navigable and could hence form a link in the overland route to India, a vital Imperial artery in the days before the Suez Canal. While in Liverpool, preparing to set off for the Middle East, Fitzjames risked his life in extremely dangerous waters to save a drowning Customs House official. He was granted the Freedom of the City of Liverpool in consequence and awarded silver medals by the London Shipwreck Institute and the Royal Humane Society.

The Euphrates Expedition proved no less exciting for Fitzjames. It involved the extremely difficult and dangerous transport of two disassembled steamers across the Syrian Desert, and their assembly and subsequent descent of the river. One steamer was wrecked on the journey, but the other with Fitzjames aboard reached the Persian Gulf safely.

Fitzjames was promoted to the rank of Lieutenant on his return and was posted to H.M.S. *Ganges*. He took part in the bombardment of Muhammed Ali's coastal fortresses in Syria and the Lebanon in 1840. During this time, he served with James Walter Fairholme, a man he much admired. In May 1841, Fitzjames sailed for the Opium War in China aboard the flagship H.M.S. *Cornwallis*. He served with distinction in this conflict, commanding a rocket brigade at Chusan and participating in the storming of the Bogue Forts. He received a wound at the capture of Ching-Kiang-Foo.

Fitzjames made the acquaintance of several officers in China, including George Henry Hodgson, Charles Frederick Des Voeux, Henry Thomas Dundas Le Vesconte, and Surgeon Stephen Samuel Stanley These men would later accompany him to the Arctic. On December 23, 1842, Fitzjames was promoted to the rank of Commander and appointed to H.M.S. *Clio* in which he served until October 1844 with Le Vesconte as his second in command.

After leaving the *Clio*, Fitzjames was recommended for overall command of the upcoming Arctic expedition but was passed over due to his youth and lack of experience in icebound waters. He was instead appointed commander of H.M.S. *Erebus*, third in command after Franklin and Crozier. Crozier was absent in Italy during the early part of 1845 and Fitzjames was given the task of selecting and recommending officers and crew. His election accounts for the preponderance of his friends and previous shipmates among the officers of the *Erebus*.

Fitzjames' career was remarkably successful given the overabundance of naval officers in the years following the Napoleonic Wars. Most officers languished at home on half-pay with little or no hope of finding a post or receiving promotion. Yet Fitzjames was continuously employed and advanced fairly rapidly. In fact, he was promoted to full Captain in December 1845 after he sailed for the Arctic. Had he survived, he would undoubtedly have experienced a long and distinguished career in the navy.

The conditions on board the *Erebus* and *Terror* would have been better than on the larger ships of the line Fitzjames was used to. There would have been overcrowding, certainly, especially at the start of the voyage. But the ships' complements were small enough (sixty-seven aboard *Erebus* and sixty-two aboard *Terror* on leaving Greenland), and the task so focused, that a certain camaraderie would have developed. The crews were also hand-picked. Many of the sailors were whalers from the ports of Hull and Peterhead or the Orkney Islands. Contact between officers and men ("people" as they were called on navy ships) was also probably more prevalent than on most other vessels, and Franklin had a reputation for keeping a relaxed, easy-going command. Yet, class barriers, especially between rough sailors and the young, educated officers, would have been surmountable only on the most superficial levels. Nonetheless, all on board would have been bound by a common feeling that they were participating in a great endeavour.

Written records by sailors are extremely rare, but the officers of the day wrote voluminously. James Fitzjames was a prolific letter writer throughout his life, recording his hopes and experiences for his family and friends in England. In fact, his journal to Elizabeth is written in the form of an extended letter. The first part he sent back in the supply ship from Disco. The rest was lost with the expedition. The Inuit told Hall that, in the wake of the disaster, they found papers beside the dead Europeans scattered over their lands. With no written language, no use for the papers, and no knowledge of their import, the Inuit gave the letters to their children as playthings. These were soon destroyed. Perhaps this was the fate of Fitzjames' journals. Or perhaps they lie wrapped in canvas in a shallow pit beside a collapsed shelter and some lonely bones.

In any case, they once existed and might have read much like this book.

* * *

North with Franklin has been a labour of love. From the moment I read the surviving fragment of the journals of James Fitzjames, I knew I would have to tell the rest of his story. From the onset, I felt a close kinship to the man. I would have liked little more than to meet him over a glass of port and discuss his world and mine. So I read his letters and the letters of his friends. I read the books he would have read and marvelled at the inventions that changed his world. I researched his culture and immersed myself in his life and times. I read the stories the Inuit told Hall and others of their encounters with Franklin's men alive and dead. James Fitzjames became my friend. The writing of this journal, more than a century and a half after he dipped his quill pen into ink, has been more than recreation, it was rediscovery; the uncovering of a voice long silent and a glimpse into the mind of a man who lived and died in a world very different from our own.

The journal you hold begins when Fitzjames leaves Greenland and offers a final good-bye to civilization. It is speculation based on what we know, with one major liberty taken. Scattered through the first few weeks of the chronology, and out of context, are segments of the original journal Fitzjames sent to Elizabeth from Disco. A sanitized version was published in *The Nautical Magazine* in 1852 and as a pamphlet by William Coningham around this same time. The original, in Fitzjames' hand, exists on microfilm in the Scott Polar Research Institute in Cambridge, England.

I include these extracts for two reasons. First, to keep me honest and ensure that I remain true to the original voice. Second, to allow Fitzjames his say, directly. His story and his words, however few, must be given a place.

Bringing Fitzjames back to life was my primary purpose but, implicit in this task was an attempt to explain the mysterious fate of Franklin and his men. For this purpose I used the published Inuit testimony where it conformed to a coherent narrative. The trip to Back's Fish River was not an escape, but a desperate hunting trip to secure food and keep scurvy at bay. Despite illness still haunting the sailors (probably due to advanced lead poisoning amongst some of the men), one of the ships was remanned by a portion of the crew and sailed farther south. Not everyone died in 1848 and some, at least, escaped as far as the western shores of Prince Regent Inlet, the spot where Fitzjames died in 1849. Since this is Fitzjames' story, I make no attempt to explain what happened to the other parties who split off in 1848.

Fitzjames leaves the journal wrapped in sailcloth and cached somewhere on the western shore of Prince Regent Inlet in the summer of 1849. It is conceivable that such a document could survive the years. That no physical remains have been found is less important than the survival of the voice of James Fitzjames. Rediscovered here, it gives us a window through which we can glimpse the flickering ghosts of a vanished time.

This is a work of plausible fiction, although the recent discoveries of the wrecks of the Erebus and Terror and the ongoing recovery of the wealth of artifacts on board each vessel will undoubtedly radically change our perspective on the course of the disaster. Since my primary objects are, to bring Fitzjames to life on the page and to create an engaging narrative, I have made no attempt to update the story from the original text published first in 1999. Recent discoveries would only require minor changes and would, in any case, certainly be overtaken by future research into the wrecks. If my tale is true to my friend, James Fitzjames, I am happy.

Summer, 1845

HER MAJESTY'S SHIP EREBUS, OFF THE COAST OF GREENLAND,
SUNDAY, JULY 13, 1845, 11 P.M.

My Dearest Elizabeth,
We are begun. All the endless preparation is done. The supplies are loaded and we have said a last farewell to civilization, or what passes for it in this barren land. We weighed anchor on the tide last night, beneath the most beautiful clear sky you could imagine. The sea was as flat as a glass and peppered with a most remarkable assortment of icebergs which shone on the horizon like a twelfth cake with each occasional gleam of the midnight sun. This really is the most extraordinary of lands we have entered.

Around eight the wind picked up and has moved us quite briskly northwards all day. There was some discussion before we sailed as to whether we should head straight across Baffin's Bay to Lancaster Sound or sail north and around the top of the ice. A Dane from Lievely who had married an Esquimaux came over to visit us at Disco and indicated that this was the one of the mildest seasons and earliest summers ever known in these lands. We are presented with a very open year for ice, but the pack—as a solid mass of sea ice is called—can still be a formidable obstacle in the centre of the bay.

It was decided that we should sail north along the coast in the direction of Cape York and yet be prepared to take advantage of any favourable winds or intelligence from the whalers we shall meet. It is generally agreed that we shall be in time if we reach Lancaster Sound by the first of August or thereabouts. Everyone is very sanguine about our prospects and I wrote to William that I would shake hands with him on February 22nd next.

Yet, I cannot stop myself from wishing for some small hindrance to keep us in this land for a winter—we have ample supplies for three years and our scientific work would benefit greatly from the extra time. I do not think one can get to know this place without experiencing it when the sun is both never down and eternally set. So if I am not back with you as my promise to William, do not fret for I shall be enjoying myself in complete security and comfort.

My dear sister—for thus I think of you just as I think of William as my brother—and wife of him I love best; I leave you knowing you as a person and no longer a mere description in one of William's letters. I feel the parting from you full as much as from William—and of course the children. I am often to be found taking much pleasure in the remembrance of my little friends. My time on land between the *Clio*'s return and this leaving was so brief, and busy, that I scarce had time to do one quarter of the things I had promised myself. My memories are too much filled with details of supplies and crew lists and the like. However, foremost in my mind is the short time I had to become acquainted with Elisabeth and Robert. Their visit to the *Erebus* at Greenhithe breathed a fresh draught of life into the dull air of a sailor at dock with their eternal questions concerning every knot and billhook they espied. In particular, Elisabeth's opinion that the rigging made the ship look as if it were held in the web of a spider and her scream of fright when she stumbled over a coil of rope which she mistook for a snake shall make me eternally look upon the tools of my trade with fresh eyes.

Perhaps you will think I am foolish to care for little children—but so it is. I was as much pleased with little Elisabeth's expressions of regard—exaggerated though they were—as I should have been with the more studied and carefully phrased, but perhaps less genuine expressions, of grown up people.

I hope to celebrate Elisabeth's birthday (this one or the next) in Behring's Strait or close by it. Little Robert, the son and heir, will be three or four by then and I promise I shall find time to devote to my Godfatherly duties.

After all your anxiety that I should keep a journal for your especial perusal and here I am already rambling on and wearing out the porcupine quill. But I have never been one to waste the hours lying abed more than necessary and can always find some dark corner of the night in which to put down my thoughts. Indeed, I have managed to keep up my official journal which I will submit to the Admiralty upon our return, but it is dry piece of work talking in the same official voice of all our doings from the weather to a man being flogged. Not fit reading for a lady fair, so I shall use it only to refresh my overfilled memory. These writings will be mere notes to please you, of such things as may strike me, either in the form of a letter, or in any other form that might at the time suit my fancy. So I do not feel obliged to fill a page every day. To keep my thoughts fresh I shall not read over what I have written, so you must excuse all inaccuracies.

And so having made a beginning and my excuses I will to bed. I wind up this and call it a letter just for the sake of adding that I am as ever your affectionate friend and almost brother, James Fitzjames.

July 14—A fine day and we make steady progress. The air hereabouts has the clarity of desert air, but with a cold sharpness I have not experienced before. It is most refreshing to both nose and eye, imparting a hard-clarity to the views which I have never perceived through the soft, moisture-laden air of England.

The coast of Greenland is in sight—a rugged place of black rock cut by white furrows and ravines of snow and some of the most magnificent glaciers the equal of any in Switzerland. The whole is canopied with a mass of clouds and mist. In bold relief, at the foot of this black mass, the most fantastically formed and perfectly white bergs shine out. Grand scenery, but desolate beyond expression.

Our time at Disco was longer than we had hoped, the off-loading of the transport being a more arduous undertaking than expected—but we used the time to advantage. We commenced by beating up to the Whalefish Islands, which are in the bay formed by the south end of Disco and the mainland. There we planned to clear the transport. By some mistake, Reid, our Ice-Master, fancied we were wrong, and led us away up to the end of the bay, thirty miles to the mouth of Waigat Channel. It was not an auspicious beginning for our expert on the ice conditions of this land, but no harm was done. In fact, the wind favoured us right around the bay which was full of the most glorious icebergs packed close along the shore. But for the loss of a morning, it would have been the most delightful sail. I went on board the *Terror* that evening, and found Crozier aware of the mistake. He fancied we had given up the idea of going to the Whalefish Islands. It was around midnight that we finally ran into a bay. Of course, the sun was up all this time, it being almost as bright at midnight as at noon.

We were met by five of the local Esquimaux, in the smallest possible canoes, all in a row. The two going ahead kept near the ship and piloted her into a safe place among the rocks, where we moored in a channel just four times the ship's breadth, and perfectly landlocked. Feeling brave the following day, I resolved to try one of the Esquimaux craft. They are very small and necessitate the removal of trousers to enter them. I paddled about happily for some time but at last over I went and remained there, upside down in a most undignified position until rescued.

One of the party gave a quite remarkable display of skill in repeatedly severing a weighted string hung over the stern from a distance of several boat lengths with nothing more than a type of small throwing dart which they use to bring down birds in flight.

The Esquimaux have the most unusual aspect, being short and stocky, like folk used to a life of hard labour. They have very flat and wide faces. Some resemble a type of face I came across in China to such a degree that it made me wonder on the origins of these odd people. Many came aboard and traded for whatever they could. They were particularly taken with any metal which they could fashion into spear points. In exchange they offered many items made of sealskin. Our crew almost universally smoke clay pipes and many obtained tobacco pouches from the natives who, although they do not much use tobacco themselves, make the pouches for trade with passing vessels. It seems the European influence on these lands extends to establishing new trade customs.

Crozier went quite overboard and kitted himself out with a complete outfit of native clothing. It consists of a shapeless jacket and pair of leggings, cunningly sewn from the complete skins of several local deer and still bearing the distinct aroma of the wilds. He also procured a pair of skin boots, or mukluks as they are called. I cannot imagine what he will do with this clothing or how strange he will look in the Strand dressed—and smelling—like an Esquimaux. When I joked him about it, he replied with a serious explanation of the principles by which air is trapped in layers beneath the clothing and, warmed by the body at the centre, serves to protect the wearer from the extremes of the local climate. He even went so far as to explain to me that the Esquimaux have been living in these lands, in all probability, since before Caesar conquered Britain and, for all their savage appearance, must have learned something of adapting to its vagaries. He really can be quite humourless at times. None-the-less, I could not deny the natives a superior skill to mine in the handling of their small craft.

I used this time to take magnetic readings with an early version of the 'Fox,' which we find quite cumbersome and awkward to use. Still, we must make what we can of it as there is no scientific supplier in these parts. I was frequently very wet and cold at this work; but plunging into cold water, when I got on board, made me quite warm. I could not help thinking of the Frenchman who, after a long account of the misery of the rain and fogs of England, wound up with—'Pour quitter ce triste sol je m'embarque à Liverpool.'

The land of Disco was bold, black, and topped with snow. The seas were covered with bits of ice, which rushed through the channel as they broke away from the icebergs with a noise like thunder. Every man was allowed on shore and they ran about for a sort of holiday, getting eider duck's eggs, &c; we collected some very curious mosses and plants, also shells. Le Vesconte and I spent a day on a small island surveying. It was very satisfactory to me that he took to surveying, as I said he would. Sir John was much pleased with him.

I also spent a day on land with Fairholme measuring angles of the magnetic lines of force of our dear old Earth. It is important work, but tedious in the extreme as it involves sitting for long hours in a little square wooden house recording minute variations in the movements of a tiny, suspended needle. To add to our woes, we were continually bitten by very large mosquitoes and I fancy we each lost some pounds of flesh. I have saved you one of the beasts.

Both the *Erebus* and the *Terror* are very heavily laden, the *Terror* less so since she left some supplies in Disco. The *Erebus* is, without doubt, the sturdiest ship I have ever been on. She is not overly large, being 370 tons to the *Terror*'s 340. Both ships are 'Bomb' vessels, built solidly at first to carry the mortar cannons that were used to bombard Napoleon's coastal fortifications.

Oddly the *Terror* is the very same vessel I rescued south of Lisbon when I was a lowly fifteen-year-old first class on the old *Pyramus* in 1828. We found her seventy miles south of the detestable hole we were blockading. She lay on a bed of sand surrounded by rocks with the surf beating over her tremendously—her crew living in tents and six other merchantmen wrecked nearby. She was refloated and towed back to England, very leaky and with the pumps working continuously. I thought then she would see no more service in His Majesty's Navy yet here she is on this new adventure.

Both ships were much strengthened for the ice they encountered while with James Ross in the Antarctic, and they have been further strengthened with oak beams and iron hull sheathing for this endeavour.

We draw some seventeen feet fully laden which a few feel might handicap the work we have ahead of us. Thomas Blanky, the Ice-Master on *Terror*, was with John Ross from 1829 to 33 and saw as much as any man of the kind of waters we must navigate. He has expressed the opinion privately—but what can remain private in the confines of a ship at sea—that the waters are shoaly and treacherous and that we would have done well to bring a small yacht with us to take out if the going got tight. I think he worries overly for our aim is to sail through the open spaces near Banks Land and, when possible keep well clear of narrow passages which may well be ice-clogged traps.

Both ships are very full with three years' provisions and coals for the engine. The engine on *Erebus* takes up space most inconveniently. It is an entire locomotive (which but a few months ago was running on the Greenwich line) with only the wheels removed and set by crane in our aft hold. It weighs fifteen tons and its bulk makes passage below deck quite a trial at times. Many of the crew are not to be convinced of its import, especially as it can only push us along at a poor three or four knots. Still, I am certain we shall have reason to be thankful for such foresight when we have need of a push through the ice and the wind is uncertain or contrary.

Some men of vision, Sir John Ross among them, even talk of a day when flotillas of ships powered by steam boiler alone will conclude all recourse to sail. It is a stirring idea especially given Ross's unfortunate experiences when he had to dismantle and dump the unworkable engines from his *Victory* at Felix Harbour in 1829. Yet perhaps he is right for certainly the steamer *Rattler* was of great assistance to us on our way to the Orkneys. Perhaps the day will come when we see the great navies and merchant fleets of the world steaming around the globe without a care for the movements of wind and tide! For all that they may change our world, the engines are, as Irving on the *Terror* says of their trials, prone to make the most dreadful puffings and screamings and will undoubtedly astound the Esquimaux not a little.

Meanwhile, our deck is covered with coal piled chest high and casks of food and liquor, and there is but a narrow pathway fore and aft which must look to the untrained eye as if it winds around like fallen knitting wool, yet which in fact defines the most convenient routes that the crew must take as they go about their sometimes complex tasks.

We sit very low and the two ships handle rather like logs in the water. You will please picture to yourself our having a smooth passage between the icebergs for we had enough rolling and pitching on our way across the Atlantic to last us all the voyage. The old *Terror* pitched so much she appeared as if tossed around by some playful undersea serpent—but no doubt we appear to do likewise from her decks. We can only hope that we do not meet with an unseasonable gale before we make Lancaster Sound and the opening of the passage.

I have no fear but that we shall complete the passage before we have time enough for scientific work and adventure, and if we do not, what wrong can befall us? Since Parry revived our English claim to these northern lands in 1818, all the expeditions, even those that met with misfortune, have lost but a handful of men, and most of those through accident or some pre-existing medical condition. Surgeon Stanley had to invalid one man home from the Whalefish Islands and Peddie did the same for two in addition to both the *Terror*'s Armourer and Sailmaker who Crozier classified as "perfectly useless either at their trade or anything else." So we are now 129 hardy souls in two of the sturdiest ships ever to set sail. We have the best of supplies and the keenest hearts that could ever be wanted. How can we not succeed?

But here I am rambling on about hearts of oak when all you want to hear is gossip of my shipmates and stirring tales of adventure. All I can pass on in this regard is that our Purser, Osmer, beat me soundly at chess this evening. I pray the voyage is long enough so that I may improve to such sufficient degree that I might take a game or two from him before we reach home.

July 15-16—I was beginning to write last night, but the ship was tumbling about to such an extent that I went to bed but had to turn out again immediately and get the top-sails reefed, as it blew very hard in squalls. The ship pitched about as much as I ever witnessed. Reid is a most extraordinary rustic and prognosticates endlessly on all manner of topics, nautical and otherwise. After the experience at Disco I am disinclined to give much weight to his sayings, but they are undoubtedly quaint and sometimes amusing. Today he was saying that he does not like to see the wind "seeking a corner to blow into," and followed this with a rough comment on the impracticality of kilt wearing in windy climates.

The weather moderated this morning, and all day we have had little wind and tolerably smooth sea. This allowed us to get the proper 'crow's-nest' up. The construction is a hooped canvas cylinder attached at the main-top-gallant-masthead (if you know where that is). According to Reid, who will have the peculiar privilege of being perched up there to search out channels through the ice, this particular crow's nest is a very expensive one.

Blanky on the *Terror* proclaims this to be a very open season, much like the one he experienced when he sailed these waters in 1829 with old Captain John Ross. Of course the weather cannot be taken as a good luck omen since Ross and his crew spent four years trapped in the ice and were given up for dead before they were rescued. But you need have no fears for us. I am told by Osmer that we could easily make supplies last a farther one or even two years taking no account of what fresh meat we might obtain with musket and ball.

Osmer is a delightful fellow. He was with Beechey in the *Blossom* in 1821 when they went to Behring's Strait to look out for Franklin. At the time Sir John was surveying the north coast of America, and was within 150 miles of Beechey; Osmer was also at Petro Paulowski in Kamschatka, where I hope to go, and served since on the lakes of Canada. It is said that if the Purser is plump then the crew eat well. If there is any truth in this saying then we will surely benefit for Osmer is almost as broad as he is tall and his skin exudes a most ruddy glow. I was at first inclined to think him a stupid old man, because he has chins, takes snuff, and has an extraordinary nose; but he is as merry-hearted as any young man, full of quaint dry sayings, always good humoured, always laughing, never a bore, takes his 'pinch after dinner,' plays a 'rubber,' and beats me at chess—and, he is a gentleman.

By the time you have read a quarter of this poor document you will have a fit picture of all my messmates. We have the following whom I have or shall from time to time give you descriptions:—First Lieutenant, Gore; Second, Le Vesconte; Third, Fairholme; Purser, Osmer; Surgeon, Stanley; Assistant-Surgeon, Goodsir; Ice-Master (so called), Reid; Mates, Sargent, Des Voeux, Couch; Second Master, Collins; Commander, of himself you know better; and over us all, Sir John Franklin, the hero of so many past adventures in the lonely and unexplored regions of the world. But for now I must to bed. Good night sister.

July 17—A wonderful clear evening. Osmer came from on deck dancing with an imaginary skipping-rope. I said to him, "What a happy fellow you are, always in good humour." His answer was, "Well, sir, if I am not happy here, I don't know where else I could be."

He has an extraordinary facility to remember and recount the details of our provisions, and we take comfort in having him recite what will keep us from want in the months to come.

"Why, sirs," he says, "we need fear nothing. We have sixty-one tons of flour; sixteen tons of biscuits; fourteen tons each of salt beef and pork; ten and one-half tons of sugar; nine tons of concentrated soup; four tons of chocolate; three tons of tobacco; a ton each of tea, soap and candles; 8,000 cans of preserved meat, soup and vegetables; 3,684 gallons of liquor; 900 gallons of lemon juice; 170 gallons of cranberries; and 200 pounds of pepper to season it all."

Of course all this is supplemented by the personal supplies that all of the officers have brought aboard and we look forward with some anticipation to the treats which will, on occasion, grace our mess table. For myself, these personal supplies are modest, comprising some ox tongue, crystallized fruit, Abernethy's crackers, and of course the preserved goose you and William so kindly furnished.

Our victualling schedule for the men will be one pound biscuit or flour; two and one-half ounces sugar; one-quarter ounce tea; one ounce chocolate; and one ounce lemon juice per day; one-half pound preserved meat every second day and three-quarters pound each of salt beef and pork, and one pint of soup twice a week. Surgeon Stanley is of the opinion that the preserved meat should be fed preferentially to the sick, and I tend to agree. We also carried ten live oxen, but they were slaughtered at Disco with the intention of freezing the meat but the unseasonably warm weather has meant that we have had to eat it as quickly as possible. At least the beasts provided us with a few meals of fresh meat to remember in the months of salt beef to come. As important as the food for the body, we carry food for the mind in our library of 1,700 books. They will make these Arctic nights pass with alacrity.

It is now well past the witching hour and with thoughts of giant hams and Milton dancing in my brain, I must extinguish the candle.

July 18—Passed within hailing of a whaler today. She confirmed the openness of the ice and stated that we should have no difficulty in the crossing if we should only catch a fair wind. For the moment it still leads us north toward Cape York.

I wish I could convey to you a just idea of the immense stock of good feeling, good humour, and real kindliness of heart which fills our small mess. We are very happy, and our opinion of Sir John improves very much as we come to know more of him. He is anything but nervous or fidgety; in fact, I should say remarkable for energetic decisions in sudden emergencies; but I should think he might be easily persuaded where he has not already formed a strong opinion.

As you know, the rumours abounded in Admiralty circles in England that the first choice to command this expedition was James Ross, but that he turned it down because of the exhaustion he felt after four years battling the icy southern ocean on his magnificent circumnavigation of the South Polar Lands. He also harboured a quite natural desire to share time with his young wife and family. Sir John had just returned from his unhappy experiences in Van Diemen's Land and was, I believe, anxious to undertake some action whereby he might restore his reputation so unjustly slandered by the colonials and escape the worries of political circumstance. He was the most senior Arctic officer available having led two extraordinary expeditions to explore the coast of America. Sir John also commanded the *Trent* on Buchan's attempt to reach the Pole in 1818. The only hindrance against him was his age of fifty-eight which is considered excessive by some, including a few of the junior officers on this expedition. But any grumblings have vanished. Sir John is a remarkable man and, if anyone is to lead us through this adventure, it must surely be he.

I dine with Sir John each evening the weather permits and he also enjoys the nightly company of two others from the mess. This evening I was present with Gore and Le Vesconte, and we discussed our orders.

"We must make all haste," Sir John began, "through Lancaster Sound and Barrow Strait to Cape Walker. From there we shall set course to the southwest and sail through the uncharted waters between Banks and Victoria Lands. I hope to emerge on the coast of the Americas near Point Turnagain and from there make Behring's Strait in good order."

"You do not hold then," Gore asked, "with the theory that an as yet undiscovered land fills that part of the globe?"

"I know not," Sir John smiled. "There may be land there as you say, but it will not be of one piece—we shall find a way around it. Simpson and Dease traversed the coast almost to the foot of Prince Regent Inlet and I am confident there must be a way through to the coast, possibly several."

"What of the northern route across the Polar Ocean?" interjected Le Vesconte. He is of the school, led by Barrow, which believes in an open ocean lying to the far north and that if only the rim of drifting pack ice around it is penetrated, a short, clear route to the Orient will be found. Like many neophytes, Le Vesconte has boundless enthusiasm for his beliefs and expounds upon them at the least provocation.

"If," said Sir John with heavy emphasis, "after our best attempts, we find the southern route to be blocked by ice or land, then we shall turn north and try to find a way east by Wellington Channel. Our orders are very clear and we shall follow them to the best of our ability, regardless of what unsupported theories are currently in vogue in some quarters of the Admiralty."

Poor Le Vesconte looked crushed, but said nothing more. I felt sympathy for him, but he was well aware, as are we all, how Sir John feels about Barrow's theories. Le Vesconte was asking for a rebuff in bringing up the topic.

The fair wind continues and we are making some seven knots, good for these vessels. The sea is tolerably smooth, though we do roll a little; but this ship has the happy facility of being very steady below, though from on deck, she appears to be plunging and rolling greatly. Already we are becoming fond of the old *Erebus*. She is what is commonly known in the service as a 'happy ship,' not least the result of the cheerful community we are developing aboard her. I sometimes miss the community on land, not least the company of yourself, William and the little ones, but to belong to a band of fellows engaged as we are in one laudable purpose and confined in a small area with but the vastness of the natural world surrounding, is a situation which cannot be reproduced elsewhere. My new world fosters such joy that I cannot help but be satisfied with the life I have chosen.

I sometimes think that in any case I am not fitted for what is commonly called society—by this I mean tea and bread and butter society—and that I am much better in a position of the sort I now occupy than dallying about in the humbugging world. This is all to say that your roving brother-in-spirit is content with his lot despite only being with you in thought, which I most assuredly am. Good night.

July 19—The life below these cold waters is quite extraordinarily plentiful and is providing continual delight for Goodsir who, though an Æsculapian by trade and lately curator of the Edinburgh College of Surgeons, is only truly happy in the presence of some unusual or hitherto unknown denizen of the natural world. He is a splendidly entertaining fellow and has the useful facility of being able to impart his enthusiasm to any idle hands he comes across and to make them uncomplainingly aid him in his explorations. He is what I believe is called 'canny.' His upper lip projects beyond his lower and his lower begins his chin thus producing a gradation, but a whisker comes down beyond the chin so you imagine there is more of the chin than meets the eye. He is long and straight (like a can of pump water) and walks upright —on his toes, with his hands tucked up in his jacket pockets. He is perfectly good humoured, very well informed on general points, in natural history learned, appears to be about twenty-eight years of age, laughs delightfully, cannot be in a passion, is enthusiastic about all 'ologies, draws the insides of microscopic animals with an imaginary-pointed pencil, catches phenomena in a bucket, looks at the thermometer and every other meter, is a pleasant companion—in all an acquisition to the mess. So much for the appearance of Mister Goodsir.

This evening he held us all in thrall with tales of his attic domicile in Lothian Street, Edinburgh which he termed 'The Barracks.' "It was rented," he said, "for the princely sum of £17 per annum. As I recall, I shared it with my two brothers, two fellow doctors, a monkey, tortoise, dog, cat, eagle, king crab, chameleon, and various assorted guinea pigs, birds, fish and amphibians, not all of whom helped with the rental, and some of whom were a considerable surprise to the other residents of the house.

"When one of our non-human guests passed on as nature intended, we would, in the name of science, dissect and study it. Naturally an assortment of skins could always be found hanging to dry in all manner of corners.

"It was the ideal setting for the free expression of opinions in the numerous and sometimes heated debates we undertook on scientific, political and moral matters. On occasion, we drew outsiders into our discussions. Once even that famous man of science Louis Agassiz. The discussion that night was warm enough to melt even the great sheets of ice that our learned visitor believes once covered all of Europe."

We were no less entertained by Goodsir's descriptions of some of the more eccentric professors at the college including the eminent man Harald Redvers who was in the habit of continually eating cranberry tarts throughout his lectures and of stopping in mid-expostulation and staring out the window for periods of several minutes while his students sat with pens poised and struggled to prevent their eyelids from drooping too far.

Goodsir is very much in favour of new ideas in science and, in this way, occasionally comes into conflict with Stanley who is more of the old school. The other day, the pair became quite heated in a discussion of the propagation of that scourge of our cities—cholera.

"Impure air—" said Stanley, expressing the traditional view, "there can be no doubt that during an epidemic, a 'cholera cloud' hangs over an infected city. Inhalation of the miasma affects the lungs, turns the blood the characteristic black colour one often observes, and the patient is killed by asphyxiation. The purging and vomiting which accompany the progress of the disease are but secondary symptoms."

This was all presented in almost biblical tones and brooked no dispute. However, Goodsir disagreed.

"Well," he said after a pause for thought, "an increasing amount of scientific study suggests that the disorders of the bowels in cholera are primary. This would indicate that the bowel is the site of initial infection. If so, then the cholera must be passed through something ingested, impure water perhaps."

Stanley only grunted, and the discussion remained somewhat academic until Goodsir, perhaps injudiciously, said, "The worst thing is the harm done by old-fashioned treatments. Warm baths, bleeding and the administration of brandy, calomel, and opium are less than useless and only worsen the patient's condition. A far more logical approach would be the replacement of the lost bodily fluids through the injection of a salt solution to the bloodstream."

"Rubbish!" Stanley scoffed. "Unsupported, modern nonsense. Contaminated water is bad enough, but to suggest injections when the patient is in an extreme condition borders on the lunatic."

I am not qualified to judge, but, as Goodsir put it, his ideas appeared to warrant more attention. In any case, it is only Stanley who grumbles at Goodsir. To the rest of us he remains a delight.

Today we pulled up enough codfish for a good feed or two for all hands, and we bring up more starfish, shells and other curiosities than even Goodsir can accommodate. This evening I sat up trying to read a watch by the light of certain blubbers which are remarkably jelly-like and which emit a bright phosphorescent light when shaken in a basin. As a practical method of illumination they will never supplant the gas light, but as a novel illustration of the varied wonders of the natural world, they more than suffice.

Of the larger life, we commonly see whales and porpoises dancing about the ship. The most unusual are the 'bottle noses,' a species of whale, about twenty-eight feet long; their heads are very peculiar, and unless they are so close as to see their beak under water, one fancies their foreheads are snouts poking above the water. Walruses are also very common at times. Sometimes we see shoals of several hundred, tumbling over one another, diving and splashing with their fins and tails, and looking at us with their grim, solemn-looking countenances and small heads all bewhiskered and betusked. They look so serious that Goodsir suggested, jokingly I trust (but then again he did once make a pet of a seal which he fed on milk) that we capture one of these beasts and set it up on deck as some kind of local dignitary which we could consult on matters pertaining to our voyage, much as the Greeks attended their oracles when they wished the future to be made clear. I told Goodsir I had no wish to know the future, that it would take care of itself in good time and that, in any case, to my understanding the Greek oracles were notorious for leading their questioners false.

Sometimes I feel we are all just inquisitive schoolboys who have climbed the wall of the local manor and are at play in some vast garden all unawares.

July 20—Pitching heavily, breeze increasing steadily from ESE. The cloud came on as the sun was lowering to the horizon in the form of a bank which was painted the most delightful rose-red by the dying light; it then rose in the form of an arch, and I expected wind; but, the cloud overspread the sky, and all we have is this breeze. Barometer rising as rapidly as it fell, and I have been prognosticating a sort of gale for the morrow in consequence. It was calm last night, cloudy all today. Passed the day working and making observations with Le Vesconte, when the sun did peep out. There is nothing in this day's journal that will interest or amuse you and I am not in a humour for describing any more messmates.

July 22—Blowing hard for two days, a circumstance which I did not relish since it brought many large bergs down upon us. Reid, however, put us at ease. I was not overly taken initially with his rough manner, and his misplacing us at the Whalefish Islands so soon after our first encounter with the ice inspired little confidence in his purported knowledge of the ice. Yet, gradually, I am coming to see some of his benefits. Not least is the amusement his broadly-accented comments bring.

Reid is a Greenland whaler from Aberdeen and amuses us constantly with tales and quaint remarks about ice and catching whales. He is a most original character—rough, intelligent, good humoured and honest hearted, unpolished, but not vulgar. When I asked him of his experience of bergs and whether we might not get into difficulties should a gale blow up, he answered, "Ah! now, Mister Jems, we'll not be worrying about the bergs.

We'll be having the weather fine, sir! fine! No ice at arl about it, sir, unless it be the bergs—arl the ice'll be gone, sir, only the bergs, which I like to see. Let it come on to blow, look out for a big 'un. Get under his lee, and hold on to him fast, sir, fast. He'll not tipple over and, if he drifts near the land, why, he grounds afore you do."

This I interpreted to mean that there was little danger in our undertaking yet it is hard not to be in awe as these huge blocks of ice and snow are borne down upon us.

I had intended to write last night but having sat down at my desk, I suddenly found myself in bed and falling asleep. Picture me if you will in my cabin struggling to add a few words to entertain you. My cabin measures some six by seven and seems quite commodious, though not as large as it looked in the *Illustrated News*. My bunk occupies one wall and is joined to the opposite wall at the head by my desk. I have a bookshelf and a chair and below the bunk are large drawers for all my possessions. Your picture hangs above the desk and has excited some comment from those of my companions who are uncertain as to whether it is quite proper for a bachelor such as I to carry a solitary picture of his cousin's wife! I do not take the trouble to explain the special bond which unites us for those who know me understand and those who do not will either come to know me through this adventure or not regardless of whatever explanations I might proffer. In any case, I trust that you look upon my presumption with approval.

My cabin is one of ten around our mess which is an open, well lighted place of red wood and painted birds-eye maple, with comfortable room for ten although there are rarely that many with those on watch. Sir John's cabin is large but he ends with little more space than the rest of us. Much room has been given over to Goodsir and his classification activities, and to Stanley who is quite expert at skinning and preserving birds of all sorts. In all the whole has something more of the aspect—and smell—of a scientific laboratory than the cabin of a ship at sea. This troubles Sir John not a bit. He is convinced of the great import of our scientific endeavour and encourages Goodsir in his work. In fact he said that, important as our discovery of the Northwest Passage will be, it is our scientific work which will live on after us.

July 23—A fine sunny day, quite warm and the air clear. Ice glistening in all directions. The only problem is the complete contrariness of wind, so we can make no headway. "But you have your steam engines," I hear you say. Indeed we have, but the decision has been made to save our irreplaceable coal supplies for the tighter work of pushing us through the ice, rather than burning it as we drudge along making precious little headway toward our goal.

July 24—A clear, fine sunset at nine, and Goodsir examining 'mollusca,' in the microscope. He is in ecstasies about a bag full of blubber-like stuff, which he has just hauled up in a net, and which turns out to be whales' food and other animals. It is all part of Sir John's instructions on the necessity of observing everything from a flea to a whale in the unknown regions we are to visit. This afternoon, seven or eight large grampuses came shooting past us to the southwest, which Mister Goodsir declared delightful animals. Last evening a shoal of porpoises bounded about the bows of the vessel as she plunged into the sea, and a bird called a mullimauk, a sort of peterel, wheeled over us. The Arctic folk say the bird, when seen in open water, is a sign of approaching ice. We need no such indicators. Today I counted 180 icebergs within sight of the masthead, and yet they are widely spaced and as long as a secure watch is kept, pose no threat.

It is but a month since I saw my first iceberg, a poor snowy one about six or eight miles off as I recall, but now I am quite accustomed to them. Before making their acquaintance, I had fancied them to be large transparent lumps or rocks of ice, but that is not at all the case; they are mostly like huge masses of pure snow, furrowed with caverns and dark ravines. They come from the glaciers which run off from the Greenland mountains. We should see them no more as soon as we enter Lancaster Sound.

Sir John told us at dinner of a tight spot he was in with Buchan at Spitzbergen in 1818.

"We were in a bay, at the foot of a large glacier," he said. "Our attention was all on mapping the rugged coastline. All of a sudden, we heard a mighty crack. Upon looking up we observed a huge piece of ice sliding down the face of the glacier. It fell some two hundred feet and crashed into the water in front of us, sending up much foam and spray and almost swamping the boat. The ice disappeared for several minutes before bobbing back up to a height of some 100 feet. Water was cascading down its sides as it rolled over and commenced to drift out to sea. I estimated the weight of ice at near 500,000 tons and, certainly, the noise of the crash was heard upwards of four miles away."

The natural phenomena at these latitudes are quite extraordinary. The light is quite sharp, making distant things appear much closer than they actually are. There is also a phenomenon, called 'ice-blink' by Reid, which is the reflection of the sunset and ice on clouds which is truly quite striking, resembling nothing so much as a large town on fire some twenty miles off. Sometimes the clouds move off, like a blanket being withdrawn and leaving an orange-coloured arch above a well-defined dark, clear, cold horizon. I do not think I have ever smelled air as crisp as this. Every odour, from the tang of the sea to the rather more pungent fragrance below decks, seems exaggerated and I find myself more aware of my surroundings than I have ever been (with the exception of the thrill of entering a military engagement). I suppose that since our senses are our only windows to the world, any change in what is perceived will alter our temper. Certainly in this world where sight and sound and smell are heightened I feel unusually alert.

July 25—The wind does not hold steady for long in these waters and we are making poor progress. We lie about sixty miles south of Cape York and can go no farther until a favourable wind comes to push us across the bay. It is frustrating as the season is moving on, however, we are making good use of the time.

This morning we got under the lee of a huge berg and made fast with the ice anchors. It was an undertaking I did not relish since, at Disco, I had witnessed one about 200 feet high topple over and come down with a crash like an avalanche, but in fact this berg seems as solid as if it were rock anchored to the sea bed. It is a large, irregular mountain of ice, upwards of 150 feet high and some 600 feet across. The ice, where it is shewing on a vertical face, is a deep blue, like thick coloured glass in some places. But the surface is not smooth and the ground is quite easy to walk on, being rough and a dull opaque white. There is a wave-cut ledge on the lee side which makes a perfect jetty for us. We have gone 'ashore' and set up a magnetic observatory some distance from the ships. As I told you in my letters from Disco, Sir John has especially charged me with the magnetic observations, and this is a splendid opportunity to collect readings where no-one has previously done so. It is exciting work but I cannot but hope we are not delayed too long.

July 26—Today around noon we were met by a whaler, the *Prince of Wales* out of Hull, with Captain Dannet commanding. We exchanged pleasantries and offered an invitation to supper on board but, unfortunately for our social agenda, a favourable wind came up (favourable for the whaler), and Captain Dannet felt he could not let it go so we parted company. Our island of ice has become quite homey with our observation huts scattered over it and men walking everywhere for exercise, but I wish for a fair wind to speed us on our way also.

July 27—This morning we came upon a further whaler, the *Enterprise* from Peterhead captained by Robert Martin. This evening a few of us accepted the kind gentleman's offer and dined aboard his vessel. It was a most enjoyable occasion much given over to talk of our prospects which were universally spoken of in a sanguine manner. The whalers are fine hearty fellows from the north country and they regaled us with tales of the whaling fleets. It is a most adventurous and interesting profession, but not one which I could take to, the whaling boat carrying such a disagreeable odour with her as I have ever smelled. It comes from the barrels she carries which are full of oil rendered from the whale fat, or blubber, heated over large fires on some suitable beach. Captain Martin laughed at our sensibilities and invited us to visit one of his rendering stations on the Greenland coast where, he assured us, the smell is one hundred times worse. We used the urgency of our passage to excuse ourselves from his hospitality.

The *Enterprise* has had a good season, the ice being open and allowing her into northern bays which were filled with whales. Reid and some others passed over letters for Captain Martin to take back. Had I been more conscientious with my writing I would have had more than these few pages which I did not think worth the trouble of sending. God willing, you will be reading them soon enough and your mood then, after we have sailed home in triumph, will perhaps be more sympathetic to my rude ramblings.

Many of our men are past whalers from Hull and Whitby, or else from the Orkney Islands and Peterhead. Several have past shipmates aboard the *Enterprise*. There was much shouting of messages between ships, but no opportunity for the crews to mingle. Just before I went across to dine this evening, I was approached by a little old Orkney man. "Beggin' pardon, sir," he said as I was about to disembark, "but Bill Fowler has pit some o' ma words on paper an' would ye consider the takin' o' the writin' for they lads tae tak hame fer the missus?"—By which I took to mean that William Fowler, the Paymaster and one of the few of the people to have learned writing, had taken down a message for the old man's wife which he was asking me to deliver over to someone on the *Enterprise*. It is a favour I have not been much disposed to undertake for the men, for it can quickly become a burden, but for him I made an exception. I have come across him before.

When we docked in Stromness in the Orkneys in June, we feared that some of the crew from those parts would repent their decision to accompany us. As was usual at this port, no leave was allowed. But the old man approached me then and begged to be allowed ashore. He had not seen his wife in over four years, so I let him go to Kirkwall, fourteen miles off. I also allowed the Captain of the Foretop, Robert Sinclair, who had not seen his mother for fourteen years, and one man from each mess, to go ashore for provisions. They all came on board after their leave; but finding we were not going to sea till the following morning, four men (who probably had taken a 'leetle' too much whiskey, and among them the little old man who had not seen his wife for four years) took a small boat that lay alongside and went on shore without leave. Their absence was soon discovered, and Fairholme, assisted by the Bailie, brought all on board by three o'clock in the morning.

I firmly believed each man intended coming on board (if he had been sober enough), especially the poor man with the wife—but according to the rules of the service, these men should have been severely punished—one method being to stop their pay and give it to the constables or others who apprehended them. It struck me, however, that the punishment is intended to prevent misconduct in others, and not to revenge their individual misconduct. Men know very well when they are in the wrong—and there was clearly no chance of a repetition of such offence until we reached Valparaiso, or the Sandwich Islands; so I got up at four o'clock, had everybody on deck, sent Gore and Bryant, the Sergeant of our Royal Marine contingent, below and searched the whole deck for spirits, which were thrown overboard. This took two good hours; soon after which we weighed anchor, and made sail out. I said nothing to any of the men. They evidently expected a rowing, and the old man with the wife looked very sheepish, and would not look me in the face; but nothing more was said, and the men have behaved not a bit the worse ever since.

I don't know why I tell you all this. I had meant to say just a little about icebergs and our guests, and say that when we came back on board I found that Le Vesconte had organized an occasion to celebrate your brother reaching the august age of thirty-two. We had many toasts with some splendid champagne and much talk of old times in China and Syria. Not one of us expressed the least iota of regret and none would rather be anywhere than exactly where we are unless it be with a fine following wind heading into Lancaster Sound. I toasted your health dearest Elizabeth and you were, as you ever are, close in my thoughts. I will try to write a letter tomorrow which the *Enterprise* may take back to England for me. And now I really must say goodnight; it is past one o'clock. God Bless.

July 28—We have a fair wind! Around noontime it turned to the northwest and we got in such a rush to bring the magnetic equipment on board, cast off and make the most of it, that for two hours or so you would have thought our friendly berg was home to a colony of black ants busily going about their business.

Around 3 p.m. we finally cast off and, with a final wave to the *Enterprise*, set course for Lancaster Sound. I am sorry we did not have the chance to return the hospitality of those stout men and, more important, pass on to them a short letter for delivery to you, but we must take what the fates offer and make the most of it, and if they suddenly give us a fair wind we cannot turn it down.

There is a feeling amongst some that, if we make Lancaster Sound by the first or second day of August, and if the ice remains as open as it is, we may complete the passage this year and set through Behring's Strait before it becomes blocked for the winter.

I hope not.

I have my heart set on spending a winter in this strange land we are approaching, and if we rush through there will not be time for proper readings of the magnetic phenomena which are of the utmost importance in advancing our understanding of that mysterious force, or time to collect adventures with which to regale you upon my return.

July 29—At dinner today, Sir John reaffirmed his doubt that there is an open sea around the Pole. He treated us to his belief that it might even be possible to reach the Pole over the ice by wintering at Spitzbergen, then going in spring before the ice broke up and drifted to the south, as it did with Parry on it. Fortunately, Le Vesconte was not one of the diners and so did not have to hear his cherished theories so put to the test.

Sir John pointed out how desirable it is to note everything, and give one's individual opinion of it. He spoke delightfully of the zealous co-operation he expected from all, and his desire to do full justice to the exertions of each. "We are the only vehicle," he reminded us, "for the transport of knowledge from this far corner to the great seats of learning. It is a heavy responsibility and one which must be given prominence."

He then told all the officers that he was desired to claim all their remarks, journals, &c on our return to England. This is common practice and will serve to provide material for his narrative of our voyage, and indeed he shall have my journal for what it is worth. This I shall regard as an extended personal letter and thus not feel constrained in what I say to you by the possibility of it being perused by other eyes. Thus I shall feel free to mention my fellow adventurers' little faults, failings, and peculiarities—in all charity of course—for the entertainment of your inquiring mind. But enough for now. Good night and God bless.

August 1 & 2—All yesterday it blew very hard, with so much sea that we shipped one or two over the quarter-deck, by which I got a good drenching once. The sea was of the most perfect transparency—a beautiful, delicate, cold-looking green, or ultramarine. Long rollers, as if carved out of the essence of bottle glass, came rolling toward us; now and then topped with a beautiful pot-of-porter head. By evening the wind moderated, and was calm at night. This morning the wind was quite fair, but instead of having clear weather as with the northeast wind, it came to the southeast, and brought hard rain and thick fogs all day.

We are now, however, (11 p.m.), going three knots and a quarter in a fog with the *Terror* close in on one side for fear of losing sight of us. Sir John will not cut sail and we are having fun navigating the bergs which loom at us out of the fog like huge, ghostly mountains. I calculate we are some forty miles off Cape Horsburgh, the most western extremity of Devon Island, and should raise Cape Warrender tomorrow and be in the Sound.

Reid still amuses us. He has just told me how to boil salt fish when it is very salty. He saw Bridgens, the Officers' Steward, towing it overboard, and roared out, "What are you makin' faces at there? That's no' the way tae get the sarlt oot." Apparently, when the saltfish boils it is to be taken off the fire and kept not boiling.

This is Saturday night. Reid and Osmer are drinking 'Sweethearts and wives;' and they wanted me to join. I said I had not the one, and did not want the other. Good night.

August 3—In Lancaster Sound—the gateway to the Northwest Passage. This morning broke fair with a stiff following breeze. Sir John read the church service today and a sermon so very beautifully that I defy any man to hear and not feel the force of that which he conveys. He took for his theme the Lord's placing of the bounty of the earth here for our use and talked of our obligation to use said bounty to the maximum. Our task, in coming to this unknown place and discovering what bounty there may be, is thus one sanctioned by the highest Authority.

I was in mind of the first Sunday he read, the day before we sailed, when Lady Franklin, his daughter, and niece attended. Everyone was struck with his extreme earnestness of manner, his real conviction. I like a man who is in earnest.

About noon we espied Cape Warrender and by 4 p.m. had land on both sides of us. I allowed the whole crew to scramble up on the rigging and perch on the mounds of supplies to better glimpse this land we have come to explore and challenge. The day was clear and the panorama quite delightful. The sky was a pale-blue, separated from the darker, fuller blue of the water by two narrow strips of black mountain on the far horizon.

We have left the bergs behind and sail now amongst broken pack ice which paints uneven blotches of pure white over the deep blue carpet of the waves. I hardly think there was a man on board either ship who was not deeply touched by the sight. This is where we start, a gateway to another world and the entrance to the Northwest Passage. How long until we sail through the gate at the other side, no-one can say, but sail through it we shall. I find myself quite overcome by the scene, in a way I never felt amidst the exotic poverty of China, or the dusty, ancient tombs along the Euphrates. As you know, I have not the gift of poetic expression, but today I felt something of the power which drives poets to fashion the world around them into verse. Common language is so poor a carriage for our sometimes soaring thoughts.

In honour of the occasion, I ordered a cask of beer opened and Gore led the men in three hearty cheers for Sir John. At dinner there was much merriment and discussion of our chances. Certainly, luck has been smiling on us so far. Those who have been this way before say they have never seen such little ice in the Sound. In fact, when Sir John Ross first came this way in 1818, it was so ice clogged that he dismissed Lancaster Sound as a mere inlet ending in a mirage of mountains. No-one is flinching from our undertaking and everyone's cry is, 'Now at last we are into the Passage.' I am not of a philosophical turn of mind, but a day such as today, when we first truly enter these lands, cannot help but begin one reflecting upon our place in the great scheme of things. The war in China was a fine adventure, but in the service of human affairs. Here there is naught but nature on every side, pure and unsullied. It is difficult not to feel we are doing God's work, or at least pursuing human goals of which He approves. Do not think I am turning into a Tracterian, but there is not one of us who does not feel deep within himself that we are fulfilling some larger purpose.

At dinner, we drank to Lady Franklin's health at the old gentleman's table. All we ask is what any man hopes, that the fates do not play cruel with us. If not, we shall be home before you know it with answers and stories that will make you hold your breath. God bless us all. Good night.

August 4—Weather continues fair but the wind has dropped and we make very slow passage. The ice remains light in mid-channel where we sail, but is piled up somewhat along the north shore.

Do you remember, on the day you bid us farewell at Greenhithe, the dove alighting on the masthead to give us an omen of good luck to carry on our endeavour. I am often put in mind of that as if the memory of it were a talisman which I can carry with me, and perhaps, knowing as I do your love of all things feathered and beaked, you too will be thinking of that same bird and our thoughts will be linked.

I am continually amazed at how the imagination of the people was caught by our expedition before we sailed, even those who had not the slightest wish or desire to set foot in more than six inches of ocean water, and how all took such pride in what we were setting out to do and revelled in the discoveries we would make in almost unimaginable seas so far from their ken. When the steamers *Rattler* and *Blazer* left us by the island of Rona, some seventy or eighty miles from Stromness, they both, despite the heavy swell and wind from the northwest, ranged alongside us, one on each side, as close as possible without touching, and, with the whole force of lungs of officers and men, gave us not three, but a prolongation of cheers—to which we responded. Having done the same to the *Terror*, away they went, and in an hour or two were out of sight, leaving us with an old gull or two and the rocky Rona to look at. But it is the memory of those good wishes that means so much to us.

I was in mind this evening of the talk there was before we left England of a brevet promotion; if this be true, I think it more than probable that I shall get the rank of Captain, although I shall know nothing of it until we have made a passage of Behring's Strait and collected our messages in Russia. With the idea that I may now be a mighty Captain, I took a glass of brandy and water at ten o'clock. Allowing for the difference of longitude, this answers to half-past seven in London. I drank your health, *in petto*, fancying you might be drinking wine. In fact, we took an imaginary glass of wine together, and I don't care how soon we may take a real one.

Now I am laughing, for Reid has just said, scratching his head, "Why, mister Jems, you never seem tae sleep at arl; you're always writin'!" I tell him that when I do sleep, I do twice as much as other people in the same time. Now, I must to bed.

August 5—The weather continues fair with no wind so we make little headway. It is frustratingly slow. The ice is thickening, but still easy going with Reid at lookout in the nest.

We have a monkey on board named Jacko, oddly the same name as the one which shared Goodsir's accommodation in Edinburgh, yet this one belongs to one of the seamen, William Mark. It turns out, to everyone's surprise, that Jacko is a lady. It is not overly cold yet, although Jacko sports a new blanket, frock and trousers which the sailors made for her. She, as appears characteristic of her species, is sometimes a most damnable pest, getting in to everything and helping herself to whatever catches her fancy.

Each of our vessels also has a canine passenger. Ours belongs to Gore and is Neptune by name, a breed known to game keepers as buck-dogs, but more commonly called greyhounds, very thin and long, but fast in the run. It is grey and so fits with the name, but they can come in all colours. Parry, in his journal of the 1823 voyage, mentions one he had that was a black colour.

Neptune is skinny and has little fat, though he is strongly built and quite powerful in the chest and shoulders. I fear somewhat for how he will manage when the cold of winter sets in. The *Terror* has a hairy beast of the species named for Newfoundland and oddly called Diogenes though there appears little of the cynic in him. It belongs to Lieutenant Little and it seems to me that it will fare better in the cold than Neptune—but then, Parry's dog survived in good health and there is even a picture in his Journal of a Second Voyage of the beast frolicking on the ice. The *Terror* also boasts a cat, a rather large orange beast which should be at least a match for the rats which will soon be plaguing us. I hope we do not regret not having one of that species on board with us.

Francis Crozier has dined on board whenever the weather permits, often with Hodgson, who was ill on the voyage here, but is quite recovered now. Crozier is a splendid fellow and we all have the utmost respect for him, his knowledge of the Arctic lands (he even speaks some of the strange dialect of the Esquimaux of the region) is immense and second only to Sir John himself. He has an unfortunate tendency to take himself too seriously, but is good enough company for any evening, although I have fancied on occasion that I have detected a tiredness of spirit about him. Certainly, we have all been busy with the preparations and the leaving, but there seems about Crozier something more; perhaps almost a weariness with the world. At first I suspected that it might be a measure of resentment at the fact that I had been charged with selecting the officers for our adventure, but until February, Crozier was in Italy and we could not wait if we were to catch the season in good time. I also suspected it might be disquiet at not being given the magnetic work, which he was in charge of when second to James Ross in the Antarctic, but this responsibility was not announced until we were well at sea. In any case, he has been most helpful in teaching me the workings of the Fox instrument, and offering advice on the most efficient way to undertake the readings. All said, I think he is much too generous of spirit to hold a petty grudge for long.

I tend now to put his weariness down to age; at forty-eight, he is much senior to most of the young bucks who officer our vessels (even your dear brother at thirty-two feels, on occasion, the weight of additional years in comparison to babes such as Couch and Sargent), although he is, of course, still ten years short of Sir John's age. I combined this fact with exhaustion from the trials of commanding the *Terror* for four years in the Antarctic. In addition, apparently Crozier's sugar and tea did not appear as we unloaded the supply vessel, Fortnum and Mason's having addressed it to 'Captain Fitzjames Terror' although I saw nothing of it. By an unlucky twist of fate, they managed to correctly send the bill and poor Crozier ended up paying for goods which ended up God knows where. It is such small things as this which can set the temper of a man in the narrow confines of a ship at sea, and yet I am convinced there is more.

Sir John feels much the same. There is also a certain tension between Crozier and Sir John, although both do nothing to make it obvious and are very close. On one occasion, when we dined alone in his cabin, Sir John confided in me his concern that Crozier has not had his former flow of spirits since we sailed.

"However brief the duration of our voyage," he said, "we shall all be confined closely in each other's company for some time and, consequently, subject to any disturbance of temperament."

I replied that I felt Crozier's temperament would settle with time and that we could ask for no-one better as second.

"Maybe," Sir John replied thoughtfully, "but did you know, James, that Crozier proposed and was rejected by my niece shortly before we sailed?"

I answered that I did not.

"It is the truth, and it was the second proposal of its kind. As you know, my wife Jane is not one to sit idle while I am engaged in duty. To aid her, she took on a companion, my sister Isabella's daughter, Sophia Cracroft, prior to me taking up my position as governor in Van Diemen's Land in 1836. The two became very close and I was glad Jane had Sophia's company on the occasions when I could not be present—some of these far-flung colonies can be the dullest of places if one is not occupied with work.

"In any case, when the *Erebus* and *Terror* wintered in Hobart in 1840, Crozier became most attached to Sophia. Unfortunately, Sophia had eyes for James Ross, who was not at this time married and, when Crozier proposed shortly before he sailed, she turned him down.

"This spring, they were re-acquainted through the preparations for this voyage and Crozier, believing, I fancy, that his chances would be better with Ross now married, proposed once more and was similarly rebuffed.

"I am convinced that Sophia acted as nothing but the perfect lady and never gave Crozier any false indication, but she is a sprightly thing and her effervescent temperament can be misconstrued on occasion. I was in agreement with her decision on two counts, first that Crozier is considerably her senior and temperamentally a world apart, and second and somewhat selfishly, I did not want Jane deprived of her companion.

"It is not good to carry unrequited love to sea, especially to the lonely places we are bound, and I hope it is not this which preys on his mind."

"I am sure not," I replied. "Crozier is certainly not a man to let something such as you describe interfere with his duties."

I was speaking the truth, but it is not merely the performance of duty which is required of a ship's Commander. A crew very soon become extremely adept at judging subtleties in their officers' behaviour that we would never give account to under normal circumstances. The slightest change can lead to all sorts of rumour mongering and, if there is any dissatisfaction to begin with, to some quite serious disturbance.

The unlikely image of Sophia Cracroft and Crozier together is so odd as to be almost laughable. As you know she is small statured and almost ethereally delicate in appearance. Crozier is a large man, broad as well as tall, and his mane of prematurely white hair and pale complexion put one in mind of an aged lion. She could almost fit in his coat pockets—yet I hear she is strong willed and would not easily take to a life of 'second-in-command.'

But here I am gossiping on like a society hostess, but that is what it can come to in such a closed community as we have here amongst the ice floes. It is far too easy to become retrospective and to dwell too long and too morbidly on past misadventures and woes. It is even difficult enough to think back sometimes on close friends and relatives without becoming sad and in the doldrums. But see!—How easily it can happen even as I write to you, dear sister. I shall endeavour in this long letter to keep a high and light tone. This is not to say that I shall tell you only of the good and not mention any bad that may befall us, but I shall try not to sink into the darkness of despair whatever we may encounter. As I have promised not to read back any of this work, you must take the responsibility upon yourself to please skip past any outpourings from the darker side of my spirit.

And now I must to bed. It is past one and the old ship is silent but for the creaks and groans of well-seasoned timber carrying us forward. Good night.

August 6—Some fog this morning which made us proceed with caution, but the breeze increased from the southeast around ten, blew away the mists and helped us proceed with our errands. At this rate, we should tomorrow be at Prince Regent Inlet which has been so well explored by Parry and John Ross. Even if it is open, which seems likely, given the lightness of the ice this year, we must sail on. It is not our orders and we cannot afford the time nor the risk of becoming entrapped in an area so far from our goal.

At dinner this evening on the *Terror*, Sir John talked about the supplies left by Ross at Fury Beach and speculated on their probable condition. As a midshipman, Crozier helped deposit this cache and well remembers what was laid there. Apparently, John Ross spoke to Franklin of the supplies and suggested them as a possible goal for any party that might have to abandon these vessels on the far side of Boothia. Ross also promised to mount a relief expedition for his old friend in three years should he not have received communication from us by that time.

So you see, we have many possibilities and some fine friends looking out for us should we require it, but failure is the farthest thing from anyone's mind. How can we fail? There has never been such a well organized, well supplied, and hopeful expedition in England's long history of seeking answers to questions in the far corners of the globe.

Crozier mentioned his worry about the lateness of the season and the severity of the past winter. He felt we must take care that, with the openness of the ice this summer, we do not blunder on without having time to take a proper look around and, without sufficient awareness, become entrapped in the ice. It is, I am sure, a sensible comment, but few of us are in a mood to appreciate anything in the least negative as things have been going so well for us to this time. If honest enthusiasm and belief in self were alone enough to power ships, we should already have made passage and be docked in some Pacific port.

I do not mean to present Francis Crozier as a Cassandra always prophesying doom which no-one believes, and casting a dark shadow over all with whom he comes in contact; far from it, he is mostly cheerful and always kind and attentive, and we are all glad to have him second-in-command and have his knowledge and experience with us.

Gore appears to have taken young Des Voeux under his wing and the pair can be seen at all hours with cigars dangling from their lips, leaning over the side with nets and long poles to catch the extraordinary animals which continue to send Goodsir into ecstasies. Osmer is always there too, laughing at everything; he really is an original and delightfully dry fellow. I can think of no ship I have been on where everyone is in such a good humour, either with himself or his neighbours.

Our dinner on the *Terror* this evening was most pleasant. Crozier was in splendid form regaling us with stirring tales of the unfortunate collision between the *Erebus* and *Terror* amidst the ice of the Antarctic Sea. It seems the ships were separated by ice almost immediately after the incident and since both were struggling with very heavy seas and being battered by the ice, had to spend a number of hours apart not knowing that the other had survived. At least the possibility of large open-ocean icebergs being blown down on us here is now lessened with our passage into the relative tranquillity of these straits and inlets.

Sir John then amused us with many tales of the Indians with which he and his party met on his 1821 journey down the Coppermine River. "The natives are much like children," he began, "and must be treated as such. One I recall, the chief, whose name was Akatcho, was charged with providing hunters from his subjects and in guiding us down the river to the Northern Ocean. At first, he required that he be regarded as our equal, insisting on a salute of musketry and flag waving upon his arrival at camp.

"For all this, instead of fresh deer meat, all we got in exchange for musket ball and powder was excuses about the lack of game and the difficulty of the hunt. I was forced to state very clearly that, in future, any supplies of ammunition would be tied to the successful procurement of fresh deer meat. Almost magically, the deer became easier to hunt and our supplies increased."

"They can hardly be blamed," Crozier put in. "We Europeans arrive from nowhere with all manner of wonders which we distribute for reasons that must appear strange to the local populace. The temptation to increase the gifts by trickery or theft must be immense."

"True," Sir John answered, "when dealing with peoples who have had but little contact with Europeans, but Akatcho and his tribe had been trading on a regular basis with the voyageurs of the Hudson's Bay Company and knew all about the value of goods and how to acquire them. Why, when we supplied some diluted rum, they immediately complained that it was watered to a greater extent than usual and we had the devil's own job convincing them that this was indeed a new drink which was everywhere being drunk this season in London.

"No, I do not blame them, but they have not the sophistication of our society and are thus more closely similar to children who have also yet to learn the rules by which to live in company."

This should have ended the discussion but, like a terrier with a rag, Crozier kept on.

"But perhaps it is not that their society is simple, but rather that it is complex in a different way. After all, we have not their skills, as Fitzjames discovered with the kayak at Disco, in those many areas which are essential to comfort in these lands."

"Comfort!" Irving interrupted. "I would not call sleeping in an ice house comfort. Give me stone walls and a roaring fire any day."

This provoked laughter, but Crozier was not to be turned aside.

"You may laugh, Mister Irving, but I have seen these Esquimaux igloos and I can assure you that they are infinitely better suited to the land in which their owners live than a dwelling of stone with a fireplace that must of necessity remain empty for lack of trees."

"And on this point at least," Sir John added, "I must agree with Mister Crozier. At Fort Enterprise on the Coppermine expedition, some visiting Esquimaux built a snow dwelling which was examined in detail by Doctor Richardson. He proclaimed it the most ideal sort of structure of such efficiency that a single oil lamp sufficed to heat the main sleeping area which measured some twelve feet across and eight high. Moreover, the snow walls allowed such a transfusion of soft light that the interior resembled nothing so much as a fine marble hall. The whole dwelling complex was quite large and, in addition to the main sleeping chamber, included pantries, kitchen, porch and several cunningly designed ante-chambers which prevented unwanted draughts of cold air.

"In all it was a quite remarkable structure and the natives must be given full credit for its invention. Nonetheless, I must also agree with Mister Irving that there is little to compare with a comfortable chair and a glass of port in front of a roaring fire."

We then moved from a discussion of the natives to a comparison of our crossing of Baffin's Bay (twenty-three days) with those who had been this way before. Parry holds the record—nine or ten days—a thing unheard of before or since. On his next voyage he was fifty-four days toiling through the ice and did not get in before September. No expedition, except John Ross's, has ever been able to leave Disco before the 4th or 5th of July, though some sailed from England a full month before us. Ross, on his first voyage got away by the 16th of June, and was, I believe, a month going sixty miles farther, so we have not done badly.

August 7—Off Prince Regent Inlet. It looks quite open, unlike the waters ahead in Barrow Strait which become increasingly heavy with ice. The open path down the inlet is an enticement, but to what? No-one knows if Boothia is an island or not and whether we may find easy passage around it to join with the seacoast mapped by Simpson and Dease—but our orders to proceed to Cape Walker are clear. Sir John is not a man to set off on some private escapade in the face of unambiguous instruction whatever the seductions might be.

The thickening ice pushes us to the far shore of the sound, that is to say, away from our goal at Cape Walker. But this is not all bad for we shall perhaps be given a chance to examine Wellington Channel into which we shall proceed if our more southerly route is blocked. The prospect pleases Le Vesconte, as it will give him a chance to examine the beginning of what he regards as the best route to the east. I do not hold with an open northern ocean and we have discussed his ideas at some length in a friendly fashion, much like the debates we used to have around the fire at home. Our disagreements not withstanding, Le Vesconte improves, on closer acquaintance and it is a joy to see his swaying, bowed figure on our cluttered decks. His height and Roman nose give him an imposing appearance quite out of keeping with his temperament. Only when he smiles and flashes his gold teeth does one realize that Le Vesconte's sternness is of one's own imagining.

This evening in the mess, Graham Gore played the flute for us. He plays dreadfully well and kept us all well entertained. As Crozier pointed out, he has an honourable nautical name, it being a Gore who brought Captain Cook's vessels home after the Commander and Second died on the third voyage. Crozier also pointed out that he himself was a Mate on the *Doteral* in 1818 under a Captain James Gore. Our Gore was in China although I never ran into him there, has curly hair, mutton-chop whiskers, a prominent nose, permanent half-smile and eyes with a definite sparkle to them. He is a man of great stability of character, a very good officer, and the sweetest of tempers, is not so much a man of the world as Fairholme or Des Voeux, is more of Le Vesconte's style, without his shyness, draws sometimes very well, sometimes very badly, but is altogether a capital fellow.

To continue my tour around the mess, Couch is a little, bullet-headed, black-haired, smooth-faced inanity of a fellow—but good humoured in his own way; writes, reads, draws, all quietly. Is never in the way of anybody, and always ready when wanted; but I can find no remarkable point in his character, except, perhaps, he is, I should think, obstinate. He is much in with Sargent and has occupied himself capitally with an illustrated signal book of Sir John's copied from one of Parry's. Sargent, a nice pleasant-looking lad very good-natured but no energy of character although he is most assuredly artistic, and I fear of not *too* much sense, but fortunately he does not (as is usual in such cases) fancy himself very clever. It is good to see friendships develop between the young Mates—as long as there is no unnatural element to it.

Stanley, the Surgeon, I knew in China: he was in the *Cornwallis* a short time, where he worked very hard in his vocation. Is rather inclined to be good-looking, but fat or flabby as if from drinking beer, with jet-black hair always parted and swept forward in front of his ears which gives him a supercilious look when he smiles—very white hands, which are always abominably clean, and the shirt sleeves tucked up—giving one the unpleasant ideas that he would not mind cutting one's leg off immediately—*if not sooner*. He is what is called a 'good fellow'—inclined to be coarse if it were the fashion—is vulgar to a certain extent but thoroughly good-natured and obliging, and very attentive to our mess although he tends toward touchiness and must be handled with care on occasion, particularly, as we have found, where some of the new ideas of medicine propounded by Goodsir are concerned.

Fairholme, as you know, was with me on the *Ganges* at the bombardment of Beyrouth and in China. He is a smart, agreeable companion, and a well informed man and is forever off with Le Vesconte in Mister Halkett's India rubber boat which, you recall, they were first testing when you came to Greenwich to bully me into spending more time with you and the children before I sailed. He has a square face which can appear most severe on occasion—a boon when dealing with some recalcitrant crew member. His only flaw is a certain confusion with figures and he is forever transposing dates and numbers to the consternation of his watch companions.

Des Voeux I knew in the *Cornwallis*. He went out in her to join the *Endymion* in 1841, and was then a mere boy of sixteen. He is now a most clever, agreeable, light-hearted, obliging young fellow, and a great favourite of Hodgson's, which is much in his favour besides. He wears eyeglasses and is in line to inherit the Baronacy. Gore has very much taken to the lad and takes much trouble to improve his navigational skills.

The Second Master Collins is the very essence of good nature, and I may say good humour—but he is mad, I am sure—for he squints to himself with a painful expression of countenance when he is thinking (or thinking of nothing)—and I can get no work out of him, though ever so willing he may be—yet he is not a bore or a nuisance—but a nonentity. We might as well be without him—we intend however to make something of him. To this end I bullied him the other day about the ship's log which is badly written and which he is to rewrite by Sunday.

Here ends my catalogue. I don't know whether I have managed to convey an impression of our mess, but you may be sure that I have tried my best to accurately describe each and every one of my companions.

Sir John is like a father to many of us and we a collection of brothers embarked upon some exciting adventure under his watchful eye. Of course there is much work to do, and it is important work; we shall bring back volumes of scientific information and, I suspect, set many of the learned gentlemen of the Royal Society on their ear. But we carry it all out with such good cheer that it seems more like garden play than work. I sometimes cannot believe my luck being here with such a fine, energetic bunch of fellows engaged in such a worthwhile pursuit.

August 8—Off the coast of the unexplored lands north of Barrow Strait (I say north, but our compasses are all but useless, being so close to the Magnetic Pole that its effects are so weak, and that of the ship's iron so strong, that they cannot well be used for navigation). I continue to take readings with Le Vesconte, but wish we could go ashore and set a proper observatory far from the influences of the ships. We have with us two portable observatories which contain no iron whatsoever and so, if we can erect them sufficiently far from the ships, will enable us to take very sensitive readings indeed. I daresay we will have the opportunity to set them up soon enough, for the ice is getting heavy and we must snake about as best we can, sometimes going ten miles for the gain of two or three toward our goal.

The ice is very different from the bergs in Baffin's Bay or by Greenland, not standing up hundreds of feet in the air and threatening to crush us from above, but rather lying like an uneven carpet all across the water and threatening to nip us from below. But it is a carpet continually in motion, heaving with the waves and breaking up and reforming with paths through or 'leads' as Reid calls them. At times there is a network of leads through which we can sail with relative ease, at others we follow but a single path which may or may not take us where we wish. But it is never a worry for long, since the wind, currents, and tides keep the ice-pack moving and changing and we need just patience to find a way through. But we move ever more slowly and, unless we find a wondrous open ocean somewhere before us, I am beginning to think I shall have my wish of spending a winter up here.

The coast is very spectacular hereabouts, being composed of massive, brown cliffs which rise several hundreds of feet above narrow rocky beaches. The tops of the cliffs seem level and probably constitute a flat plateau. The coast here too is flat with precious little to afford a harbour if one were required.

Elizabeth, it is a wondrous and a strange place we have come to and I shall have much to tell upon my return but for tonight I am done.

August 11—My apologies, the last few days have been very hard and I have not been of a mind to write. On the 9th, we met ice solidly packed from shore to shore. For a time we imagined that we might be trapped for the season, uncommonly early, dangerously exposed in the open channel and a great disappointment after splendid good luck till now. Reid appeared unconcerned, however, saying, "Just you wait Mister Jems, she'll no' be solid yet, one o' they leads will come for us afore long." And sure enough, around 4 p.m. we heard a loud crack not unlike the report of a large artillery piece, but sharper. I was aft with the instruments and rushed forward thinking the worst had happened but not being able to imagine what it might be. I was met by Reid wearing a large crooked grin, saying, "Ah Mister Jems, there she be arl right," and pointing to a wide lead which had appeared almost magically not twenty feet from the bow. It was little wider than the *Erebus*'s beam and snaked about in all directions, but seemed to be heading approximately to our bearing. Then the hard work began. We opened the ice saws, each twelve feet long, rough bladed, and weighted at one end, and I ordered the crew over the side.

The procedure when making way through ice is to have the men cut a channel to the nearest lead. This is done by digging two holes in the ice with axes, the width of the ship apart. The ice saws are dropped through the holes, weighted ends first. The upper ends are roped to pulleys which are attached to tripods of ship's spars. The saws are raised and lowered by pulling on ropes running through the pulleys and thus the ice is cut. The tripods and saws are gradually moved forward as the cuts are made and the separated ice broken and either hauled up onto the surface or, if the underside of the ice is smooth enough, pushed underwater and to each side. It is a laborious process, but one which there appears to be no avoiding if we are to progress through the ice. I was timing the men, and the best they managed was to cut through three feet of six-inch-thick ice in one minute, fair going I thought.

We have brought much gunpowder with us in order to make charges to break the ice before us, but this method needs thicker, strong ice to be effective (not the soft thin stuff we encounter this early in the season where the charge simply blows a hole through and does not break the ice up). While the ice is being cut, the remainder of the crew must take to the ropes and manhaul the ship through the new passage toward the open water. It is hard, slow, backbreaking work, but the men take to it with a will, many having performed just such feats on previous whaling voyages. There were a number of injuries, most minor and due to men slipping on the smooth ice which has not acquired a covering of snow, and Surgeon Stanley had no difficulty in patching them up.

In three hours we had reached the open lead and set to firing up the steam engines. We had to sit some considerable time and wait for the *Terror* which was farther from the lead and had more work to do. At last, around nine in the evening, she too was in the lead and we proceeded under steam power with some caution. Fortunately the sky was clear and we had a full moon, so even when the sun was below the horizon, it was still light enough on deck to read by, and we continued to make progress. The engine seemed at first to perform well, although it made a noise rather like some huge hissing mechanical dragon, and we made some progress parallel with the coast. At about 5 a.m., by which time it was already fully light, Gregory the Engineer came on deck to report that there was a failure in one of the valves and that steam was escaping in a dangerous manner. I immediately ordered the fire damped and we resorted to sail and teams of men on the ice hauling. This is how we proceeded these last two days, alternately steaming when the boilers were working, sailing when the wind was fair, and hauling at the other times.

Our path has been a zigzag through a bewildering array of leads which open and close at the whim of some undersea current or the pressures of ice being driven from some unknown channel. The main difficulty is that the ice is being driven back along Barrow Strait, so that at the times we are trapped in the ice, we are going back the way we have come and must struggle to even stand still. This ice work is strange, and not at all like what I am used to. Even the Euphrates, with its continually shifting sandbanks, treacherous shallows, and false channels, was nothing like our struggle through this always moving ice. At times, the leads are no wider than the ship, and I can hear the sound as it grinds past the hull, and already our black and yellow paint, which looked so splendid in the May sunshine of England, is looking sadly worn and chipped. The noise of the ice is worrisome to hear, but we have not yet, thank God, been in any ice under pressure. The men take to the work with good heart and Reid remains ever cheerful, merely regarding the ice as a minor inconvenience.

This a.m. we followed a lead which was taking us almost directly to shore in the lee of a stubby point of land. As the sky was blackening, or I should say greying since it was laden heavy with rain, and the wind was freshening against us, we kept on in and are now lying at anchor in its shelter. It will not do us as a winter bay, but Reid is convinced that the wind is good at this time of year and will open the ice in the channel and allow us to proceed at a better rate in a day or two. At present, rain is falling heavily and the wind is fresh. The sky is low and the clouds speed past above us just above mast height. In breaks we get glimpses of the ice in the channel which appears to be moving at a rapid speed past us and which firmly closed our lead long past, but the ice in our shelter is calm and we sit close in to the shore which is composed of rough, jagged rock leading up to towering cliffs of which we have only seen the lowest 100 feet beneath the rushing clouds.

The *Terror* sits close beside us and Crozier and Hodgson came over for dinner. Crozier too is of the opinion that this wind will do us good and clear at least some of the ice out of the channel. Osmer and I managed a game of chess, the first for several days. He beat me soundly.

August 12—The storm continued against us all last night, although the wind abated to sudden short squalls by morning. Around ten we espied some leads of open water and cut a passage out to them to recommence our tedious passage westward, but as we went, the leads became more numerous and wider until, by mid-afternoon we were sailing with some ease in relatively open water. It seems Reid was right and the ice has all been blown farther down the channel. Since the whole channel appeared open, we set course across to the shore of North Somerset which may be a continuation of Boothia. Our speed is still slow as there is much ice around, but the backbreaking work of cutting and hauling is done, at least for now.

August 13—The weather continues fair and the ice light, although it is heavier up against the Somerset coast. We progress west some ten or twelve miles off land, which is much different from the cliffs we have seen recently. To be sure, there are some cliffs but not of the same uniformity. Altogether the land hereabouts is more hilly, in keeping with its namesake, but of course the hills are much higher and there is no grass nor any of the apple orchards for which that delightful English county of Somerset is so justly renowned. I would be nowhere else at this moment; yet to sit with you beneath an old oak and sample some cold roast duck and a glass of cool cider, would be most pleasant!

But we are well looked after; bread and biscuits are baked in ovens whenever the weather permits and the meat is of good quality. Our canned supplies, provided by the contract with Goldner's Patent Preserved Meats, are not so good and some have been found leaking their contents already. I suspect this is a consequence of rushing to fill the supplies before we left and of purchasing them from an unknown and untried supplier simply because he managed to quote the lowest price. The food in the cans which are not leaking are of good quality and we have dined on the soups, vegetables and meat on a number of occasions. I shall distribute cans to the crew on special occasions.

The officers eat Mister Goldner's produce more regularly to stave off the stultifying effects of salt meat, but the sick I have ordered fed exclusively out of the cans. Stanley feels, and I agree, that the quality and variety of diet offered by the cans will aid the men in regaining their strength. Not that our sick bay is full. Stanley has the usual number of shipboard accidents, including a man with a bad axe wound from slipping while at work on the ice, with which he deals with admirable efficiency. It is one of the most important things for the state of a ship's crew to have a good surgeon. So many are but butchers with a bit of book learning, and we are lucky in Stanley who is much experienced and able to deal with any and all ailments to the patient's satisfaction. There is also one man in sick bay who shews every sign of consumption. Why he did not tell us before we sailed, as all the crew were charged to do, I cannot fathom. This Arctic world, the cold and the hard work, are not for the weak. I fear he may be a casualty if we have a long voyage.

But back to our diet, we must each drink our share of cranberry or lemon juice every day to ward off the dread effects of scurvy which is the main problem on these long voyages. Fortunately, we also have a good stock of brandy and port, which Sir John distributes before and after dinner as appropriate. Last evening, he regaled us with the story of his unforgivable treatment when governor of Van Diemen's Land. Apparently, the settlers thereabouts formed very strong cliques and retained a strong allegiance to the former governor. They resented Sir John's liberal-mindedness on many matters and were constantly disloyal to him. Sir John maintains that this is often to be expected in the more remote colonies, but what was unforgivable was the local society ladies' treatment of Lady Jane.

I have only had the pleasure of meeting the old man's wife on one occasion, when she sailed on board from Greenwich to Greenhithe on the Thames, but even at that, I was struck by her forceful personality and energy. She is a very cultured person and would, I am sure, have railed heavily against the parochialism of the inhabitants of a small bleak island at the ends of the Earth. In any case she was treated very shabbily and Sir John cannot forgive the Tasmanians for that. He shewed us a rebuttal of their complaints which he had arranged for publication after we sailed. It is, I think, a very reasoned document, although he was advised against publishing it for fear of annoying the friends of the colonials in the government. I think Sir John is happy to be free of the machinations of politics. He strikes me as a straightforward man, happy to be carrying out orders and working in the hard simplicity of exploration. Of course he misses his wife and children most dreadfully, as I miss you every day, dear Elizabeth.

Oddly, on earlier voyages, I envied the men with families and sweethearts their connections home, the memories they carried with them whatever the circumstances, and the delicious anticipation they felt before a return to port. I would joke them about the enviable freedom I had without the burden of responsibility, but secretly I sometimes wished I had more of a home to return to than my rooms at the club in town or the generous lodging of some friend. Now that I have a home, for I think of you, William and the children as my family no less than Sir John or Fairholme think so of their wives and kin, I find that the thought of you now produces an almost exquisite longing to return which, when felt to the full, is a distraction from one's duties and a trouble to the heart. Now I sometimes find myself envying the carefree emotional state of young Le Vesconte or Des Voeux. Not that I would trade places with them, I merely say this to show you the effects you have on your poor brother even at such a great distance.

But I am in danger of becoming maudlin, I must to bed. Sir John's most excellent port has made me sleepy and over voluble. Good night.

August 14—We have discovered a new channel to the south, and named it Lady Jane Sound. It is wide, but much ice clogged except down the east shore where there is open water leading to the tantalizing unknown. I estimate that we are little more than 350 miles from the strait discovered by Simpson and Dease and where there should be open sailing along the coast. It is tantalizing indeed and Crozier came over for a conference this evening.

"It is opportunity," he said. "This land offers precious few and we cannot afford the luxury of neglecting even one."

I argued for pushing on to Cape Walker. "The open water is not wide and it may lead us into difficulties, and it is unpleasantly early to be beset for the season. Parry made considerable headway to the west before he wintered at Melville Island and we should follow his route farther before turning south for the coast."

"Aye," Crozier went on, "Parry did make many miles westward, but it was all along the Melville Island coast. He could make no headway to the south and reported remarkably heavy ice in that direction.

"But this is a warm season. That ice may well be broken up this year."

We fell to silence waiting for Sir John's opinion.

"You both make good points," he said thoughtfully. "But I am inclined to Mister Fitzjames' view, not least because our orders require us to proceed past Cape Walker before turning for the continental coast. We cannot know what the ice will be this year and I am of a mind to follow our ordered route to the best of my ability before deviating from it. Should we return this way, Lady Jane Sound remains an option."

I could tell that Crozier was not happy with Sir John's choice or my arguments, but he held his peace. Only time will tell who is right.

August 15—Fair weather with only a slight breeze, yet in the morning it was enough to push us along at two or three knots. Spent the day taking readings. We have crossed the mouth of Lady Jane Sound and have Cape Walker close on our port beam. It is but an island off the coast of a much larger body of land lying off Somerset which we have named Wales Island. By afternoon the ice had thickened and we were forced to tack away from the coast and work with care. The ice is still very broken but heavy; thankfully, the weather is calm. If a wind got up we would have the devil's own business not being severely battered by the ice.

August 16—What disappointment! All day the weather remained clear and the breeze fair although the ice remained heavy and we had to move onward with caution. At first we were encouraged by the land falling away to the southwest, but around 2 p.m. we espied a distant line of white in the water which could only be hard pack ice. By four we were close up to it and our hearts fell. It is the heavy pack of Parry's describing, a vast moving wall, a glacier on the ocean. Blocks of ice are thrust up to great heights and the whole moving mass is groaning and crying out as if in agony. It is as if the ice were a giant living thing which would crush us as thoughtlessly as we would step on an ant. I have seen nothing like it.

This must be the source of the ice which kept us pinned in our small bay but a few short days ago. We stood off and watched in silence. There is no way through. The ice river dashes any hopes of making progress to the south past Cape Walker. Consequently, we are now following the edge of the ice to the northward. Small floes and blocks of ice are continually being thrown off by the ice river and make a close approach impossible. Even at our distance of a few miles, we must pick our way with care and the going is slow, but we must stay as close as possible to see if there is a way through to the west. Was Crozier correct?

August 17—A frustrating day. The weather remains fair and the wind calm but favourable, yet all we can do is tack back and forth in front of this impenetrable wall. There is no way through, even where Parry progressed toward the shores of Melville Island. Byam Martin Channel is completely ice clogged too—discouraging, even though we know it would only lead to further disappointment in the north were it open. A discussion at dinner resolved that we shall wait longer and see if a change in the wind will open a path for us. No-one who has seen the ice river can believe that it will offer a lead, yet we have no choice other than to retire with our tail between our legs.

August 18—All day the ice being freed from the river increased around us, requiring a close watch be kept. Toward evening the wind swung round and large masses of ice were borne down upon us. It was almost as if the ice were reaching out to grasp and draw these two puny interlopers into its realm. We are retreating to the northeast as the wind freshens.

August 19—We continue to run before the ice and passed close by Lowther Island. This afternoon we examined Lady Jane Sound again through the telescopes, it being a considerable distance to the southward. It seems the wind has closed the lead we saw but three days ago—is this a missed chance or was the opening merely a siren attempting to lead us into the icy fastness of some blocked inlet? We shall not find out this season. We are finding some shelter behind Griffith Island and working in toward the south coast of Cornwallis Land where there is open water.

August 20—This afternoon we crossed the mouth of Wellington Channel which is open and an inviting prospect. The ice is still flowing past us from the westward, but remains broken enough that we can make way through it. We watch the ice silently, because all understand the danger of the wind getting up, the ice suddenly thickening around us, and our expedition being carried helplessly back out of Lancaster Sound. Then all our efforts would be for naught as it would be too late in the season to return and we would be fated to spend a winter in the open, unprotected ice—a possibility that even Reid with his rude philosophical view of the ice does not relish. The mood is low and even Osmer took no pleasure in his defeating me at chess.

This evening we pulled in behind Beechey Island at the eastern point of the entrance to Wellington Channel. It is not a true island, being attached to the mainland by a narrow isthmus of rocky beach which forms a bay sheltered from the ice of the main channel. All are agreed that it would make a suitably protected winter harbour. Barrow Strait continues icy, but Wellington Channel appears open.

Captain Crozier came over for a council of war this evening. He had the grace not to mention our discussion of several days ago.

"We could not ask for better winter quarters than these," he began. "I admit it is still early in the season, but the ice is very capricious and were we to venture too far from here, we might not be able to return and hence become beset in a position much less favourable. Our time here before travel becomes impossible could be well spent in exploration and in a small-boat survey of Lady Jane Sound, preparatory to our continuation that way come next season."

Again, I had to disagree.

"Wellington Channel is ice free," I declared. "I cannot hold with the idea of an open Polar Ocean, but we are charged with examining this strange land and we must take every opportunity to increase mankind's knowledge of it. That end would be better served by a full excursion by both vessels to determine the extent and heading of Wellington Channel. Even if we are blocked, it will finally put to rest the Polar Ocean idea."

Our differing opinions were put forward with no rancour or bad feelings. The responsibility of decision is Sir John's alone.

"Again," he said, "Mister Fitzjames' proposal fits most closely with our orders to sail north if a southern route is blocked. Time and circumstances alone will tell if Lady Jane Sound was a missed opportunity, but we must use to the full what time remains of this season. Tomorrow we will round the point and investigate Wellington Channel."

Le Vesconte is of course delighted and talks of nothing but forcing our way through to the open Polar Ocean and perhaps even reaching the Pole itself. He maintains that the currents which have been observed continually in motion in Baffin's Bay and also through Behring's Strait, combined with the observed northward migration of birds and animals, and the apparent break-up of winter ice from the north when observed from the shores of America, all suggest a northern climate milder than that found around the Mackenzie River—and thus, the presence of large quantities of water in a fluid rather than a solid state to the north. All that will be required is the penetration of the rim of pack ice around this open ocean and the pole—as well as an easy route to the orient—will be ours.

I cannot believe it. The river of ice beyond Cape Walker was immense beyond belief, and it seemed to be flowing, albeit very slowly, *from the north*. Thus there must be to the north a reservoir of ice of such size that it completely covers the Arctic Ocean and any land which may be present there and for all seasons. On this point at least, Sir John, Crozier and myself are agreed. There is certainly a risk of besetment in unfavourable circumstances, but we did not come here to avoid danger, and the potential increase in knowledge is worth the risk. We are engaged in work the import of which will only be truly judged by future generations.

Listen to me, waxing eloquent and blowing myself up pompously. I must to bed while my vanity can still fit within my small cabin. Good night.

August 21—In open water again, what joy. It took us most of the morning to struggle through the ice and round the point. The wind was moderate and not favourable, so we had to tack much, not easy when your way is blocked by numerous large pieces of ice. We used our engines which remain uncertain, but by noon, the ice was thinner and we began making progress up this unknown passage.

The channel is wide and trending to the northwest; Le Vesconte is in quite a frenzy over what he imagines our chances to be. He is a permanent fixture in the bow when he cannot persuade Reid to let him take a turn in the crow's nest. "We shall be well on the way home by Christmas yet," is Le Vesconte's eternal refrain, but he continues to be an invaluable help with the readings of which we have collected much in the clear weather of the last few days. All have brightened with the prospect of some more open water for our hulls. To our east lies the unexplored west coast of North Devon and, to our west, Cornwallis Land.

Wellington Channel narrowed around four, but almost immediately opened out as the coast of Cornwallis Land swung to the west and that of North Devon fell away to the northeast. Ice is packed hard and heavy along the Devon shore, but it is still open by Cornwallis. By evening we thought we could see a point of land to the north, but whether it is a new undiscovered isle or part of North Devon where it swings back to the west to form a large bay, we cannot tell. This we named Point Parry on our charts.

Tonight we have the most magnificent display of the Aurora Borealis, with the entire sky being wrapped in shimmering curtains of light: blues, green, and reds. The light forms a wall and the colours roll along it as if following the folds of the stage curtain at the opera. It is bright enough to write my journal by on deck when the sun is below the horizon. This is truly a most amazing phenomenon and we take it as an omen of good fortune to come.

August 22—We have left the shores of Cornwallis Land which we now suspect to be an island since the land fell away sharply to the west and south. The ice is very heavy to the west, but we are mostly protected by a line of islands, the most southerly of which Sir John allowed me the honour of christening Elizabeth Island after the dearest sister any sailor could hope to have (I seem to have fallen into the habit of addressing you thus—I hope not against your will for truly I think of you as such. I have long called William brother, since the days of us growing together in my uncle's house and cousin is such a poor word for the closeness I feel for both of you. So, for the present and since there is no-one here to contradict me in the privacy of my journal, I shall continue to refer to you thus and you may scratch out the offending words upon my return). In any case you will be immortalised on the Admiralty Chart forever, but I fear you will never see your very own island, and the pressure of the lateness of the season means that your enterprising cousin-brother cannot take the time to set foot upon it for you.

Tonight we lie only ten miles off Point Parry. It is in fact a part of Devon and we have named the bay to our east James Ross Bay after the commander of our brave ships, and of Captain Crozier, on the Antarctic circumnavigation. The channel is narrowing to the northeast between the extension of Devon Island and what we presume to be Bathurst Island which extends much farther to the north than does Cornwallis. The ice is heavy but there is a wide expanse of open water along the Devon shore which we shall follow as far as is possible tomorrow.

August 23—Today we reached latitude seventy-seven degrees, our farthest north, and the farthest we shall go in that direction. All morning we sailed in a wide lead until, around 1 p.m., it closed ahead. I climbed the mast to see what I could. Ahead the coast of Devon swings to the east and Bathurst to the west presenting a view of a vast expanse of solid ice as far as the eye can see. This must be the Polar Ocean and the source of the heavy ice we encountered past Cape Walker. No-one could ever hope to find a passage through this and I suspect it offers no open water at all from one year to the next.

Poor Le Vesconte. I let him climb the mast to gaze on the hopeless vista ahead. He is disappointed, but taking it well. We can go no farther north this way. Not even Barrow will be able to maintain the fiction of an open Polar Ocean in the face of our report. An important piece of work, if only a negative one.

Tomorrow, if our lead shews no signs of closing, we shall take readings, and then work our way back down to our wintering place.

August 24—Weather clear and a large party from both ships went ashore. We have collected many of the most northern readings ever. We went also to hunt, which resulted in only five or six partridge since Sir John would allow no party to travel any great distance from the ships in case the wind changed and our lead closed.

Le Vesconte, Irving and I climbed a hill, almost 1,000 feet by my judgement, to confirm what we glimpsed yesterday from the mast. What we saw to the northwest was indeed an apparently limitless tumult of ice stretching as far as the eye could see and so completely solidly packed as to offer no hope of ever navigating through. Vast towers and castles of ice are everywhere cast up to great heights as a testament to the power of the elements in this region. We appeared to be on a peninsula reaching up from Devon and, far on the northern horizon, we observed several points of land which I suspect represent islands in this sea. To the southwest, we can clearly see the north coast of Bathurst Island which is of considerable extent.

Poor Le Vesconte was silent as he looked upon the death of his dream of an open Polar Sea, but he roused himself and together we erected as large a cairn as possible in the time available, and in which we stowed a message giving some bare details of our journey and discoveries so far. When we returned to the shore, we discovered Fairholme and the others busy measuring the air and dragging the shallows in search of whatever strange life they could find to interest Goodsir. Around four the wind swung around from the northwest and freshened and I judged it prudent to return to the ships. This evening it came on to rain and the wind increased and began pushing ice down upon us. We are retreating, but it is slow work. At least now with the open Polar Sea notion to rest, our way for next year is clear, as I think it always was in Sir John's mind; we will follow our instructions come what may and head for the continental coast.

And now it is past one and I must to bed. If this weather keeps up, I fear I shall be hard at work for the next few days. Good night.

August 30—At last we are back beside the island which bears your dear name. It has taken us five days to retrace a journey that took us less than two only a week ago, such are the vagaries of this peculiar and ever-changing place. But now we are more secure in the lee of sheltering Elizabeth Island.

The weather today was fair and you can now be content that your brother at least has set foot upon your island. Fairholme and I set up one of our wooden huts and our instruments, and we will sit in it tomorrow and watch and record the movement of our various needles. Today I had the chance to wander around and picked up some interesting looking mosses and lichens for our collection.

Elizabeth Island is low and, I am sorry to say, not overly imposing, but perhaps it has a hidden sense of fun which only shews itself by the light of the Aurora. It takes the form of an oval, about four or five miles across and some twenty long and trends nor-nor-west, pointing almost directly at distant Point Parry. It is surrounded by rocky beaches which lead rapidly to moderate cliffs, the top of which form a level plateau cut by numerous small rivulets. There is some grass and sedge, and purple saxifrage and a tiny yellow poppy add some colour. For birds there are the ducks and geese which are everywhere in this land and a small reddish brown wading bird, about nine inches long, which Fairholme assures me is a phalarope. Fairholme kicked over a sizeable bone which he believes once belonged to some species of deer. I have collected a modest-sized rock from the base of the cliffs which I shall bring back and you can place upon your mantle as a conversation piece, for which of your lady friends can boast of owning a piece of an island bearing her name?

We plan to return to Barrow Strait down the west side of Cornwallis which appears more open at present. It is certain now that we shall winter in the ice, if possible, back at the sheltered bay by Beechey Island. But now I must to bed, happy in the knowledge that, if I cannot set eyes on you dear sister, at least tomorrow, I shall set foot again upon your island.

August 31—Overcast and cold. The wind has moderated to a light breeze and swung around from the southeast to bring us the lightest of rains, so light that it is almost impossible to tell if the drops around one fall or hang suspended in the air. But for all its subtlety, this rain has the power to find the least crack in one's clothing and soak one through in a very short time, which Fairholme and I found out as we sat in our little shack. Reid says it is called a 'scotch mist' and I can believe such devilishly contrary weather originated in the bleak hills and glens of our northern neighbour.

Not that I have the least to say against the inhabitants of that land, except perhaps to comment on their sensibleness as far as finances are concerned, for many of the crew are from there, particularly the most northerly islands. They are a very hardy race and put up with the most rigorous work without a word of complaint. They are silent and one might almost think them morbid, or 'dour' as they say, but it is just a consequence of the dryness of their humour which does not find expression in the slapstick which sometimes entertains us so.

I overheard two men talking on deck last evening, the piles of supplies allowing a close approach without observation. They were both old in looks, although in years probably not past forty, the look being a consequence of many hard seasons on the whalers, and both had the lit clay pipes which all the crew have, clamped firmly between their teeth, so that their conversation was a series of mumbled comments which escaped from the sides of their mouths. They were discussing Neptune, who was lying apparently asleep atop a pile of rolled canvas.

"Yon dug'll no survive the winter chill," says one.

"No, I daresay," says the other.

"He has nay fat on him at arl," continued the first.

"No, I daresay," replied his friend.

The conversation, if such it could be called, continued in this vein for some time, with the first man making an observation about Neptune and the second man responding with "No, I daresay," occasionally interspersed for variety with "Aye, I daresay."

At length the first man stated, "Why, he's sae skinny noo, he's like nothin' more than package o' soup bones in a sack."

The second man considered this for a while before replying, "Aye, I daresay we'll have tae look tae the monkey for supper when arl the cows is gone."

Both found this last amusing and chuckled roughly before lapsing into silence. Such strange, gruff humour is common amongst the people below decks, and I like to hear it for as long as men are joking, dry though these jokes may be, they will be happy in their work.

This evening the breeze has picked up and we commenced our return passage down Cornwallis Island to complete our circumnavigation. Good night dear sister.

September 4—First I shall say that I am still well, but at times in the last few days it was my considered opinion that the words farther up the page would be the last I would write to you.

We set off as planned down the coast of Cornwallis Island and for the first morning made good progress. We were sailing in a channel between the stony beaches and the heavy ice pack, in width about ten times the length of the ship. It was tight going, but the land fell away from the beach rapidly, so we had sufficient way beneath us. The channel could be easily seen extending far ahead of us along the coast. Around noon the wind dropped and, as we observed the channel narrowing ahead, we lit the boilers and proceeded under steam. Around four, the *Terror*'s engine failed and we had to wait while her crew examined the faults. We were not concerned since the wind was beginning to pick up from the northwest which would allow us to make way under sail again. What we did not immediately realise was that the wind from that quarter would also rapidly drive the heavy ice on shore.

We noticed about dinner time that the channel was narrowing ahead and that large blocks of ice were becoming detached from the stream and drifting across our path into shore. No-one slept that night as we spent a very nervous time avoiding the ice and attempting to make headway south. The going was particularly hard for the *Terror*, whose engine refused to work. By first light—I judged we were about half the way down Cornwallis Island—both ships were held tight in a solid carpet of ice pushed hard against the shore.

Reid was in a worry that the pressure would increase and that we would be 'nipped,' that is the hull would be crushed by the floes. He knew of cases where this had happened to whalers and, although we are in much sturdier vessels than the whaling ships, I had seen the power of the ice west of Cape Walker and had no doubt that, if it wished to crush us, our hulls would stand up no better than if they were paper.

We set to work cutting an open channel, but it soon proved impossible, the pressure of the ice being so great that any channel would close as soon as it formed, and the men on the ice were in danger from sharp blocks of ice being thrust up. In fact, around noon of 2 September, the pressure increased around the *Erebus* and she was lifted up, a most strange feeling, and canted over fully five degrees. In one sense, I found it encouraging that the ice pressure pushed the hull up in the air rather than nipping her, but it was a worrisome sensation and no-one relished the thought of being wintered in such active ice.

The *Terror* was in even worse straits. Being closer to shore when the ice closed, she was in imminent danger of being driven onto the beach where already some of the ice was pushing with deep groaning sounds. The sense of being absolutely helpless as we felt ourselves lifted up and as we watched our sister ship being pushed onto the rocks was very unsettling, although, if we are to live with the ice we must learn to accept its power with some philosophy.

That night was even worse than the one before as we listened to the noises of the ice. I had left England with the vision of ice as being quiet, immobile material, moving only down a mountain valley when impelled to do so by the force of gravity, and then only at the pace of a snail. I assumed it was certainly capable of holding a ship fast, but doing little more. I could not have been more wrong. It is a living malevolent thing, in continual motion at the whim of wind and tide and does so with such a variety of unpleasant noises, cracks, groans and howls, that it seems almost to be crying out alternately in terror and then in anger. I cannot help but remember what the poet Coleridge said of it,

The ice was here, the ice was there,
The ice was all around:
It cracked and growled, and roared and howled,
Like noises in a swound!

By the morning of the 3rd, we were in a serious position. Our list had increased to almost ten degrees and we were in danger of losing our coal overboard. The hull was making such loud noises of protestation that I felt sure it would give way and we would plunge to the bottom of the sea.

The *Terror* was no better off. She was aground on the beach and in risk of being pushed so high up that we would never get her afloat. I gave orders to prepare to abandon ship and was organising the crew to move our supplies onto the ice when a lead opened. Reid, who was in the crow's nest, a most unpleasant place to be on a ship with a list such as ours, yelled that he espied a lead to the south. The wind had moderated somewhat and the ice was quieter which I took to be a good sign. Every fifteen minutes Reid called out the heading of the lead and it soon became apparent that it was heading toward us at a considerable speed. As the pressure was eased, I sent men onto the ice to cut away around the hull and by late afternoon we had righted and were sitting secure in a pond of our own making.

Meanwhile the crew of the *Terror* was hard at work cutting ice away from her seaward side and hauling her off the beach. All night, by the light of torches, we continued working and by this morning were in the lead and were joined by the *Terror* around eleven. Everyone heaved a sigh of relief, but the work is not over. To be sure, the pressure is reduced in the ice, but it could build again at any change of the wind or undersea current, and we are still surrounded and must follow uncertain leads and cut and haul our way along.

We found by experimentation that in these conditions, a soda water bottle filled with charge and sealed by a Bickfords fuse, when set off some two feet down a small hole in the ice, is very effective in cracking the surrounding ice and allowing the men to haul it aside. So we do make progress and I take heart in that, but now I must to bed.

September 5—Another tedious day of cutting and hauling, but we are, at least, some miles closer to our destination and our luck holds. When our steam engines are working, it is merely a matter of cutting away the ice ahead and steaming slowly forward. When they are not, as with the *Terror*'s at present, there are but three ways to proceed; 'warping,' whereby a hawser is attached to an anchor in the ice ahead and the ship pulled forward by hauling in the cable using the capstan; 'towing,' when the ship's boats are put in and pull the vessel along—although this is not good in ice if the leads are irregular and narrow as it becomes difficult to manhandle the oars; and 'tracking,' which involves sending the ship's company on the ice to pull on a cable attached to the foremast, rather in the way a barge is towed on the much less hostile canals of the midland counties. All these methods are slow and all require prodigious exertions on the part of the crew. The engines are blessed when they work and cursed when they do not. Ahead we see Barrow Strait and should be well into it tomorrow.

September 6—The hard slow work continues, but at least we are back in Barrow Strait. There is little open water and we are loath to follow leads out toward the centre of the Strait as we fear being unable to return to our goal at Beechey Island.

September 7—Another tiring day, we have passed the south end of Cornwallis Island and thus completed its first circumnavigation. Had we known the dangers, I do not imagine we would have examined the west coast at all. Even the waters of Wellington Channel are not as clear as they were when we sailed up them. I am too tired to write more today.

September 9—Still off Wellington Channel. We can see the cliffs of Beechey Island, but the ice is heavy around us and pushes us where it will with no regard for our intentions. Yesterday, the *Erebus* was carried far out into the Strait while the *Terror* was held immobile where she lay. Fortunately, the wind subsided and we were able, by warping and tracking, to regain our former position. We move with almost imperceptible slowness and can only wait for a lead to open and take us in the direction we wish to go.

September 10—The weather is calm and clear, quite beautiful if it were not for our perilous position. The drift east is very slow and the ice so heavy that cutting a lead is little more than a way of keeping the crew occupied.

September 11—Almost there, we made some progress today along a lead which took us almost to a point level with our goal. Unfortunately, the path then turned out to mid-channel. We are some three miles from the shelter of the bay and I think we will be able to cut our way through tomorrow. Not much time to think of little Elisabeth's birthday.

September 14—Safe at last. We have had three days of the most terrible work, cutting and hauling ourselves through the ice to our anchorage. We are in a small bay on the coast of Beechey Island, well sheltered and probably not a moment too soon, the sea is freezing fast.

Some of the crew are in sick bay as a result of our gruelling work. One man who fell into the water was immersed for several minutes before his companions could get a line to him and haul him out. He appeared near death, but some warmth and brandy revived him somewhat. Stanley had to remove two fingers from the hand of one man who was frozen during the work off Cornwallis, they were blackened and had begun to rot, but most of his patients are merely broken with exhaustion and will recover with some canned food and rest.

Erebus led the way into the bay which we have named Safe Haven Harbour. *Terror* followed and now both ships sit, about 400 yards apart, in flat ice some three inches thick. This will be our winter home, and a finer more protected harbour we could not wish for. Had I known in advance of the trials we have so recently undergone, would I have been so high-and-mighty about our God-given duty to increase mankind's knowledge? I think so. Progress of any kind implies a risk and a leaving of past securities behind. If it were security we sought, we should never have left the Thames.

This is almost to the day that Parry was secured at Winter Harbour in 1819 to begin the first winter that men spent in the Arctic lands. He, of course, was some 300 miles west of us on the south coast of Melville Island and must have had much luck to avoid the ice river we encountered. Some disappointment at not matching his feat, but our goal is elsewhere and we will attain it next season.

Sir John read divine service today and we gave thanks for what we have accomplished to this date. Our hopes of completing the passage in a single season have not been fulfilled, but surely next year will see us through. We have accomplished much. We have added Lady Jane Sound, Point Parry, James Ross Bay, the distant northern points, and of course Elizabeth Island to the charts, circumnavigated Cornwallis Island, examined Point Walker more closely than anyone else, reached seventy-seven degrees north, and proved there is no way through to the 'Arctic Ocean' by Wellington Channel. We have collected enough specimens to keep 100 Goodsirs happy for a year and have filled journals with scientific readings. We are well positioned to complete our other tasks next season and return to our homes in a year or two at most.

Our short summer, so incomparable with the long insect-haunted days with which you are familiar, is now over. Our luck has held, and I have my wish of wintering in this strange place. It is an odd feeling to be safe after the adventures of these past few days, and hard to believe that soon our main difficulty will be keeping ourselves entertained. Perhaps by the spring I shall be Osmer's match at 'the game of kings.'

How I shall miss you and the rest of the family in the darkness ahead, but we have made a good start and shall, with luck, emerge next summer by the coast of Russia. I hope I have given you a good account of our doings, certainly they have not lacked interest for those of us engaged in them, and I hope you have been amused or interested by my poor account. Whether I will find sufficient of note to keep you amused in the long months ahead we will see. Tomorrow I shall make a start by describing our situation. For the meantime, God bless you and good night.

Winter, 1845/46

September 15, 1845—Overcast and light snow today, very cold on deck. The mood in the mess has much lifted with our reaching a secure berth, at least as secure as this land allows, but we must soon begin work on our winter preparations. Sleds need to be constructed for the transport of supplies to the camp we shall establish ashore, and our scientific instruments and building materials must be ferried to the sites we select for our work. The wooden houses such as Fairholme and I suffered in at Disco will serve as magnetic laboratories although, if suitable, we will use local rock and, once we have snow proper, we shall try our hand, under Crozier's direction, at the construction of snow houses in the manner of the Esquimaux.

Our scientific work is of the utmost importance and Sir John is much in favour of it, one might almost call him a zealot in this matter, and the one sure way to be in his favour is to carry out any scientific task with diligence and precision. I sometimes feel that our scientific work is of greater importance than our explorations and the completion of the passage, although it was the last that so took the public's fancy and was covered so extensively in the newspapers. In fact I have a copy of the *Times* with me which was published after we sailed, but was delivered by coach at some northern port, I forget which. It reads:

> *There appears to be but one wish amongst the whole of the inhabitants of this country, from the humblest individuals to the highest in the realm, that the enterprise in which the officers and crew are about to be engaged may be attended with success, and that the brave seamen employed in the undertaking, may return with honour and health to their native land.*

This was certainly something we saw in the places we stopped and in the small vessels which cheered us on our way, and we feel that we carry with us all the good wishes of everyone at home for a speedy and safe conclusion to our voyage. Of our success, there can be no doubt, although the vagaries of this land make an accurate prediction of when and exactly how we shall achieve it, somewhat difficult. I hope that with all the cheering that will accompany our triumphant return, the delight at our geographical discoveries will not hide our other scientific achievements; they are of great importance, for only by increasing our knowledge of the sciences, can we hope to understand the world and mould it to our designs to create for our people the most perfect of societies in which to reside.

But, I suppose it is difficult to arouse the people's enthusiasm for sitting day after day in a cold hut recording the movements of a tiny needle every hour. But the movements of that tiny needle will tell us more about the very forces which power our world than the discovery of any sea-route to China. The magnetic work is my responsibility, and it is, Sir John tells me, the main thrust of our endeavour, never-the-less, we will also be measuring atmospheric refraction, hydrography and, when we are at sea, oceanography. We do not anticipate that travel will be possible during the winter months, but in the spring, before the ice breaks us free, we will undertake exploration of the coasts around our temporary home. It is little enough to occupy our minds or bodies in the ten months or so we can look forward to being here, but we must make of it what we can. In the meantime, Good night.

September 16—Snow continuing. Crozier came over for dinner this evening and we toasted our good luck. Sir John, probably reminded of his ordeal on his expedition to the Coppermine River in 1821 by the crewman who fell in the water, expounded at some length on the best way to warm up a frozen man.

"The man must be stripped completely," he said in that tone of his which brooks no discussion. "Two others must do likewise and then lie down beside the first, one on either side. All three must be wrapped in whatever blankets are available, so that the warmth from the two healthy men will revive the third. Buffalo skin blankets work best, but any will do. It is truly wondrous to see one apparently dead revived by this method.

"The trick is to revive the frozen man slowly. The error of giving in to the impulse for a speedy revival can be seen in the experience of Doctor Richardson after he gallantly attempted to swim the icy waters of the Obstruction Rapids on the Coppermine River on my first expedition there in 1821. Richardson had lost the use of all four limbs and appeared dead when we pulled him ashore. In our concern, we wrapped him in blankets and placed him before a roaring fire of willows. In truth he revived and went on to the fame of which we are all aware, but in our enthusiasm to help him we placed him too close to the blaze. In his numbed state, he did not notice and, for some considerable time after had no feeling at all down the left side of his body. In fact, a full five months after the event, he still complained that he had not the strength on that side that he had recovered on the other."

I hope, dearest Elizabeth, that you do not think me vulgar in my reportage of Sir John's tale. I fear that the fairer sex does indeed exert a moderating influence on the roughness of men and that this influence is waning the longer we endure without that company. On the other hand, I must justify my words with my earlier promise to tell you truly of all our doings and this I can only do if I include even that which might cause slight offence. I take refuge in the Bard and while I live shall, "tell truth, and shame the devil."

We also discussed plans for the coming season. Tomorrow we will begin building on shore and move such supplies as are necessary for our land camp. A priority will be the construction of a blacksmith's shop to manufacture nails, sled runners and the replacements we need to restore the engines to working order. I shall be kept busy with the magnetic readings which will be taken throughout the winter at a number of sites established sufficient distance from the vessels and our shore camp.

The main problem will be in keeping the men occupied, but we have the experiences of Parry and Ross to draw upon. Crozier is in favour of organising theatrical entertainments as a way of diverting the crew. He entertained us at dinner with tales of his role as Sir Lucius O'Trigger in Sheridan's *The Rivals* on board Parry's ship. Sir John feels that plays are a 'low' form of entertainment and that we should encourage higher pursuits. Certainly we will have classes in reading and writing and in mathematics and geography for those that want them, but I felt that something more was necessary. At length we settled on a ball on the ice at New Year such as the one James Ross held in the Antarctic, but we shall avoid large scale theatricals. Odd that Crozier was so much in favour of thespian activities, I should not have thought him that way inclined.

September 17—Beautiful clear day. The ice and new snow sparkle as if some benign giant had sprinkled diamonds as far as the eye could see. We almost seem to be sitting in an amphitheatre. Both ships face in to the shore, that is to the southwest. Close by are the cliffs of Beechey Island looking down upon us. They are over 600 feet high and very flat on the top. Across Erebus Bay are the cliffs of North Devon stretching west toward the entrance to Wellington Channel and east back toward Lancaster Sound. Between is the narrow neck of land joining Beechey Island to Devon—it is low and composed of dark, broken rock where the wind has blown the snow clear, much like the beaches at the foot of the cliffs. The darkness of the cliffs is in notable contrast to the white of the snow of the last two days, and I almost feel as if they are watching us so small and insignificant amidst the grandeur of this world. Behind us is the open channel, but we need not fear ice being forced in on us from that direction, since Parry's experience, and ours so far, suggests that the winds here blow always from the northwest and we are protected from that direction by the island and isthmus. Barrow Strait is completely choked with ice and we were lucky to find this haven in time, this late in the season we cannot expect the ice to break-up again before next year. We do not expect hard winter to set in before November and must occupy ourselves before then in preparations. There is much to do.

Sir John, Gore and myself dined on board *Terror* in honour of Crozier's birthday. A fine repast highlighted by a magnificent ham which Sir John presented to the mess, although the wines were not of the quality kept on the *Erebus*; Crozier not being a man of Sir John's refinement in appreciation of the vintner's art. The atmosphere too in the *Terror*'s mess is not as free and easy as our own. It is true that the tenor of a mess is determined by the nature of the Captain or Commander, whether or not he dines there, and Crozier is a man less inclined to indulge in the little luxuries of life than Sir John. As for your brother, he feels that, since we have the craft and ability to preserve fine foods and carry them with us, why should we not allow ourselves the undeniable pleasures of a few luxuries?

Crozier's cabin has not the appearance of a scientific laboratory that increasingly characterises Sir John's. This is partly due to Peddie and Macdonald not having the scientific turn of mind of our own Goodsir and Stanley, whose collections increase weekly, but mainly due to Crozier himself who denies them access to his space and requires them to prepare their specimens in the confines of the officer's mess. Admittedly, the Captain's cabin on the *Terror* is not as commodious as our own, but I suspect Crozier to be more jealous of his space even at the inconvenience of the other officers who must put up with all manner of skinned beasts and fowl. This, of course, is his right.

At dinner, Irving told us of his time in Australia and of the strange animals there. In this he was joined by Sir John, who was in that part of the world with Flinders, and who could describe the natives and the fauna very vividly. "The natives of those parts are most remarkably primitive," he told us. "They are coal black, naked and painted with bright dots and lines, and they sport the most amazing crops of wire-like curly hair imaginable. The squalor they live in is most dreadful, grubbing for roots and existing on the barest of foods. They have none of the refinement or interest of the islanders to the north."

"Certainly they are not the inhabitants of Eden which the Sandwich Islanders have been taken for by some biblical scholars," added Irving.

This produced a laugh, though I fear one of vulgarity since the promiscuous attractions of the Sandwich Islands and Tahiti are well known to all who have sailed to those parts.

"Indeed no," continued Sir John, "no-one would find the inhabitants of Australia attractive in the least degree. However they must be watched for they are a treacherous people and one of our sailors was pierced four times by their crude stone-tipped spears and was lucky to escape with his life.

"But the true excitement on that voyage occurred on the return home. We were in three vessels, the *Cato*, *Porpoise* and *Bridgewater*. One night, in a storm, both the *Cato* and *Porpoise* came to grief on an uncharted sandbar. I was on the *Porpoise* with Flinders and we managed to remove all the crews of both ships onto the sandbar, which was of considerable size and stood some three to four feet above the water. We had an uncomfortable time, but knew that the *Bridgewater* would come in to take us off at first light.

"Imagine our consternation gentlemen, when daylight exhibited not one trace of the vessel. At first we feared that she too had come to grief and it was only considerably later that we learned that her Commander had sailed her in good order into Bombay where he had reported us all lost. Why he did so we shall never know since the *Bridgewater* was lost with all hands on the next leg of her journey home.

"In any case we were stranded and had to make the best of things. We had many provisions, including a herd of sheep, and both ships remained aground for several days before foundering, but we could look forward to no rescue in such an out-of-the-way location. Flinders, the true explorer, first set us to lay out his expedition charts to dry on the sand. Unfortunately, it was almost a disaster, as something frightened the sheep and they stampeded across the paper. I have heard that their footprints may still be seen if you consult the maps in the library of the Royal Society.

"For our succour we had to look to our own devices and Flinders accomplished one of seafaring's most remarkable small boat journeys in sailing one of the *Cato*'s boats the 750 miles to Sydney to secure our rescue."

I hope, in my old age, I can look back on a life half as full of adventure as Sir John's. If so, then be assured that you shall not escape my re-telling of my adventures well into our mutual dotage, but for now good night.

September 18—Continues clear. Le Vesconte and I went ashore to Beechey today and climbed the cliffs. Neptune insisted on coming with us, a rare event, since he rarely strays far from Gore, but I suspect that like the rest of us, he is frustrated with being confined for so long and, since his master was kept busy on the ship, jumped at any opportunity to escape for a few hours. And escape he did, making great sport of frolicking far and wide over the land. The ice and snow do not appear to bother him and he is not troubled by the growth of clots of ice on his feet which seem to cause long haired breeds such problems.

The ice is some seven or eight inches thick out in the bay, but much thinner along the shore. It is adequate for a man to walk on, but will not bear the heavy loads we must drag ashore to build our camp. The top of the cliffs is indeed flat, the effect of standing upon it being somewhat like a Gulliver standing on a table belonging to the Brobdingnagians. There is three to four inches of snow on the ground, although it is blown clear from the high points and fills in the low by the wind which blows lightly from the northwest. Vegetation seems limited to a few poor grasses and sedges, some tufts of saxifrage, and a collection of black and brown lichens clinging to the rocks. It is a more imposing place, but not near as delightful as your own island.

The views we had all day were dramatic. From the first point where we attained the plateau, we could look over to the clifftops on Devon which looked remarkably similar to where we stood, except of almost limitless extent. Below us the ships looked puny indeed and the people working around them like tiny, busy insects. Already there is a dark ring of travelled ice around each ship and one dark line, like a narrow grey bootlace, joining our two homes. When we crossed the island, we were amazed to see completely across the ice-filled passage of Barrow Strait to the lower land of North Somerset. Even back as far as we could see toward Lancaster Sound is a solid mass of white, unbroken any-where by the least suggestion of open water. Apart from the cliffs and our small ships, the world up here is endlessly white; we take for granted the richness of colour around us in the temperate parts of the globe in a way that can only be understood when faced with such immensity of black and white as we have here.

Le Vesconte and I took a few minutes to build a small cairn on a seaward point of the cliffs. We have no illusions that it will be seen from any great distance, the work being hard, and we not having adequate tools, but we both felt comfort in putting our mark upon this land, even in such a small way. Neptune caused us amusement by also putting his mark upon the cairn and establishing, in canine fashion, that this was his territory. Le Vesconte found a rock shaped curiously like a hand with the finger extended pointing. This we placed atop our cairn pointing our future way to the south.

Le Vesconte is, as you know, not a great talker because of his shyness, but he can hold forth very well when in company with one whom he feels at perfect ease and, on our tramp over the island we exchanged some very pleasant reminiscences of the time he was my second on the *Clio* during our return from China.

"Do you remember the cheetah, Fitz?" he said. "You used to let it run loose and climb the rigging and it was many a poor sailor got a bad fright coming face to face with a wild cat half-way up the mizzen mast."

"Aye," I replied laughing, "but, if you recall, I almost was paid back. Remember the Cabin Boy who took so much fright that he ran?"

"Yes, yes, and of course the Cheetah became excited and chased him down . . ."

"Until I grabbed its tail and hauled with all my strength . . ."

"And gave the creature such a fright it turned on you, placed both its feet on your shoulders and looked you in the eye as if to say, 'What did you do that for? I was only having some sport. It is in my nature to chase things.'"

"Fortunately," I added, "it is also in a cheetah's nature to have claws like a dog not a cat and I escaped without a scratch. Although, as I recall, the crew had to beat the beast off me with iron bars."

It is extraordinary to sit on a barren outcrop of rock, gazing out upon an immensity of ice and snow and think of such things. How exotic appears a world which can include cheetahs, and how remote now appears the part of my life which brought me in contact with such beings. One aspect of the monotony of the landscape hereabouts is its ability to envelope one's senses and render dreamlike all reminiscences of a previous life.

After we built our cairn, we sat in silence for a while, each with our own thoughts about our situation. Even Neptune ceased his gambolling and lay pensive at my feet. At length Le Vesconte broke our silence.

"Fitz," he asked, suddenly serious, "I have been wondering much of late if we do right in coming to this barren land."

I expressed surprise at this odd thought. "What do you mean? Surely it is our duty to discover what we can of the world."

"I am not sure," he answered, "but lately I have a growing sense that we do not belong in this place. Perhaps no-one does, we have seen no Esquimaux nor any signs of their dwellings or travels. Perhaps there are places where no man is meant to go."

He lapsed into silence and we both gazed out over the endless ice for a time. I broke the silence.

"You are just down because we could find no open Polar Ocean," I ventured, trying to jolly him out of his thoughts.

"Yes, I suppose I am," he said, "I suppose I wanted the Polar Ocean so that we would have an easy journey of it. In all truth, Fitz, the ice scares me not a little."

Again we fell silent, I not knowing what to say I had not thought Le

Vesconte to be the sort to be afraid of some ice, but as they say, the quiet waters are most often the deepest and I had been somewhat taken aback by the power of the ice river myself. After a few moments Le Vesconte roused himself.

"Pay no heed to me," he said smiling, "it is but the prospect of a whole year without a good roast pheasant and claret that brings me down."

"Yes," said I, "but at least the company is good and the conversation will feed the mind if all we have for the belly is salt beef and leaky cans of soup."

We both laughed at this. On the way back to the ships, we collected what specimens we could and Le Vesconte was in such good humour that the dark clouds had flown by the time we climbed back on deck.

September 19—Clear in the morning, but clouds building to the west and the wind freshened this afternoon. I fear it may presage a storm of sorts, however, we are secure. Today we set to erecting roofs over our homes, these consist of large, heavy canvas sheets which completely cover the deck, being supported in a peak running the length of the ship from the masts. They do nothing to keep us warm but will help throw off what snow we may get and will help shelter us from the wind. To that last end we will also build walls of ice and snow to the northwest of the ships to protect us from the prevailing wind in these parts.

As for warmth, we are well catered for. There is a small boiler next to the stove in the galley. This invention is hooked up to a labyrinth of pipes which carry hot steam under the decks to all part of the ship. In this way we will be protected from the cold. Thus you can imagine us as warm as a caterpillar in its cocoon while the Arctic winds do their worst outside.

The only problem is that, to keep out the Arctic cold, the men stuff every nook and cranny. This not only adds to the already strong odour below decks, which can only get worse as our time here increases, but encourages the formation of a skin of frost on the walls. On cold nights with almost fifty men sleeping at the same time, the frost can attain a thickness of several inches. This would not be too inconvenient except that as well as forming on the cold walls, the frost is also melting in the warm air, so that there is continual dripping. The impression is of being in one of the tropical houses at Kew Gardens except that the smell would discourage many visitors. Each day the men must set to scraping the frost off, laborious work, but then they are in need of things to keep idle hands busy.

This evening we dined at the *Terror* and I discovered more of her officers and men. Irving I find to be a delightful chap, diligent, hard-working, and full of enthusiasm for both our venture and what we shall discover, has a scientific turn of mind and has been charged with taking our atmospheric readings. He is quite the mathematician and shewed us a medal for mathematics he had been awarded some years previously. At thirty he is already quite the man of the world, having lived in the hard bush of Australia for four years and been occupied in the exploring services in the South Seas where he twice endangered his own life to rescue shipmates—yet he does not have the conceit sometimes associated with that species—he is companionable, good-looking, a decent man at cards, and well thought of by Crozier. Beside Third Lieutenant Irving, the *Terror*'s mess consists of: Captain, Crozier; First Lieutenant, Little; Second, Hodgson; Surgeon, Peddie; Assistant-Surgeon, Macdonald; Ice-Master, Blanky; Mates, Hornby and Thomas; Second Master Macbean; Clerk, Helpman, and I shall give accounts of them as I discover them myself.

To Crozier I mentioned the monotony of the landscape as it had appeared to me on the excursion with Le Vesconte yesterday. It was a passing comment of, as I thought, no import, yet Crozier took it to heart.

"The monotony you perceived," he began, "is only so due to your lack of understanding."

Taken somewhat aback I asked, "How so? What is to understand?"

"Much," he answered. "Take snow as an example. To us it is simple stuff, merely crystallized water which falls from the sky, blankets the land, inconveniences our travels and communications and provides some subject matter for poets. It is snow only. Yet to the Esquimaux who live with it near every day of their lives, it is more. It provides them with shelter, a swift means of travel, a way of tracking game and a medium for storing the food once it has been caught. To them it is not simple stuff, but immensely complex and fundamental to their very existence and this is reflected in their very language which has, I believe, some several dozen distinct words to describe what we call snow. They see wet snow, dry snow, loose snow, compacted snow, snow that is good for travel, or building, or tracking. When we can see complexity in snow, we shall be ready to live in this land."

Crozier's outburst, coming so unexpectedly, left us in silence for a moment until Irving commented, "Well, there may be several dozen words for snow, but I am certainly more comfortable with the names we have invented for the numerous excellent cuts of roast beef."

Even Crozier smiled at this and the conversation turned to other things. Undeniably, Crozier knows much of these lands, but surely he cannot seriously believe that the natives who live here, accomplished though they may be in naming snow, can hold a candle to us when it comes to mechanical accomplishment and fitness to survive in almost any circumstance?

Anyway, dear Elizabeth, enough of your brother's special fitness to rule the world. I am almost settled in my new winter home. I daresay it will not be the standard of Pall Mall or Hampstead, but then I am used to all sorts of discomforts and I would not find many tales to entertain you in either of those places. Sweet dreams my dear. Good night.

September 20—Awoke this morning to a strong wind and snow which made work on the ice impossible except in the lee of the ship. Twice every day we must send men out to chop fire holes in the ice with axes. Fire is our greatest fear and we must have water to hand in case it breaks out. Each of the galley stoves has a desalinator built in, but we will have little use for it in the winter. Fresh water is obtained from snow melt or from the ice; oddly, the salt in the ocean water is not taken up when it freezes, so we may melt the ice to obtain drinkable water.

September 21—Snow moderating today but continues blowing hard, forming continually moving patterns on the surface of the ice in the bay. The falling snow does not lie on flat surfaces, but collects in drifts against any object which breaks the wind. It is already several feet deep to the windward of the ship. The mercury is dropping and the wind cuts through all but the heaviest garments like a knife. Thank heavens for the steam pipes.

September 22—Cleared briefly this afternoon and the wind has moderated allowing crews ashore with supplies to begin laying out building foundations on a flat beach ridge on Beechey Island. We will have the blacksmith's shop, a storehouse, laundry, and carpenter's shop, but we began today with the raising of a flag. It took much of the afternoon to build the foundation for the pole, but now the Union Jack is flying over our winter home.

Looking at it, I could not help but reflect upon all the diverse places around our world which lie beneath the protection of this cloth, and indeed, upon the multitudinous opportunities available to a young man of vigour and imagination in those places. I do not count myself particularly adventurous, certainly no Napier, yet I have already in a little over three score years travelled to such diverse corners of the Earth as China, Mesopotamia and the Arctic wilds of America, where shall I go next? I cannot forever count on an exploring life in the Navy, there are too many of us half-pay officers seeking employment, and I fear that the urge to explore, at least these barren lands, will wane with our successful return. Perhaps if I cannot acquire a suitable posting I will see what wonders India has to offer, and thin my blood again with the warmth of a tropic sun, although I do not think I am suited to a life of commerce.

But I race ahead, we have not yet settled to our winter home and there is much yet to do here, and of course, whatever I do, I shall undertake a quiet spell in your company. Meanwhile, good night.

September 29—A week and no words for you. The weather has remained moderately fair, cloudy and breezy but pleasant enough for the work in hand. Every day the mercury falls a few degrees more. We have completed the ice walls and our ships begin to look like the central bastion of some white-painted fortress, I think our vessels now are secure and comfortable homes for the coming months. On shore, our storeroom is complete and we have transferred much of our scientific equipment to it. The smithy is almost done and William Smith and Samuel Honey will soon be working like Hephaestus at the forge to supply us with our metallic needs.

Since metal is an anathema to my own magnetic work, I will set out tomorrow with a sledge party to make a hut for readings, from stone if possible. I will go to the west, up into Wellington Channel, some way past Cape Spencer. I will take Couch and six men. Across the bay, in the other direction, Le Vesconte will take Des Voeux and do the same work on Cape Riley. We will thus have two stations set a considerable distance from any interference. A third base station is to be set up by Irving on Beechey, but it will primarily be concerned with atmospheric readings.

Goodsir trawls every day through our fire holes, collecting whatever manner of creature he likes and taking readings of the water temperature. He finds little in our bay, but still manages to exclaim with joy at all manner of wonderful beasts observed through his microscope. Osmer has been so busy arranging our supplies on shore and on the ice in order to give us some more room on board that we have had little time for chess, although he still beats me when we do sit down. I expect to be away from the ships for but a few days and will take pen, ink and paper with me to record interesting phenomena and activities which I shall transcribe for your diversion upon my return.

October 10—Well, a longer expedition than I should have liked, but we are all back safe and well as of yesterday. Le Vesconte returned the day previous, having not gone so far.

We set out early in the morning with the traditional prayer for sledge parties, 'O Lord of life and death, have mercy upon those that are appointed to die.' This rather discouraging send-off was followed by three rousing cheers as we set off to the west and Le Vesconte to the east. We made good time at first, hauling over the smooth ice of the bay across the spit, but we soon ran into some rough going as we left the cover of Beechey Island. There was much work in hauling the sled over hummocks and ridges in the ice, some twenty or thirty feet in height; still it was easier than trying to make progress along the beach which, although flatter, was poorly covered with snow and composed of sharp rock which cut up our boots fiercely and held back the sled runners. Despite this, we made good progress, myself being out front and Couch and the men in harness.

The sledges are heavy brutish things made from solid beams and nails. They can take much punishment, but the work with them is gruelling and called by those who have performed it on previous occasion 'pully-haully.' Each sled weighs close to 1,500 pounds and is pulled by seven men, meaning upwards of 200 pounds per man. This is bearable on the flat, but there is precious little flat hereabouts and the work involved in manhandling a full load up a twenty foot high ice ridge is painful indeed. Perhaps the worst problem is thirst, for a man must drink copiously to replace the moisture lost through sweat, and yet melting ice or snow is a laborious process. The boot soles have much difficulty maintaining a secure grip on the ice, and the men are continually slipping and falling and must scramble to regain their footing and take up the strain so as not to disrupt the rhythm of the others. We all had veils to wear over our eyes to prevent snow-blindness, but the weather remained overcast and we did not suffer that painful malady, nor was sunburn a problem nor frostbite, although men commonly had frozen extremities when we stopped to rest.

The work would kill a man not in the peak of fitness and many have stories of men falling stone dead in the traces, or returning so worn out that they take weeks to recover and are never good for hard physical labour again. Even for myself, who had no hauling to do, the work was hard because the trail had to be broken and frequently I had to go on ahead some distance to scout a route, only to find it unsuitable and retrace my steps and try again.

We travelled for two days before we found a suitable route up the cliffs. It was a narrow, snow-filled gully, quite easy to climb, but hard to drag our equipment up, but drag it up we had to, since if we set up at the foot of the cliffs, the mass of the cliffs themselves would affect our needles. Upon reaching the top, we made camp. There was plenty of flat rock about with which to construct a hut and we set too immediately. It must be constructed entirely without metal. We kept metal objects to a minimum, bringing no canned food with us and keeping our cooking and eating utensils a good distance away in a tent. Also, when we enter the hut to take readings, we must make sure that no metal is on our person, a belt buckle or pocket-knife being sufficient to upset our instruments.

On the third day, it began to snow and by mid-afternoon, the wind had strengthened so that we were in the midst of a blizzard. At times we could see no farther than our hand before our face and had to rig up a line from the hut to the tent so that no-one would miss their way and become lost. Our hut was not complete and we had to arrange a canvas over one wall and the roof, a great inconvenience since we could not secure it firmly and were continually having to tie it back down. However, I am happy to say that what was built of the hut stood up admirably to the battering of the gale, and the tent performed well although we had to be continually weighing it down and packing snow around it to prevent it blowing back to Lancaster Sound.

The worst of this inactive time was for those in the tent not engaged in readings. Although they have more space because of the absence of the readers, it is still painfully cramped and one cannot move position without the permission of those beside one. Over the ground we spread a Macintosh upon which we laid a buffalo robe, hair down. Each man has a sleeping bag made of a heavy blanket and covered with canvas to keep out moisture. When we are asleep it is so cramped that we must lie beside each other, head to toe, like so many logs of wood along the length of the tent which is rectangular, being little over six feet wide and seventeen long. The door of the tent has a system of flaps to prevent snow coming in and a bowed area to assist the cook of the day. The cooking chores we rotate, two men each day, and it is not a welcome task, requiring that those on duty rise some two hours before their mates in order to heat water for tea over our small oil stoves. In these low temperatures it can take that long to get meltwater to a temperature sufficient to concoct a lukewarm, but palatable drink. The bags are covered with another robe and a farther blanket to keep the fine fall of condensation which is continually forming on the tent walls just as it does on the inside walls of the ship.

In these conditions, every hour is a hardship and we prayed for the storm to abate and allow us some freedom of movement. The blizzard lasted five full days and offered us no chance to complete the hut and return with the empty sled.

The magnetic camps will be manned at all times through the winter months by two men and they will be relieved and supplied at regular intervals. While we were there, we trained all the crews in the use of the instruments and rotated the readings as frequently as possible, still the men were bored within the confines of their tent or the hut. Couch and I were rarely together since we did much of the readings and were also training the men. Couch is very quiet, but a quite interesting chap on farther acquaintance. He is remarkable for his sensitivity, feeling for the hardships of the men hauling even though he himself is in the traces with the rest. At the camp, he began work on an improved, lighter sled design. His goal is to devise a light sled which would be easier to pull but which could carry almost as much equipment.

To pass the interminable hours we talked a little and on occasion played some cards, but I missed the conversation of the mess and Osmer's chess games. For my part, I occupied myself with planning the location of food caches which we will lay out either this year before the hard winter sets in or very early next spring. These will be used in about April or May as depots for sledging parties which will set out to explore as much of the land surrounding us as possible before we are released and on our way.

The 8th dawned clear and there was not one of us who was unhappy to see the sky and an end to the snow. We rapidly completed the last of the hut construction, packed up a few supplies, said our farewells to Couch and Seaman Best who will take the first spell of readings, and set off. Best seems to be a conscientious worker and takes an interest in our science. I hope I will be able to turn him and a few others from the lower decks into worthwhile helpers. Unfortunately, our scientific work is such that it cannot be performed by the ordinary sailor who may be good at obeying orders, but has not the education or patience for taking precise readings and for observing phenomena. Of course the officers have the full responsibility for the scientific work, but the nature of the magnetic work, with several spread locations, makes the use of some seamen for readings inevitable.

Best is an interesting chap, not as rough in appearance and more softly spoken than many of his fellows. In fact, he speaks very well and I have never heard him resort to the coarse language which is universal below decks. I suspect there is in his past more than the common grind of most of the people. I think he will work out and there are a few others whom I have my eye upon as likely candidates.

The going was much easier on the return, the sled being much lightened, so we stopped frequently to cut a path through the more difficult stretches or to build ramps up the steepest inclines for succeeding travellers. On the evening of the 8th we met Des Voeux and the relief party from the ship and wished them luck as they set out to relieve Couch. We arrived back at noon on the 9th. A small adventure, but one which I feel will prefigure much more of our work, although I will get little chance to undertake the exploration, being tied to the ship and the magnetic camps. But now it is well past midnight and I must retire.

October 12—Parties are already out laying in caches for the spring and our forge is blazing away on shore. Couch returned this afternoon with the relief party, Des Voeux having taken his spot at the observations. Goodsir has given up collecting beasts through the ice and now spends his time scraping the different kinds of lichens off the rocks and examining them under his microscope. He produces the most extraordinary drawings of what he sees and seems eternally engrossed in the world through his glass. Our preparations are well in hand for the winter and will continue to progress satisfactorily as long as the weather remains moderate. Des Voeux and Irving have both expressed the opinion that we should be engaged more heavily in exploration while the weather holds. Sir John has forbidden anyone going out of sight of the ships unless it be on a required task such as relieving the magnetic camps or establishing supply depots. Having seen how the blizzard set in while we were setting camp, I can only agree with him; there will be ample time for exploration in the spring, since we cannot reasonably expect the ice to break hereabouts before the second week of July at the earliest.

October 13—Overcast and windy. Dined on board *Terror* in some comfort with so many officers out on sledging journeys. Couch is busy instructing the carpenters on his design for a light sledge after the fashion of the plans he drew at our camp, which he hopes we will be able to use in the spring with greater ease than the heavy ones we currently have.

"Young Mister Couch's work is worthwhile you think?" Sir John asked me.

"Yes indeed," I replied. "On two counts. First, his work, if successful, will increase the range of our exploring parties in the spring, and second, I sometimes despair of turning him into a good sailor. He would rather mope around on the ice with Sargent than work on celestial readings, so it can do nothing but good to have him pursuing an interest."

"Couch and Sargent are close?" Sir John asked.

"Yes, as two peas in a pod."

"Then be careful, James. You know the dangers on board ship." I nodded and Sir John hurried on to less sensitive topics.

"It is quite extraordinary the new inventions which are making our life here easier. The heating and desalination systems, the steam engines."

Here Irving, who has been much involved with the uncertain performance of the *Terror*'s engine, coughed significantly and produced a laugh.

"It is true that there have been difficulties," Sir John said with a smile, "but it is no more than with any advance and our conditions here are sometimes harsh in the extreme. The benefits ultimately outweigh young Irving's inconvenience.

"And take the Halkett folding rubber boat. I suspect they will be invaluable for summer travel. A boat capable of carrying three men or supplies across a swollen river, yet it can be carried on one man's back. In 1821, Hood, Richardson, Back and I were held by the swollen waters of Obstruction Rapids for seven full days. In our starving condition, it was a delay we could ill afford and it may have cost Mister Hood his life. Were a Halkett boat at our disposal, there would have been no delay, and lives might have been saved.

"Mind you," he continued after a thoughtful pause, "it was more the treachery of the natives that led to the tragedy."

"How so?" asked Irving, betraying the fact that he had not read Franklin's account of the journey.

"They did not remain at Fort Enterprise where they were supposed to meet us at the end of our overland journey from the Arctic coast. It was only through the fortitude of Mister Back, who undertook a splendid march to obtain supplies, that the toll was not even greater."

"But," interjected Crozier, who had been silent to this point, "you cannot entirely blame the natives. They have lived in the land for generations and know its harshness. Their own survival, rather than that of some temporary interlopers, must always be of paramount importance."

"We were not 'temporary interlopers' Mister Crozier," responded Sir John sharply. "We were, as we are here, a scientific and geographical expedition engaged in important work for the increase of knowledge."

"I did not mean to belittle the expedition," Crozier added hurriedly, "it remains a remarkable achievement to this day. I merely wished to suggest that to be completely successful in these lands, we might do well to adopt some of the native's ways.

"For example, look at the sledding burden that Mister Couch is busy attempting to lighten. Even if he is successful, it will remain an arduous undertaking and subject to the whims of climate. Compare this to the ease by which the Esquimaux, for all their primitiveness, move around in all weathers using light sleds and dogs. If we could adopt some of their techniques, would not our exploration become more efficient? Indeed, Parry reports at length on the benefits of utilising dogs."

"I see, *Mister* Crozier, that you pay homage to the modern God of efficiency," Sir John was speaking lightly, but he was staring intently across the table at Crozier. "Efficiency is not everything and there are good reasons why dogs are not suitable to our exploration tradition, not least of which is the fact that we have none with us. But even if we had, good sled dogs are hard to come by and their maintenance and efficient use is not an easy task. We should require either a large number of Esquimaux drivers or much training in the art for our officers.

"And then there are our men. The British sailor is the best in the World—why? Because he works as part of a team and is trained to obey orders without question. Much of his work on board ship is monotonous, hard labour and he is fitted to that. Sled hauling is a good utilisation of the seaman's skills: teamwork, dedication, and rope work. He is ideally suited for the task of sled-hauling, not the maintenance and supervision of such temperamental beasts as Esquimaux dogs.

"We also require large sleds for specimen gathering, a significant factor given our objectives, and a walking pace of between ten and twenty miles a day is ideally suited to our purpose of examining in detail the terrain and mapping the irregular coastline.

"Our means of doing things is different, but superior, to the primitives in this land."

His point made, Sir John sat back and clasped his hands beneath his chin. Wisely, Crozier took the matter no farther. The discussion was amicable, but there were undercurrents between the two men. I think Franklin regards Crozier as a depressive influence.

As to the substance of their argument, I must agree with Sir John that our men are more suited to the hard labour of sled-hauling and we need sleds of good size to transport our scientific equipment and collection. I also have no desire to adopt Esquimaux ways, dress in stinking skins, live in a snow house, and eat raw seal meat. My uniform, bunk, and roast beef will suffice, thank you. On the other hand, it struck me as odd that Sir John, while deriding the natives as primitives incapable of learning our ways, with the same breath implies that our own Able Seamen are not capable of learning the Esquimaux ways!

The time in which we live is a cusp for our people. We are on the verge of great things. England is a great power, unchallenged militarily since the Old Duke put that devil Napoleon in his place, and with unparalleled trade and commerce throughout our far-flung outposts. We have also achieved almost unbelievable things since the end of the war, not least on account of the new inventions which sparked the discussions on the *Terror*. I feel that we can only progress in the direction we are being offered and that improvements with our machines in the years to come will eliminate all of Crozier's arguments and place us in security and comfort wherever we wish to go in the world.

After dinner, I found myself on deck with Crozier and put the above arguments to him.

"Well James," he said addressing me, as he does the officers in his command, informally, "it is true that many of our recent inventions will become much improved with use, and one day soon we may even have engines which do not break down with so much wheezing and groaning every two days of use, but I firmly believe that, while machines are perfectible, men are not.

"Even a perfect machine must be run by men and, hence, subject to human errors. Take our own situation as an example. Our machines keep us safe and warm, yet a simple mistake on our part, such as choosing one channel over another, could bring it all to naught and place us at the mercy of elemental nature. I believe we should work on the perfection of man before we worry overly about the perfection of his machines."

Crozier is undeniably an interesting man, but I cannot agree with what he proposes. Mistakes we will make, and have done I am sure, but our equipment, used with skill and fortitude, must surely carry us through in the end. If we perfect our machines, and therefore our world, can moral perfection lag far behind?

But here I am waxing philosophical again, I must to sleep before I turn this into a tract on our divinely chosen position in the world!

October 14—Overcast with light snow. One of the most interesting new inventions we carry with us—and no I am not going to re-enter my philosophical musings of yesterday—is our Daguerreotype camera. Collins seems to have taken quite an interest in the process and has placed himself in charge of all the equipment under the supervision of Goodsir, who was originally charged with our picture taking but whose scientific duties leave him little time to pursue it. Collins still exhibits little interest in his regular duties and I must still frequently take him to task on the state of the log he keeps on watch. He must be bullied or jollied along in order to satisfactorily complete the simplest work, yet at the least excuse he will struggle about with the bulky picture equipment and spend hours in the cold attempting a particular image.

I visited Collins this afternoon in the laboratory which his cabin has become. I do not understand how he survives in there. It is an alchemist's den of foul-smelling fumes emanating from the mercury, iodine, chlorine, bromine and potassium cyanide which he requires for his work. It appears as if he is eternally polishing silver copper plates or exposing them to the noxious fumes to fix an image. When he is at work, the smell, even in the mess, is almost overpowering and there is much competition to be on a separate watch from the man so as to at least have a chance of being occupied elsewhere when he is dabbling.

None-the-less, I must admit that he has managed to take several fine images now that we are at rest for the winter. The contrast between the dark cliffs around us, the ships, and the white snow and ice produces a pleasant effect, enhanced if anything by the silvery tone imparted to the picture by the process. I think we shall have some worthwhile illustrations when we return, but I shall continue with my poor sketchings all the same.

Sir John is not particularly enamoured of the process, being, I believe, disappointed with the Daguerreotype taken of him before we embarked. He was suffering from a bad head cold and looks somewhat the worse for wear; as he says, "At least a painter could have made a portrait of me looking decent."

I hope you have retained the image of me taken at that time and look upon it fondly, *de temps en temp*, as I often look upon your image in my cabin. With a final glance then, I bid you good night.

October 15—We have now set up quite a little village on shore, with our three large buildings, two smaller ones for food storage and laundry, and several tents. The forge and the carpentry shop are busy making sledges to take out our supply caches for the spring explorations. We intend to send four parties out, one in each direction along the coast of Devon, and one directly overland to the north to see if they can attain a northern shore. The fourth party shall cross the ice on Barrow Strait and examine the shore of North Somerset, perhaps even gaining a look at the coast of our proposed route down Lady Jane Sound.

Came on to snow this evening, light at first, but now is heavy and the wind is picking up from the northwest. I fear there may be a storm on the way. Broke from chess this evening to play a few rounds of backgammon on the fine leather board which Lady Franklin presented to our mess on our departure. I fared quite well against Gore and Goodsir, but Fairholme is a demon and none of us is his match.

Below decks, the men have taken to card games or 'Crown and Anchor,' betting slips of paper against their double Arctic pay. Officially it is discouraged, but it cannot be prevented entirely and, unless the gambling gets out of hand, I am prepared to turn a blind eye while we are in winter quarters. The men are for the most part a good crowd of people and there is none of the harsh caste of a first- or second-rater where the forecastle man despises the topman who despises the after guard as a silk-stockinged gentleman and so on.

Apart from the whaling men there is a good leavening of old man-o'-war hands: Wall for instance has the old cook's habit of whistling tunelessly whenever he is making a preparation with raisins so that none should think he is stealing some. He is adept at the making of burgoo, a sort of oatmeal gruel much prized by the old hands for breakfast. On the *Cornwallis* in China, fresh biscuits could often not be made because of the weather or enemy action. After a few days, or even weeks sometimes, the biscuits developed such a hardness that they could only be eaten after prolonged soaking in tea.

Even then, there was always the rock-like centre or 'reefer's nut' which would defy even the strongest teeth. The cook was then prevailed upon to grind the 'reefer's nuts', soak them, and fry the resulting porridge with pork fat. This is burgoo, a dish which would not pass at any society table and one for which I have never developed a taste. However, even though we are now at rest and can bake fresh biscuits regularly, Wall is still prevailed upon to grind up some burgoo.

At noon, to call all hands to the grog tub, Able Seaman Josephus Geater plays a lively version of "Nancy Dawson" (on land you may know it as "Sally in our Alley") on the fife. There is much singing amongst the men, especially now that we are in the ice. Often I can hear the simple strains of "Drops of Brandy" filtering down from above as the men work on some task:

And Johnny shall have a new bonnet
And Johnny shall go to the fair,
And Johnny shall have a blue ribbon
To tie up his bonny brown hair.

The marines, or 'pipeclays,' tend to keep to themselves, even to having their own songs, although the tunes are frequently the same. A favourite is "Who'll Be a Soldier" the tune of which you will know as the catchy "Craigielee." I am told it was sung by both Marlborough's and Wellington's men, but our marines have altered it to fit their particular circumstances:

A bold young marine came marching down through Greenwich town
Off to explore in afar country,
And he sang as he marched
Through the crowded streets of Greenwich town,
Who'll be a pipeclay with Franklin and me?
Who'll be a pipeclay? Who'll be a pipeclay?
Who'll be a pipeclay with Franklin and me?
And he sang as he marched,
Through the crowded streets of Greenwich town,
Who'll be a pipeclay with Franklin and me?

The Queen she has ordered the Northwest Passage to be found
On a stirring voyage of discovery
And if you'd be a pipeclay
All in a fancy uniform
Take double pay for bold Franklin and me

Take double pay! Take double pay!
Take double pay for bold Franklin and me.

And he sang as he marched,
Through the crowded streets of Greenwich town,
Take double pay for bold Franklin and me.

I quote at length as this is one of the few songs which could be even mentioned in polite company! It is good to hear. A sailor or a soldier who does not sing, even if the song is one of bitterest complaint, is a sorry being and one who will be in trouble very shortly.

Life at sea is a strange mix of companionship and resentment. The artificial throwing together of all ranks of men in a confined and isolated space can engender a great sense of belonging, one strong enough to bind together all from the lowliest Cabin Boy to Sir John himself; yet the potential for rivalries, for example between the old hands and the whalers or the sailors and the marines, is great.

On a personal level too, petty jealousies can become blown out of all proportion. Some men adapt by becoming solitary, some by expansive gregariousness. Still others compensate by developing intense relationships with one other person. This can be based on admiration, misplaced or otherwise. My Cabin Boy, George Chambers by name, I suspect regards your brother this way. He is of course a mere lad, being something around ten or eleven years of age and I do not think they have been easy years at that. He follows me around like a loyal puppy and is only happy when I notice him and delegate some insignificant chore. It is flattering to have such admiration, even from one so young, and there is a strong temptation to take the lad under my wing and encourage his progress, but I must be careful that he not become perceived by his fellows as an officer's pet. It is after all with his fellows that his future lies. To this end, I am sometimes deliberately stern with him to remind him of his place and duties.

The other type of relationship is based on the mutual attraction of like spirits. Thus Gore and Des Voeux work well together and Gore is something of a mentor to the younger Mate. Watching the pair reminds me of old Gambier on the *Pyramus* who did so much to teach me and advance my career in the Navy.

The danger of course is that the latter relationship becomes something other and that unnatural urges surface. It is unpleasant to dwell on such things, but they are, unfortunately, sometimes inevitable in a ship at sea. No difficulties of this nature have come to my notice, although I am mildly concerned with the amount of time Couch and Sargent spend in each other's company. It is probably nothing more than friendship, but I shall keep watch.

I must apologise for touching on such delicate matters, but such concerns are a part of life on board ship. Good night.

October 16—Snowing hard, and cold. We are snug in the *Erebus*, but cannot venture a few feet onto the ice before all is lost in a blanket of white and all sense of direction vanishes. Even the ice-cutting parties must remain attached by a line to the ladders, although they are only going a few yards and that in the lee of the ship. The *Terror* is less than a quarter mile from us, but might as well be in Australia for all the contact we have with her. When this storm passes we must rig a line to her to maintain communications. A large party from both ships is on Beechey Island, but we have no fears for them, they are secure in the huts and tents and have ample supplies for the whole winter should it be necessary. The magnetic camps are more of a concern, but they have sufficient food for several weeks and should suffer nothing other than loneliness.

October 17—Still blowing hard. The time is useful for us all to prepare our notes in good form to this date and to update our journals. Strange, but now that there is less to do, I find that I am sleeping more than if I were hard at work in the middle of the ocean battling waves.

The lack of opportunity for daily exercise outside will be a problem if prolonged. Stanley believes that fresh air and exercise are essential adjuncts to the antiscorbutics in preventing scurvy. Goodsir, of course, differs, maintaining that the lemon juice is all that is required, although conceding that fresh air and exercise are of themselves good and healthful activities. We have a long winter ahead.

For the most part we are following Parry's recommendations for 'promoting Good Order, Cleanliness, Health, and Good-Humour among the Ship's Companies.' The watches, four a day, are the same as when at sea and are filled by the officers, but the men are allowed a full night's rest. The morning begins with the men scrubbing the decks with sand and stones before breakfast, after which they are inspected for cleanliness and their clothing for condition and adequacy. All have purchased clothing from the Navy, although some are still in arrears for payment, and must look after it or purchase more from our supplies. On our way to Disco Sir John called all hands on deck and made an issue of clothing for every man; a jacket and trousers of blue cloth, one pair snow boots, one pair sea boots, one red worsted shirt, one pair stockings, one Welsh wig, one comforter. The clothing is free if men behave well, if not it will be charged out of wages.

The rest of the morning is spent in exercise, on the ice if weather permits, or on our covered decks at times such as now. While this is going on, the officers inspect the men's quarters and organize the men to remove any particularly thick accumulations of ice. After dinner, those not normally engaged in specific tasks, would take walks ashore, but since instructions state that the men must not lose sight of the ship, that is impossible in the conditions currently prevailing. At present, the men are mainly occupied with ropework between the decks, a few of the more promising being taught the operation of the scientific equipment. Best, for example, has taken to the magnetic work as a duck to water and is rapidly becoming invaluable in that field.

We also give lessons in reading and writing to those that need it, which is most, so that they might return home improved in skills if not in morals. We also have arranged classes in mathematics and geography to those that want it, which is few. At six o'clock, inspections of the men and sleeping places are repeated before the crew go to supper. Evening is free time until nine when all must turn in. Since every man on the ship smokes a long clay pipe, the Quartermasters, Bell, Arthur and Downing, practice a routine of half-hour nightly inspections for fire and to make sure that all fire buckets are kept full from our fire holes in the ice.

Le Vesconte and Hodgson have been occupied preparing a weekly newspaper, *The North Devon and Beechey Gazette,* which should have appeared this week, but, I fear will be delayed due to the severe weather since they cannot get to our small print plant on the shore. Wall, the Cook, is a genius at making our monotonous diet more interesting by creating dishes from the cans and salt beef. Because of the lack of exercise I have ordered an increase in the consumption of lemon juice to stave off scurvy and, to the same end, have ordered Wall to begin a small kitchen garden of cress and mustard in the galley, both of which are also very efficacious in preventing illness. I think we shall manage to entertain ourselves and keep fit in these difficult conditions, but I fear there may not be much of interest to tell you.

October 18 & 19—Still snowing and blowing hard.

October 20—Weather broke briefly today, snow eased, but the wind still strong and bitter. We managed communication between our ships, and rigged up a line. By supper the weather had closed in and we were again cut off in our little world, but this time we need merely to follow the rope to visit the world of our sister ship.

Some of the men are suffering from frostbite of their extremities quite badly, and we must make sure that they take proper precautions before they venture out. Many do not yet realise that the wind can freeze a man's flesh to the bone in less than a minute. We now inspect all parties leaving the vessel.

I was inspecting one group this afternoon on their way out to cut the fire hole. One man had no gloves on at all. I asked him why.

"The cauld dosnae boather me," he replied cheerfully. "I niver had need o' the gloves in Orkney, an' it's only a wee hole in the ice ahm goin' tae cut."

I ordered him back to get gloves on. The whaling men are better, having experienced something of what this land has to offer, although none of them has ever wintered at these latitudes.

October 26—Divine service today and I think we all gave silent thanks for the first day in more than a week when we have been able to walk out on the ice. The wind has dropped to a stiff breeze and the sky mostly clear, at least enough for a few readings. I walked over to the shore camp to find that the men there had fared well and had rigged up a complex system of ropes to allow safe passage between the various huts and tents.

Relief parties set out at once this morning for the magnetic camps. I expect this will be the pattern for the season, periods of being utterly trapped by storms, interspersed with spells when we will rush to prepare for the next one. My joy at the break in the weather would be complete if only it included a look at your face and a few minutes of your delightful conversation. But I suppose we must save these minutes I miss now so that we may have hours on my return. Good night.

October 27—Clear last night and froze hard, the mercury dropping to twenty-five degrees below *zero*. Just as I had wished you good night, Le Vesconte came knocking and told me to come on deck where I was treated to the most magnificent display of the Aurora Borealis ever. Even the old Arctic hands claimed to have never seen such a performance. It was as bright as day and the snow seemed to be lit up with the various colours of no less than six huge, waving curtains of light which swept across the sky from west to east and reached far up above our heads. As we stood on the ice some claimed to be able to hear the sound of the curtains moving. I listened hard, but could hear nothing.

To some of the old Scottish whaling hands who profess to believe that Hell is a land of ice and snow at the North Pole, the experience was doubly awe inspiring. Quite a spirited discussion ensued as to whether the curtains of light were drawn by God to protect us from a view of Hell or whether they were drawn by the Devil, or "De'il" as Reid puts it, to entice poor sailors on to Damnation. Whatever the case, we stood enraptured for near an hour before the cold and the waning colours encouraged us to return to our cosy home. If a man could transpose this display to Hampstead Heath for one night and charge the people a penny for the show, he would find himself a rich man before the sun came up.

November 1—Continues cold and overcast. Le Vesconte and I took some men on to Beechey today to try our hand at building the snow houses used by the Esquimaux. The snow here is very strange, not like the heavy wet carpet which falls on London, it is dry and in very fine flakes, so that its own weight packs it down very well. When it is packed, it can be cut rather like a very light plaster, and will hold a brick shape so that a rude wall may be constructed with some ease. I caught a brief glimpse of how snow can be more than the simple substance of my ken and how it might warrant a complex designation.

No doubt in the field of snow construction, even with Crozier's descriptions of the dwellings he had seen, we are much poorer craftsman than the local inhabitants, if there are any for we have seen none so far. However, after a full morning's work, we managed to construct a passable, if rude, shelter in the shape of an irregular dome which appeared more as if it had grown rather untidily from the earth than that which was the construct of men.

I am not yet convinced that I should enjoy passing the night in one, despite Crozier's claims as to their efficiency. Of course we are not yet sufficiently adept to construct antechambers and tunnels to keep the wind out. Perhaps when our skills improve, we may undertake such refinements, for now I shall settle for my bunk on board ship.

Dined on the *Terror* and Crozier treated us to a description of the Esquimaux sleeping arrangements.

"Inside the snow houses," he told us, "they build ledges or platforms on which they sleep naked wrapped in skins. The skins they wear, which are never washed from one season to the next and thus offend the nose quite strongly, dry well in the course of a night, unlike our woollen clothing which must be worn wet to sleep to prevent freezing. I suspect it is more pleasant to put on warm skins in the morning than to awaken in frozen wool. Future expeditions might do well to acquire skin clothing for travel."

"Well," interjected Irving, "at least the smell would not be worse than those some of the men currently exude. However, I fear I should draw the line at eating raw seal and whale meat and fat. I do not think my civilized stomach would be up to that task."

We laughed, but Crozier merely pointed out that the Esquimaux had been living hereabouts for hundreds of years on just such a diet, suggesting that it had some properties to recommend it. He is most knowledgeable on Arctic matters, and no doubt has some very worthwhile ideas on travel and such like, but he can be most infuriatingly serious at times.

Hodgson, on the other hand, is a delight to listen to, always ready with an amusing anecdote or tale of his much beloved children. He has five, in ages from a mere babe to almost grown. His favourite appears to be a son, Henry, some ten years of age and the inheritor of his father's scientific inclination. On one occasion, Hodgson noticed a peculiar smell emanating from an attic room. Upon investigation, he discovered Richard busily boiling a large pot filled with a cow's leg joints and a sheep's head which he had acquired somehow from a neighbouring farmer. On inquiring as to the boy's purpose, he was informed very seriously that the lad was merely rendering the flesh so that he might examine the structure of the bones more closely.

The story delighted Sir John who is much taken with science and regards Hodgson as one of our expedition's most diligent practitioners.

The mates, Hornby and Thomas, are an odd pair and are inseparable despite their disparate characters. Hornby has been in the Navy since thirty-four and, I fancy, is a touch put out at still being a Mate. He is quiet and you would not notice his presence were it not for his attachment to Thomas who is a most energetic, voluble, noisy, witty, warm-hearted prankster, forever getting in trouble for the cause of some joke or other. He is an orphan, the youngest of the officers at no more than seventeen and thus known universally as 'the Baby.'

Apparently when he heard of this expedition, he approached Hodgson to recommend him for a position. His description of himself as 'steady and zealous and with a scientific turn of mind,' caused not a little hilarity amongst those who knew him.

Even a glimpse of Hornby and Thomas together is enough to provoke smiles. Hornby is tall, almost Le Vesconte's match in that department, skinny and much stooped over, a common characteristic in tall men used to the narrow confines of a ship. He has a long face which puts one in mind of a sad old horse and a mouth which is permanently drooped around the corners.

Thomas, on the other hand, is short, even for his age and runs a little to chubbiness. His face is round and always wreathed in smiles at some private joke, giving him the appearance of a cherub contemplating some new trickery. To see them together is a study in contrasts and I have overheard them referred to as 'the long and the short of it.'

Second Master Macbean is an extraordinary fellow, with some of the rude Celtic charm of Reid, but a fund of lore on animals rather than ice. For many years, he was gamekeeper on an estate near Edinburgh and regales us with tales of the poachers he was continually battling. On one occasion, the lord insisted upon setting up tripped muskets to take poachers on his land. One was triggered and wounded an innocent man out for a walk. The landlord's comment was, "Ah well, the purpose of deterring poachers is as much served by hitting an innocent man as a guilty." After that Macbean set only charges and not shot in the guns.

He has also enlightened us on the best way to entrap a pheasant.

"They are no' intelligent birds," he said smiling, "and they do love the raisins above a' other food. The trick is tae find a path that they use in the woods and scatter a line o' raisins doon it. At a suitable point, turn the raisin line aff the path and intae a canvas sack wi' the remainder o' the raisins in it.

"The bird, no' bein' very smart, will follow the line, stick its heed in the bag and, thinkin' because o' the dark that night has fallen, will go tae sleep. It is then a simple matter tae wring its neck."

This produced much jollity, although none of us were certain that we were not being spun a line. As we settled down, Macbean added without a hint of a smile, "Beggin' the pardon o' the present company, pheasants hae no' the intelligence o' a Sassenach Lord wi'oot his servants."

Sassenach is the Scots dialect for an Englishman; such is the rough forthrightness of this northern race! But it was all told with such a lack of guile that we could none of us take offence, besides, we all know the type of person of which Macbean speaks.

It certainly put me in mind of Stanhope and the dinner party last Christmas that I was fortunate enough to attend with your good self and William. Do you recall how the insufferable man took such vocal offence at being seated farther down the table than the Welshman Owen and his charming wife? Sometimes I feel that if there is one thing which will stop the progress of the English in this world, it will be the airs of such as Stanhope.

Surgeon Peddie is an Edinburgh man. His hair is red like my own, but he has the reddish, almost abraded-look to his skin shared by so many of his countrymen. I suspect it is a predilection for the national drink which causes such an effect, none-the-less, Peddie is most companionable as far as I can see. He has not the disturbing cleanliness of Stanley, but is a model of medical efficiency, having once removed a man's gangrenous leg in twenty-three and one-half seconds. He has with him a set of the Scottish bagpipes, which he plays some evenings on deck. The sound carries remarkably over the ice and is clearly audible on the *Erebus* and even at the camp on Beechey. It is not unpleasant though perhaps the subtleties are an acquired taste, and seem strangely suited to the bleak landscape in which we find ourselves.

Macdonald, the Surgeon's Assistant, is the very opposite of Goodsir. He too is charged with the examination of all sorts of strange creatures that we might come across, but does so with little of the enthusiasm of our companion on the *Erebus*. He is a nice enough fellow however, witty and with a certain charm, able to entertain in a dry sort of way at table, is attempting to cease the habit of smoking too many cigars, is almost Fairholme's match at backgammon, and has been on whaling expeditions to

Davis Strait.

Helpman the clerk, when I first set eyes on him on the *Clio*, I took to be a typical member of a certain species of accountant, eternally with small spectacles balanced on his thin nose, tall in stature with a stoop, which gives one the impression that he is about to pounce upon, and examine minutely, some tiny fallen number which has escaped his imposing ledger. On closer acquaintance, I found a delightful fellow, well versed in the classics and able to quote anyone from Cicero and Virgil to Bulwer-Lytton and Carlyle. He has already pointed out to me some interesting works in our library which I think will help to while away the hours of darkness to come. My only concern regarding him is that he is not physically strong and may not bear up well when subject to the rigours of the places we find ourselves.

Little is perhaps the oddest of the *Terror*'s mess. He is companionable enough, and can enter into a joke with the best of them, but he has a very strict attitude to the crew, allowing them no leeway and abiding strictly by the rules of service which, while they may be appropriate or even essential on a long ocean voyage, may not be suited to the situation in which we find ourselves. As in the case of the old Orkneyman, it is my feeling that an interpretation of the rules to suit our circumstances is more befitting. In any case, these are sketches of the *Terror*'s mess, not in such detail as my own messmates, but I will perhaps embellish the pictures as I come to know them better in our confined winter quarters. And now I must retire.

November 4—Winter is upon us. Today we said farewell to the friendly old sun which barely managed to shew us its rim over the horizon at noon. What a night is before us.

November 13—We are in 'hard winter' as Reid calls it. For the last two weeks, the mercury has not risen above fifty degrees of frost day or night. We have had little snow, but it is continually overcast and there is a steady light wind from the northwest. A dull twilight is the best we can manage around the middle of the day. For the most part we move around like shades from Dante, each almost unrecognisable in layers of wool and face masks to keep out the biting wind. The cases of frostbite have slowed as the men become accustomed to the precautions one must take in these regions and the sick bays are not too busy. The man with consumption is worsening, spitting blood and becoming very weak. He has a brother on board who is much concerned. The Leading Stoker on the *Terror*, Torrington, is in much the same state—why these men did not declare their condition before we sailed I do not know. Bringing weakened lungs to this land is a death warrant, not to mention the burden they present to their fellows.

But enough of death, our newspaper is now published on a weekly basis and does much to lift spirits with some amusing articles and pieces of scientific interest. I have stated the goal that every man on board ship shall be able to read the paper before the voyage is through.

Our orchestra is now formed and practices whenever it can. It would give pause to a patron of the London Philharmonic Society, but in volume it has no peer. Peddie we have limited to the occasional solo on his pipes, otherwise he would drown everyone out, but we have two violins, an oboe, clarinet, and Gore's flute. For percussion we have arranged a collection of drums, cymbals and chimes which are played with gusto by Goodsir. The sound is not unpleasant, but I feel some refinement is required. We also, in the crew's mess, have a mechanical hand organ of the sort you may see on the street corners. It is much appreciated, so much so that its use must be restricted to special occasions. When this occurs, the noise of popular tunes can be heard throughout the ship and the monkey, Miss Jacko, takes to dancing wildly on the mess table in a variety of clothing made for her by the men. Neptune, on the other hand, is less impressed and tries mightily to squeeze himself into a dark corner farthest from the entertainment.

November 14—Blowing harder today and snowing some. We have managed to set out three depots for our spring travel, but it is becoming too cold for more. All the parties are back in and we must settle down to the real wait, the only excursions will be to the magnetic camps and those routes are well worn by now. The sameness of the days does not easily lend itself to a daily inventory of events to interest a sophisticated lady, and you may have already noticed that the gaps between entries is growing. I have never claimed to be able to tell you tales of interest with any regularity, thus I will add to this letter when I feel I will be capable of entertaining you in some small way. For the present, good night.

December 1—A new month, the last of our first year. We have had a few days of blizzard, but, for the most part, the weather remains cold and blowy. The ice in Barrow Strait is very thick now and the pressure is immense, pushing huge slabs high into the air, where they remain like the broken peaks of some frozen mountain range. I am glad we have this sheltered harbour, to be beset in that would be a frightful experience indeed. I have just completed Mister Dickens' *A Christmas Carol* and enjoyed it immensely, not least for the memories it provoked of Christmases very different from the one we face; I can easily see why it was so popular last year.

I was discussing this evening with Fairholme the possibility of the world one day being tied together with a network of wires carrying Mister Wheatstone and Mister Cooke's electric telegraph. Fairholme informed me that a demonstration of the technique had been carried out in America before we left by Mister Morse, and maintains that it is only a matter of time before wires carry messages around the globe at incredible speed. What an exciting world we live in when so much is possible. Perhaps one day it will even be possible for us to communicate, in some way as yet undiscovered, with those at home. It is hard to believe, but anything may be possible and an invention which would allow me to communicate with you dear Elizabeth, would be worthwhile indeed. With the minds of men such as Wheatstone, Faraday, Stephenson, and MacIntosh working, what can the future not hold? But now, for me it holds a good night's rest. Good night.

December 2—Well, my 'good night's rest' was not to be. I tossed and turned and had the most unsettling dreams, the most vivid of which placed me behind a wall of the clearest ice through which I could observe you, and the children, but through which I could not make myself heard nor even my presence known. I awoke with an uncommonly sore head and all the marks of a proper attack of the cold. I suppose it is our close, damp quarters which encourage these attacks, I must attempt to get more fresh air, cold though it is, and more exercise when I feel recovered.

December 8—Another blizzard begun today and almost a disaster. A relief crew led by Irving was returning from the easterly magnetic camp when the snow set in around noon. Somehow they lost the trail, which is well marked with cairns and solidly beaten down, and wandered up against the cliffs. It is difficult to believe how easy it is when the snow is blowing hard to lose one's way. It becomes quite literally impossible to see one's hand held before one's face. You could walk but three feet past the foot of Nelson's Column and not suspect its existence. All sense of direction vanishes and, if the path is lost, one is doomed to wander aimlessly until found or stumble by luck on one's destination.

Irving realized their error at the cliffs and turned in an attempt to regain the path. They could not do so and became irretrievably lost, stumbling hopelessly amongst the chaos of upturned ice floes. At length, they abandoned the sled and struggled on in what they thought was the correct direction, but each time they came up against the cliffs. They were close to utter exhaustion and could not have kept on much longer when they stumbled over the line strung between the two vessels and followed it back to the ship where they arrived at supper and were warmly greeted by their shipmates. No serious harm was done and we shall retrieve the sled when the storm moderates, but the episode illustrates how rapidly the most routine activity can become dangerous due to the treacherous nature of the climate.

I have finished Hawthorne's *Twice Told Tales* as you recommended a full year ago. They cast an interesting light on the sometimes harsh Puritanism of our former colony which now lies to the south of me. I have almost a yearning to visit that place, perhaps not the New England of Hawthorne, but rather the wilds of Fenimore Cooper, whose, *The Pathfinder*, I think I shall read next. Sir John has many tales of the northern wildernesses of Canada which also catch my fancy.

It is now completely dark from noon to midnight and vice versa, a most extraordinary phenomenon which somewhat unsettles the more superstitious of the crew. Light is provided by the moon, clouds permitting, and by the Aurora which can be as bright as day on occasion. The cold remains intense, the mercury freezing solid on occasion which indicates seventy degrees of frost!

The ship is warm inside although the ice build up and consequent damp are continual problems, but it is the men at the shore camp and the magnetic stations who suffer most. Their habitations are frequently so cold that they can derive little comfort except when asleep in their bedding, and candles develop the annoying habit of burning down within a thin skin of frozen wax, shedding but a ghostly memory of their former light as they do so.

Our main discomforts on the ship are the rats which seem to thrive and multiply in the damp warmth surrounded by our voluminous supplies of food. They will eat anything from leather harnesses to frozen casks of sugar, only the cans are proof against their attentions. One crewman even awoke last week to find one brute gnawing on his toe which had slipped out from beneath his blanket. I think they must soon be given a dose of arsenic and sulphur.

December 13—The blizzard ameliorated on the 11th and we took the opportunity to deal with the rat problem. That night, the men all took to tents on the ice or slept at the shore camp and we lit burners of sulphur mixed with large amounts of arsenic between the decks. This is effective, but a hard task for those who must tend the fires, for the fumes are almost unbearable and prolonged exposure will result in most unpleasant ailments.

On the 12th, I sent a party in to remove the kill which were laid out on the ice like the proud bag of some successful hunting party. The total count was 207, which is a lot for a vessel of our small size. The ship still smells unpleasant below decks, but at least it is a change from the overpowering smell of people closely confined, and we are assured of a festive season relatively free of the vermin. Our entertainments continue and we are preparing a grand ball to be held on the ice at New Year.

December 25, midnight—Merry Christmas my dear sister, you have been much in my thoughts these past few days and I have missed you sorely. I take comfort in the hope that we will be together for the season next year when, together, we can read these rude entries and wonder at the world in which your brother celebrates now. There is much joviality aboard, due not least to the extra issue of rum I authorized. Watches must of course still be kept, but the 'lights out' regulation (a delightful irony in a land where we have not seen the sun for weeks), was relaxed and just a few moments ago I could still hear the strains of the hand organ echoing through the ship. "Hearts of Oak" has reverberated numerous times and I now hear the men setting in to "Spanish Ladies" with a will:

Farewell and adieu to you fine Spanish Ladies
Farewell and adieu all you Ladies of Spain
For we've received orders to sail for Old England
And perhaps we shall never more see you again.

We'll rant and we'll roar like true British Sailors,
We'll range and we'll roam o'er all the salt seas,
Until we strike soundings in the Channel of Old England
From Ushant to Scilly 'tis thirty-five leagues.

The songs of the sailors take me back to the *Pyramus* and the *Cornwallis*, but they are mixed with the shanties of the whalers and some Scottish airs of the Orkney men, often in that strangely soft, lilting and totally incomprehensible tongue that some of them speak amongst themselves. Whatever it is, I like to hear the people singing.

The entire crew dined on Mister Goldner's canned produce and, I think, all appreciated the change from salt beef and hard biscuits. Myself, I was less enthusiastic, almost breaking a tooth on a sizeable lump of hard solder concealed in the soup; indeed, many of the cans have large protuberances on the insides of the joints which look like some odd growths of nature, but result simply from the haste with which the order was filled before we left. We continue to find occasional cans blown and leaking but they are not many and the contents are generally good. The empty cans we fill with rock and earth (not as easy a task as it sounds when you realize that the ground is frozen as hard as iron and even the smallest indentation must be achieved with a pickaxe) and build them into a large cairn.

Crozier wished to place a message beneath the cairn as is the custom of all visitors to this land, but Sir John felt that we will be here until July and that a message interred now would give precious little information and, perhaps even a false impression, to those who might follow us. In the spring we shall deposit messages at the extremities of our exploration journeys and leave a detailed one here for the sake of posterity. Our conversation at dinner, at which Crozier, Hodgson and Irving attended, centred on our plans for the spring which have not changed since I outlined them to you, but the restatement of which is important to help us maintain our focus in these dark days. We continue to collect much invaluable information on all aspects of this country and Goodsir is filling boxes and jars with specimens of all sorts. Hodgson has been charged with the collection of rock specimens, no easy task when they are frozen and often covered with snow, to ascertain the geological history of this place.

Oddly, much of the rock hereabouts is of a limy nature and contains some remnants of sea shells and corals which must have lived in a world very much different from the one we now inhabit. Strange to think of these bleak shores once abounding with life and lapped by tropic seas!

But I am wandering away from my purpose yet again. Our dinner was a splendid menu of pea soup, turkey, mutton, meat and mince pies, plum pudding and pumpkin tarts, made more so for me by the delightful and thoughtful gift of gloves from you; you see, I did wait until the correct time although I think if it had not been for your certainty that I should open the gift early, I should indeed have done so.

All in our mess had some package or other from home that they had saved for this very day. These were mostly in the clothing line, reflecting our loved one's concerns about the harshness of the climate in these parts. These special gifts were increased by a collection of items which we exchanged; for example, with much ceremony, I presented Reid with my old curved pipe for which I have little use now since I have ceased the habit. He thanked me most graciously and promptly lit up with relish. However, I have the feeling that he will return to his long clay pipe before long. Gore opened a box of the finest cigars and Sir John added a bottle or two of his special port, so we indulged in a few of the luxuries of home. All loved ones, you most fervently on my part, were toasted at least twice, and it was a jovial crew that eventually parted company.

I think all have enjoyed our Christmas festivities and it has provided a welcome respite from the monotony of our life in this dark world, but this evening has been only a part of our celebrations; on Saturday we are planning a sporting meet with races and competitive games on a flat track cleared out on the ice close to the shore. The crew are much excited by this event and are busy practising at every available opportunity. We are also continuing with our plans for a ball on the ice on New Year's Day, next Thursday. To that end, we have cleared a large area of ice and have constructed seating arrangements, and a 'throne' to mimic the interior of a real ballroom, and we will have a sheltered stage for the 'orchestra' and for our other entertainments. The area will be draped in flags and the whole lit by our oil torches. It is not what the society of London is used to, but it will more than suffice for us. And so, again, I wish you dear sister the most merry of festive seasons and, to quote Mister Dickens' Tiny Tim, 'God Bless us every one.'

December 26—Weather remains cold and with a slight breeze. We had some brief flurries of snow this afternoon, but all should be well for the athletics planned for tomorrow. All preparations are complete, and excitement is at a high pitch.

December 27—The first (and I imagine last) resurrection of the ancient Greek Olympic Games at these latitudes, 'The Great Northern Beset Sailors Festival of Sports and Athletic Endeavour,' was a great success despite the fact that we could not emulate our classical precursors by running barefoot. In fact, with the mercury indicating twenty-five degrees of cold below zero, the hardy athletes looked more like lumbering overdressed bears than reincarnations of Hermes and Apollo, but what was lacking in style, was more than made up for in enthusiasm. Each winner was crowned magnificently with a wreath of lichen and awarded an extra tot of rum to combat the cold. The highlight was the race between the champion of the *Terror* and that of the *Erebus*. Amidst much partisan cheering, I am pleased to say that our own Able Seaman Thomas McConvey proved fleetest of foot and acquired the undying honour of the fastest man north of the Arctic Circle for our ship. The proceedings were concluded with a game of football in which the *Erebus* was not so lucky, losing by a considerable margin before the sputtering torches forced abandonment.

The sporting events put me in mind of our day at the races at Epsom. Do you recall? You were so taken with that chestnut filly that I, despite William's misgivings, wagered considerably on her. When she came in next to last, you were so distraught, feeling it was your responsibility when in fact it was my own foolishness. My only concern was that you not feel badly on my account. Still our walk on the Downs cleared the air nicely. Our talk that day of childhood and family, as we strolled across the rolling green hills, remains one of my fondest memories to this day.

I have often envied others their secure, complete family upbringing which was so cruelly taken from me, although do not think that I could ever have wished for a more generous or kinder stepfamily than the Coninghams, but on that perfect day, with little Elisabeth gambolling at our feet and you, with your parasol raised against the sun, walking arm-in-arm with William, it was my dearest cousin that I envied in his domestic bliss. Not that I think I shall ever resign my adventuring, seafaring life, but to have William or Hodgson's stable family hearth to provide a centre to return to appeals more and more as the years go by.

Or perhaps it is just as this long cold night drags slowly on and we are immersed in the season where thoughts of family, comfort, and security predominate, that I find I am become less satisfied with my lot. Or perhaps it is an overindulgence in port! In any case, I must cease this groaning. Good night.

December 28—Divine service on the ice was read by Sir John. He chose as his text St. Paul's letter to the Corinthians, and few of the listeners remained unmoved by his words. It is a strange time, one when we are saying good-bye to the old year and being reminded of the loved ones we have left behind, and one when we are looking forward to next season and the completion of the passage and a return to civilisation—what a mixture of reminiscence and hope race through my mind, I pray I can sleep without the bother of dreams. Good night.

December 29—The weather continues fine although still very cold. Preparations are almost complete for the ball with no sign of a blizzard to upset our plans. Stanley told me today that poor Torrington on the *Terror* is shewing signs of pneumonia which, in his greatly weakened state (he has not eaten anything for several days now and not much before that) can only foreshadow the worst. For two weeks now he has been completely confined to his bunk and not able to endure even the shortest of walks. It is mostly the consumption, although Peddie says there are other complications in his lungs which have been made worse by the closed atmosphere below decks and by his work, although he has not undertaken any for some months now, as Leading Stoker.

Our own Seaman Hartnell is in better condition, but still very weak and only barely able to stand let alone walk any distance. Both men are given the best care possible through the not insignificant combined skills of Stanley and Goodsir (who are for once united in this cause), and Peddie and Macdonald, but there is little that could be done even at Guy's Hospital itself.

But why do I burden you with this? How hard I try to imagine your own Christmas and how it must differ so much from my own. I hope you are remembering your adventuring brother as you sail through the social whirl of London. Next year, I promise, we shall have a celebration to eclipse anything which has gone before.

December 31, 10 p.m.—The weather is holding and both ships are in a state of high expectation over tomorrow's Grand Ball. Crozier and I, as the two Captains, shall begin the festivities by leading three other pairs of officers in a quadrille. There has been some discussion as to which of us shall undertake the lady's role. Crozier finally claimed seniority and so, for the occasion, I shall be Miss Fitzjames. With that thought, I shall wish you good night.

January 1, 1 a.m.—Still awake. I have been playing chess with Osmer and have ended the year no better than I began it. We are all in high spirits and none can remember a start to a year which was greeted with such hope and enthusiasm, This is especially true of the Scotchmen among us who place greater store in this festivity than in Christmas. I tease Reid with this fact and with a statement that it was probably due to a closer historical association with a paganism than the more civilised lands.

"Aye, Mister Jems," he replied without a hint of expression, "but recall if you will the good book, 'Joy shall be in heaven over one sinner that repenteth, more than over ninety and nine just persons, which need no repentance.'" And with that he left me with my thoughts.

In the dark sameness of our winter up here, it is sometimes hard to remember all of the things we have achieved and how well we have progressed toward our ultimate goal. We are a happy band and Sir John continues the finest leader we could hope for He is firm when necessary and flexible when he can be, thus all the crews know exactly where they stand with him. The worst thing for a Commander on service is to be indecisive, that only promotes disaffection and the worst elements rise to the top—that was well shewn by poor Bligh's experiences in the Pacific—but we have no word of complaint. All our people are solid and worthy and we all believe so heartily in the importance of our goal and our ability to achieve it that I think there is no thought in anyone's mind to cause the slightest bit of trouble.

At times like this I find a tendency toward reflection and a dwelling on the distant past. Dear old uncle Robert, your father-in-law, although you were never blessed to meet him, has been much in my mind, particularly remembrances of the many kindnesses he did me and the many times he helped forward the career of a young 2nd class. He treated me no different than if I were his own son and William's brother, so much so that I fear I must have taken the role for granted.

I remember not a lot of my natural parents except a vivid image of a tall, stern man with whiskers I thought must be meant as hand-holds for the advancement of a young body up the cliff of his face, and a soft, willowy, very beautiful, as I thought, woman who would hold me firmly to her breast and coo sweet childish lyrics in my ear. I still curse the sickness that took them, and yet I cannot complain at the life I have had filled with such generous mentors as Robert Coningham and old Gambier of the *Pyramus*, and such dear friends as William, John Barrow and, of course, your dear self. So sister, I wish you and William all happiness for the New Year and hope you have given little Elisabeth and Robert a hug for me and told them that their 'uncle' amidst the ice thinks of them often.

New Year's Day, 1846—A day of such extremes I hardly know where to begin; perhaps I shall simply begin at the beginning.

The day commenced with great hope and expectation, the wind was calm, a rarity at this place, and all preparations made. We started by assembling the crews and distributing a gift of clothing from the Queen which was greatly appreciated. We also gave out a ration of chocolate and tobacco and an extra tot of rum. At the sound of a cannon shot from the *Erebus*, an honour guard formed on the ice and to a ragged burst of musketry, we made our way to the 'ballroom.' Sir John led, in full dress, followed by Crozier and myself arm-in-arm. Behind us followed the other quadrille pairs, Gore and Irving, Le Vesconte and Hodgson, and the eternally unlikely, Hornby and Thomas. We were a serious group as the occasion demanded, but I fear that behind us the parade quickly degenerated into considerably less formality.

At the ballroom we all took our places on carved ice chairs, each with our names emblazoned on the back in bright red felt. Sir John occupied a throne placed on a raised plinth, from where he made a brief speech on the certainty of our success for the coming year. This was met with wild cheers from all ranks and at a second roll of musket fire, Crozier and I led a passably good quadrille to begin the ball proper. There was much revelry, although I could not help but be struck by how bizarre we must all look dancing around to gallops and polkas in our English clothes, by the light of oil torches, in an ice ballroom, thousands of miles from the nearest civilization.

Most bizarre, and giving the festivities the air of a medieval Saturnalia, was Jacko, bedecked for the occasion as a human baby dressed in swaddling rags. She danced about waving a flag which read on one side, 'The Infant of 1846,' and on the other, 'The Year of the Passage.' Neptune and Diogenes cavorted around people's feet, completely carried away with the noise and excitement. The 'orchestra' performed admirably, although the wind instruments had a tendency to freeze after a few tunes and the mouthpieces had to be removed and hidden beneath clothing to warm up, but they performed many very good reels and country dances.

I was resting from the merriment and talking idly to Irving when he spotted Peddie approaching from the *Terror*.

"Look," he said, "old Peddie's come to join the Sir Roger de Coverley, his patients must be feeling better."

But I was not so sure; the physician's gait seemed heavy and he appeared downcast, even at such a distance. When he approached, he spoke simply.

"Torrington is dead."

That was all, yet I felt all the joy of the day fall from me like a cape cast aside. It was something we had all been anticipating for some time, but we had put it to the backs of our minds while we worked on the celebrations. Now, in his death, young Torrington had brought us back to reality and reminded us that our task is a serious one and not merely childish adventures.

I went over and told Sir John, but it was decided to keep the news from the men until the ball was over. It proved impossible. Somehow, the word seeped over from the ship and made its way through the revellers who gradually stopped prancing about and fell silent. There was a very awkward moment when everyone was simply standing around silent not knowing what to do, before Sir John, realizing that the word was already out, stood and announced the tragedy. He made as light as he could of it, stressing that Torrington should never have come to these harsh lands with his lungs in the condition they were, but the event, particularly the timing, will be taken by some of the more superstitious among the crews as an ill omen. The orchestra attempted to continue, but the spirit of the occasion had evaporated and the men began to drift back to the ships. I went back with Crozier to pay respects to the deceased.

Torrington was never a big man, being below five and a half feet, but his long illness had shrunk him till he looked no bigger than a child. He looked at peace, and was already dressed in his best shirt with pearl buttons, tucked into his pants. Peddle had tied a kerchief, white and covered with blue dots, around his head which, along with Torrington's delicate features, increased the impression that we were looking upon a child.

When we arrived, Macdonald was busy tying linen strips around the body to keep it in position before stiffening set in. Tomorrow we shall set to work on a grave and Honey and Wilson will build a coffin. The least we can do for the poor boy and his relatives is give him a decent burial as close to the one he should have had in his native Manchester.

When I returned much saddened to my ship, I went to the sick bay to see how Hartnell was doing. To my relief he seemed in good spirits, although very weak. He is still taking food and can stand and take one or two short steps with assistance. His brother was present and expressed the thought that the sick man was improving and that he would be well if he could only last through the winter. I don't know.

It is a cruel twist of fate which has plunged us into despond on such a happy occasion and I am sorry to burden you with it, but if I am to be true to my purpose, I must tell you all that will be of note, not just the happy things. The mood on board is much sobered this evening and there is no dancing or the sound of the hand organ. I must to bed and hope that the days ahead may lift our spirits from this sadness. Good night dear sister.

January 2—As if in recognition of our mourning, the sky lowered today and it began to snow, not a blizzard but a steady falling curtain of white. The men go about their duties in silence as if the presence of poor Torrington lying tied in the sick bay weighs down upon them.

Honey and Wilson are busy with the coffin which will be built of mahogany, and Torrington's messmates are busy constructing a plaque for their friend. There is an irony to mahogany wood, a reminder of sunny tropical climes, ending up serving such a sad purpose in this frozen land.

A crew from the *Terror* is also on Beechey Island digging a grave which is difficult work through this frozen ground. I went over this afternoon to see how they progressed. It is a sad spot, just upslope from the smithy. The grave was already so deep that there was only room for one man to work at deepening it and he looked like a shade from Hades, lit as he was by the smoky glow of a solitary oil lamp and swinging the pick which sent up showers of sparks when it came in contact with the frozen rock. As I stood in the bitter cold and blowing snow watching this heartbreaking toil, I had my first sense of what Le Vesconte talked of the day we built our cairn scarce three months ago—that perhaps there are places in this world where men are not supposed to go.

The funeral will be tomorrow.

January 3—The snow eased today to allow us to perform our melancholy task. Poor Torrington was laid to rest at 4 p.m. today. We gave him as pleasant a send-off as is possible in this place and much work was done by his friends. The wasted body was laid on a bed of wood shavings within the coffin and wrapped in a blue cloth shroud. The coffin was covered with the same blue wool with the outlines highlighted in white tape. A painted plaque made from beaten cans was attached to the coffin lid bearing the legend, 'John Torrington died January 1, 1846, aged 20 years', and Hodgson has supervised the making of a wooden headboard which reads:

Sacred
to the
memory of
John Torrington
who departed
this life January 1st,
A.D. 1846,
on board of
H.M. ship Terror
aged 20 years.

With as much ceremony as possible, the flag-draped coffin was lowered onto a sled on the ice and, in a cruel parody of the happy parade which took us over the ice to the Grand Ball but two days ago, we pulled the coffin, six of his messmates walking beside the sled and acting as pallbearers, over to the waiting hole.

Sir John appeared very solemn, leading the way, and reading the service at the graveside. He spoke of his sorrow at losing a man for whom he was responsible and at Torrington's bad luck at not being able to share in our coming success. It was a sober and serious yet hopeful speech, the kind we have come to expect from the man, and he has never disappointed us.

As we lowered the coffin down into the hole, it seemed almost too small to hold an adult, so wasted was the poor boy by his final illness. The snow was light and formed a thin layer on the coffin lid covering the lovingly painted plaque and, I thought, creating a blanket with which this frozen world welcomed our late comrade. We stood bareheaded in the cold air as a final volley of musketry marked our last farewell. Then each, except for the grave digging crew, returned, deep in their own thoughts, to the ships. As you know, I am not superstitious in the least, but this tragedy right at the start of our year is difficult to throw off. I hope it will be our last.

After supper tonight, the most extraordinary thing occurred. As usual, myself and two other officers, this night Fairholme and Couch, dined with Sir John. As you can imagine the conversation was slow and mostly unhappy. Our host appeared preoccupied and at the end, asked me to stay. I did so and we sat for some time in silence enjoying good cigars. Finally Franklin spoke to me, but it was as if he were addressing someone else, so distant was the look in his eye.

"This day weighs very heavy upon me," he began. "I had hoped to return with the loss of no man, but it is not to be. I pray this will be all, but I fear sometimes for what we are entering."

This surprised me since he has never made any suggestion of having doubts about our capabilities or the eventual outcome of our endeavour, in fact, chiding Crozier for making what he perceives to be less than optimistic pronouncements. By the light of the lamps, Franklin appeared as a large hunched form, dark except for the glow from his cigar.

"Seeing the coffin draped in the flag brought a black mood on me," he continued at length. "Before we left London, I was cursed with a bad case of the influenza. It was worst on the day that they took that infernal image of me. That night, sitting by the fire with a hot rum punch to ease my suffering, I dozed off.

"Jane was working on the flag with which we shall celebrate our completion of the passage. It being a cold night and, out of concern for my well-being, she draped the unfinished item over my legs for warmth. On feeling the material, I awoke and seeing my flag-draped form I was horrified and jumped up saying, 'Don't you know that they only drape flags over corpses.'"

Here Sir John paused again. At length he looked up at me and continued, "When my illness receded, I forgot the incident, but seeing poor Torrington's coffin lowered over the side in the flag brought it back to me and I cannot shake the thought that this is how I shall end in this God-forsaken place."

I could think of nothing to say. Here was the man who led us, who was our pillar, and who would brook no sort of failure in our task, talking like some superstitious kitchen maid; and yet, there was a look in his eyes which sent a chill down my own spine.

I tried to reassure him with some words on how well we had progressed and how certain I was of success in the year just begun, and I think I had some effect, for Sir John raised himself and replied, "Yes, of course you are right, it is nonsense. It has been a busy time and I just need some sleep—I trust, James, that you will breathe no word of this lapse outside this cabin."

I assured him that I would not and retired to my own thoughts and my words to you. But now it is late and I must to bed.

January 4—We have not yet recovered from the shock of Torrington's death and we are struck by another. At four in the morning, I was awakened from a disturbed sleep of only a few hours length by Stanley who came to tell me the news that John Hartnell is dead. He was very sick, but the death came so suddenly that it was a shock. Stanley feels that the cause was consumption, but he charged Goodsir, who is an anatomist by training, to perform an autopsy which was carried out this morning and found severe lesions on the lungs. So it is Weekes' and Watson's turn to set to and build a coffin, far too soon after the first, and I can hear them above me on the deck working as I write. Hartnell's friends are working on a plaque, and I have a crew on shore breaking through the frozen earth.

An unfortunate incident occurred when Stanley came to dress the body. It seems Hartnell is one of those men who is in arrears in the payment for his clothing. Regulations state that, in the event of death, the deceased's clothing must be returned to the Navy and we were faced with the possibility of burying him naked, an unacceptable thing. Fortunately, his brother Thomas came forward and gave a shirt and undershirts to clothe the body. Tomorrow, if the weather holds, we shall repeat the miserable ceremony of yesterday.

January 6—Blowing snow yesterday and slow work on the digging forced our funeral today which was calm and clear, the stars being clearly visible in the gloomy twilight of noon. I will not describe the same event as repeated, suffice it to say there are now two wooden headboards above the smithy.

Our twelfth-night dinner was a fine affair with a splendid cake made by Wall, although the day's events overwhelmed us all somewhat and it was a quiet affair. The days are weighing heavy upon me at the moment. I do not mean to burden you, although this will all be long in the past before you read it, but I must try to communicate to you a true sense of our situation, and for that I must include all. Having said that, time hangs heavy, so do not expect too much of a winter journal from me. I miss you more than ever. Good night dear sister.

January 8—Visited the two graves on the island. The crew have done a fine job of making them respectable. Each mound is covered with flat slabs of the limy rock common hereabouts and surrounded by a small 'fence' of upright slabs, none of which is easy work in this cold. Hartnell's headstone is the same as Torrington's except for the date, age (twenty-five years), and the fact that the crew, prompted by Hartnell's brother I think, added a quotation from the good book, 'Thus saith the Lord of Hosts, consider your ways. Haggai, i., 7.'

Standing before these graves, and with a supreme effort of imagination, one could almost see them nestled in a small, quiet country churchyard, enveloped by elm and oak trees and covered with a carpet of greenery, instead of this bleak, snow-covered place. I shudder to think of the loneliness of the last resting place of these two men after we have departed. How long will it be before some other curious traveller should stop to pay his respects?

January 20—Our mood has lightened considerably after the bleak start to the year. I think most have put the events behind them, though Thomas Hartnell takes his brother's death hard. We have had a small blizzard which,

I think, has served to blow much of our sadness away, and the work must continue. Yet there is little enough work in this place to keep all 127 of us busy and it is vital that the men not become bored. The routine of cleaning quarters, scrubbing the ship, and exercising is invariable and at the least gives us all a better sense of the passage of time in the darkness—not that it is pitch dark at all times. Around noon there is a period of twilight, which day-by-day increases in duration and brightness, although the dear old sun never pops her head over the horizon. Her return is awaited with as much anticipation by us as if we were all superstitious pagans praying to some elder god for a return of the light.

It is strange, I count myself a rational man, and yet the emotional desire for the return of the day can make me stop and stare off at the horizon. At such times, although I know that the sun will return in its own good time, I find myself almost willing it to struggle up and shew us its bright rim. As you will recall my telling, I felt very isolated and alone on the river expedition in Mesopotamia, but that was nothing like here. There, despite the hardship and loneliness, I always felt that there were multitudes of past generations, from Nebuchadnezzar to the desert peoples of now, gazing out at me from the dusty mounds on the river banks which had once been clothed in greenery and rung to the sounds of commerce and battle. But here it is different, there are no echoes of the past, only the silent strangeness. Certainly, there is much to learn about this land but, and although science is wonderful food for the mind, it is poor nutrition for dreams and there are precious few of those in this land.

January 21—Still dark. If only I could have captured some of the sunlight, which was such a bane in Mesopotamia, and released a bottle of it here, what a hero I should be. I have come to the conclusion that man needs sun just as much as flowers and that without it, our spirit should eventually wither and die. The men are like shades in the dusk, going about their tasks willingly enough, but it is as though they are, like the phantom crew of the Ancient Mariner's vessel, driven by an other worldly force. Only Neptune appears unaffected; content so long as he has attention and food—at times I think I envy such a simple life as he leads.

The Cabin Boy, Chambers, has ceased to be my inescapable shadow and is turning into a most useful attendant. His friendship focuses now, much more appropriately, on his companion and age mate, David Young, who attends to Sir John. The pair seem unaffected by the darkness which hangs so heavy with the rest of us—another example of how the uncomplicated perspective of youth is to be envied—and may often be seen, huddled in a corner, laughing together at some juvenile joke.

January 30—I am much in mind of the expedition to Mesopotamia these days and, I am afraid, prevailed somewhat upon the mess to listen to my stories this evening. It is, I think, a response to our long night and I do not see marked reluctance on anyone's part to hear my tales of warmer climes.

"First," I said by way of introduction, "you must imagine me sporting a long beard and moustaches and burned by the sun almost as black as the native inhabitants."

Mention of the sun produced such a wistful groan that I could not resist the temptation to build upon it.

"While building the road from Antioch, it was over 100 degrees in the shade. We could cook eggs on any exposed metal surface and from noon until late afternoon, all work ceased and we were forced to lie exhausted and sweating in our tents."

"But at least," piped up Le Vesconte, "you had the means to wash off the sweat later."

This reference to our current ripe smell provoked laughter.

"True," I continued, "but it was not all taking our ease in the sunshine. I picked up the brain fever from too much sun and was laid up for a full month. Even long after, I was subject to sudden shivering fits and ague. And that was before the cholera almost finished me; before I even had the chance to become the hero you see before you."

"But you were already a hero," Fairholme stated quickly. His comment took me aback.

"A hero? How so?"

"Was it not you," he asked smiling, "who, while preparations were being made for Chesney's expedition, saved a poor customs man from drowning at great risk to life and limb?"

"That is true," I said recalling his reference. "And a terrible fuss was made of it at the time with medals and notices in the paper, but I can honestly say that, since I acted on impulse, with no thought to the danger, it was perhaps closer to the act of a fool than a hero."

"And it is indeed true," added Fairholme, "how alike the two are and how many of one turn out to be the other. But tell us the tale."

"Very well. I was standing on deck, while we were docked in the canal at Liverpool. I was talking with a fellow officer, Laird I believe, of our provisioning. For some reason, I was holding a leg of mutton in one hand and gesturing wildly with it to make some point which now escapes me. After a particularly wild swing with the meat, I glanced over the side and observed a man being washed past on the strong tide. The situation was so bizarre that, without a thought, I jumped in and proceeded to hold the poor soul, who could in no way swim and struggled and grabbed at my legs forcing me to hold hard to his hair and collar in order to keep his face above water. We were swept a good half mile before rescue."

"What of the mutton?" asked Le Vesconte.

"I fear it did not survive. But the main consequence was that I had to put up with an unmerciful ribbing-on from my messmates over the desperate measures to which I was prepared to resort in order to put myself in line for promotion."

With general laughter the evening closed and so this hero will now retire to bed.

February 2—The sun cannot be long in shewing us its face. Every man is wishing it heartily and, around mid-day, there are always some in the masts or finding some excuse to climb the cliffs of Beechey in order to be the first to see its rays. I am certain there is betting going on the exact date and time, but I shall turn a blind eye.

February 4—The sun is back. At 11:30 a.m. it shewed itself head over the horizon. Le Vesconte was on the summit of Beechey and thus got the first glimpse, but we are all overjoyed to see its pleasant light and know that winter is coming to an end and the darkness is over. After so many weeks of darkness it is a wonder to see the friendly disc heave itself into our sight once again. It is, at present, just a momentary visit each day, but it has performed miracles for our spirits and all go about their tasks with a lighter tread because of it. I don't think I shall ever take sunlight for granted again.

We have had some extraordinary displays of the Aurora lately, but while it would still excite comment amongst London society, we have become very casual about it, only remarking on a particular brightness or an unusual pattern or colour.

The temperature remains constant around fifty or sixty degrees below freezing. Oddly enough, although it would kill multitudes in England, these temperatures are not too unbearable as long as one is appropriately dressed and has a warm place into which one can retreat. The problems occur when the wind gets up from the northwest, which it almost invariably does; this produces an effect which can chill the bones through the thickest clothing and which can freeze any exposed flesh in a few minutes.

We have few cases of frostbite, because the men are becoming good at taking precautions, but often they will return from digging the fire holes or some other task, with the telltale white spots and numbness to their faces and fingers. In most cases, the effects are very minor and disappear as the person returns to the warmth. The more serious cases, one of which we experienced today, have added to the debate ongoing between Stanley and

Goodsir.

Stanley is in favour of the traditional remedy of rubbing the affected area with snow or cold water and plying the victim with warmed wine. This is what he did today. Goodsir observed the proceedings in silence, but his attitude and expression made no secret of his doubts. When he eventually retired on deck, I followed.

"You do not approve of Surgeon Stanley's technique?" I asked when we were alone.

"Does it make sense," he asked, "to cure an ailment by application of the agent which caused the problem in the first place?"

I replied that, while it did at first sight appear inconsistent, tried and true remedies must have a basis in truth. I fear he scoffed at your dear brother.

"Tried and true!" he exclaimed. "There is little tried or true about much of the physician's art. I feel sometimes that we can do little but ease our patient's most obvious pain and watch them die."

"But surely," I interjected, "great advances have been made and more must lie just around the corner."

"True," Goodsir admitted, "we have discovered the circulation of the blood, and the surgeon's knife can, in the right hands, perform wonders undreamed of a few short generations ago, but hideous plagues still sweep through our cities and all the medical community can do is talk of 'foul miasmas,' and 'unclean air.'

"We know that the heart pumps the blood around our bodies yet we cannot with any degree of success transfer blood from one body to another. There is as much pagan superstition in the medical arts as there is modern science and, until the latter reigns supreme, I fear there will be precious little to congratulate ourselves about."

With that he retired to Sir John's cabin to catalogue his latest finds and I was left to ponder what he said. I find it hard to believe that the state of Goodsir's science is as backward as he implies. There are failures to be sure, but certainly time will rectify that.

Our attempts to adapt to these extremes of climate have been only partially successful. We have manufactured face masks which only shew the eyes and mouth, but they are unpopular since they tend to freeze to the flesh as the breath freezes and they can be painful to remove, especially from those with facial hair, which is most these days. At these temperatures, everything becomes brittle and easily broken and metal can burn exposed skin, even a simple breath in can give one the unpleasant sensation of having frozen the hairs in one's nose.

We have had more success creating boots for walking on the ice. They consist of variations of driving a number of screws through the sole from the inside and then shearing them off an appropriate length below, this provides some grip on ice or hard-packed snow, essential when hauling heavy loads.

We have also been busy making snow goggles from fine wire mesh to protect the men from snow blindness which was often reported as a serious problem by sled-hauling teams on previous expeditions, although we have had little chance to test our inventions as yet. The Navy-supplied veils are awkward, tending to collect condensation from breath and requiring constant adjustment, difficult when engaged in 'pully-haully.'

We get less snow than I expected, and what we do get blows about much. Against an obstruction, it can attain a depth of eight to ten feet, yet on flat surfaces exposed to the almost continual wind, there are but a few inches. Most of the snow arrives in short, sharp blizzards which last but a few days, but can make our lives, particularly those at the observatories, miserable. The rest of the time it is overcast and dull, with occasional days of light snow. Clear weather is a rarity in these parts, which makes our celestial readings problematical.

Couch, with the eternal help of Sargent, continues to improve the sled designs and test new variations on the runs to the magnetic observatories. A major contribution has been his ingenious idea for rigging a sail from the tent canvas and poles that the sledding teams carry in any case. It is a bulky, square thing, but with a following wind a respectable speed can be maintained with little or no effort from the men.

We continue to collect much valuable information. Osmer shews no signs of weakening his dominance over me on the chess board, despite his increased concern over the distribution of our supplies in preparation for our spring activity, which will get underway in April before the thaw makes sled travel too awkward.

Sir John has said nothing more of the strange conversation we had after Torrington's burial, and I will certainly make no mention of it. He is back to his old self, encouraging our work and talking of our plans for the spring and summer.

The moment we are released, probably around late July to judge by past records, we will head down Lady Jane Sound which should lead us close to Ross's Cape Felix, from where we should have little difficulty linking up with the open coastal waters of Simpson and Dease and proceeding on our way to the west. It is my hope that this may be completed in one season; yet, the more I see of the harshness of this land and the power of elements we face, the less I feel supremely confident in the fulfilment of our plans on a schedule of our devising. We may be required to winter again somewhere on the coast of the Americas, an eventuality which will make me grateful for the large margin of safety initially built into our plans. But listen to me being a Cassandra now. It is merely the dull sameness of these winter days which casts an unnecessarily pessimistic glow on our doings. Ignore me.

Bless you Elizabeth, good night.

February 7—Happy Birthday dearest sister. I hope you are having a fine occasion in a climate and situation much improved from ours. You have been much in my thoughts and I toasted your very good health in brandy at a time when I imagined you to be commencing your celebration. How I wish I could be with you, but I am, in spirit at least. Good night.

February 12—Have been confined by yet another blizzard these last three days but the snow has ceased and the wind is dropping so perhaps tomorrow shall be more clement. A most entertaining dinner this evening. Sir John was expansive and told us many tales of his adventures. I had not known, but he was signal midshipman on the *Bellerophon* at Trafalgar and was thus the one on board who first received Admiral Nelson's famous message. In the battle, they passed through the enemy line behind the *Royal Sovereign* and hotly engaged the *L'Aigle* and the Spanish *El Monarca*, which they took possession of. Franklin was one of only four who remained unwounded on the poop deck and was commended for 'evincing very conspicuous zeal and activity,' characteristics which are still very much in evidence in his personality to this day.

As the evening wore on he returned, as he so often does, to the events on his first overland Arctic expedition. "It was a time of such triumph and tragedy," he began. "We undoubtedly achieved much in the scientific field, but at such a cost. It tires me even now to think of the hardships we endured. No-one who has not been close to death by starvation can understand the joy evinced when we fell upon the rotting spine of a deer and ate its putrid marrow, or the fortitude achieved when we ate our daily allowance of *tripe de roche*."

"Tripe de roche?" asked Le Vesconte.

"Lichen," explained Sir John. "It grows abundant on rocks in the barren lands and can be stripped off and made into a brew which, if drunk daily, can stave off death from starvation for some time. It is not a palatable mixture and some stomachs cannot accept it. Poor Mister Hood was one such. It brought on such terrible cramps that eventually he could not take any and weakened fast."

"But was he not shot to death?" asked Le Vesconte who was listening most avidly to Sir John's tale.

"Indeed he was. By Michel, who was later summarily dealt with by Doctor

Richardson. I was not with the party at this time, being ahead at Fort Enterprise. But Doctor Richardson told me that Mister Hood was terribly weak and would not in all probability have survived even without the bullet."

Sir John paused reflectively before continuing.

"Michel was a monster. Doctor Richardson confided in me later that he had reason to believe that some wolf meat that Michel supplied to the party was actually human flesh cut from a voyager that he had murdered."

At this horrific exposé, we all fell silent. It is difficult to believe that men can stoop so low, even in dire circumstances, and I hesitated to write the above words which will surely offend your sensibilities. For that I apologise, but I must be true to my purpose.

In any case the conversation soon took a lighter turn as Sir John related a tale of love in the wilderness. Apparently, both Hood and Back took a fancy to a very comely young native maiden, the daughter of one of the chiefs of the Indians of the Coppermine. By all accounts she was very beautiful and managed to play off the two young men as cleverly as any society belle seeking a good match. Imagine! See the power you ladies have over us poor creatures when you choose to exercise it?

My contribution to the evening was a light-hearted description of the return of the king of the Greeks to his homeland in 1832 when I was seconded to the *Madagascar*. The landing was at night and I remember being very impressed by the wild, shouting Greek soldiers in their bright uniforms milling beneath the blue lanterns held by the sailors in attendance. By way of contrast, I was able to give a description of the capital of the Greek's bitter enemies, Constantinople, and this led naturally to a general discussion of the eastern question and the intent of the Russians in their move toward the gateway to our empire in India. Gore here entered the fray, and in a much more aggressive role than I should have expected from him.

"There will be no security," he exclaimed loudly, "until we have fully annexed the territories surrounding the passes into India. The natives thereabouts are treacherous beyond belief and cannot be trusted to hold to any treaty. At the least expectation of plunder or advantage to be had from our enemies, they will change sides and fall upon our backs. You need only to look to the recent disastrous retreat from Kabool to see that."

I attributed Gore's passion to the fact that he lost a dear friend in that disaster.

"But that is exactly why we cannot annex them," interjected Fairholme. "The cost of policing their territories in sufficient force to discourage their depravations and treachery would be prohibitive. And even then, the Kabool fiasco shows that an entire British army is no proof against disaster. We must work, through political means, to erect a series of neutral or friendly buffer states which we can monitor through agents and which at the very least will provide us with ample warning of any Russian designs."

So here we have in miniature aboard our tiny vessel, the issues which are currently not more hotly debated in the very Houses of Parliament. It is such a delight to be amongst so erudite and interesting companions and to partake of such wide-ranging conversations, that it is almost possible to forget the bleak world outside and the long months we face before we are again engaged in exploration activity.

I suppose these topics are dull and old-fashioned to your eye, but they are what keeps our minds active in the midst of such deadening boredom. In any case, I shall relinquish the far-flung corners of the globe in favour of my narrow bunk. Good night.

March 12—I can hardly believe that it has been a full month since I last wrote to you—not that there is a lot to tell, but I had hoped to put pen to paper on a more frequent basis. The days continue to lighten and we are eagerly noting any sign of spring. We, or at least the parties out and about on the island, see the tracks of much game—deer, wolves, foxes, grouse and rabbits—but we have seen no living animal save the crows which seem to disdainfully shun the possibility of fleeing to warmer climes. One of these creatures has apparently adopted our little ship and perches for much of the day on the rail where the men feed it scraps which it accepts with a polite little bow and a cry of 'caw, caw.' Some of the tracks have been so fresh that we have sent out hunting parties, but they have always returned empty-handed. Le Vesconte believes this is because the animals hereabouts are almost exclusively white and we dress in dark clothes and thus stand out in this landscape like an inkblot on a blank page.

We have seen nothing of the native inhabitants of this region, if indeed there are any. Certainly there used to be, as we have found several old graves and the foundations of some dwellings surrounded by discarded whale, seal and deer bones, but how old these indications are we cannot determine. In this cold, some things, if undisturbed, seem to last forever. I am sorry we have seen no people, since I was looking forward to seeing them and how they live in this land without the benefit of our many inventions, but surely we will run into them when we make the American coast this summer.

The temperature is moderating somewhat, although it shews this by becoming less certain, some days popping up to only thirty or so degrees below freezing before plunging back down to fifty. It also comes on to snow more frequently and the wind tends to be stronger, but every day the sunlight increases and, although there is precious little warmth in it, remains a source of joy. Not as much a source of joy as would be the sight of your face and the sound of your voice, but we must make do with what we can in these barren lands. Good night.

March 15—Saw a bear today. I was below when I heard the sound of muskets from on shore. I hurried on deck to see what was causing the excitement. Apparently Samuel Honey, the Blacksmith, had been answering a call of nature, when he looked up and saw a huge white bear a short quarter mile away and heading in his direction. It had its head down and was lumbering along as if following a scent. Poor Honey ran shouting back to the smithy where he was met by the other men with muskets. Seeing them, the bear headed off across the ice toward the Devon shore. They followed some way taking shots as they could, but saw no evidence that they had scored a hit.

When I came on deck, the first thing I noticed was the party of men, like black dots on the ice, straggling in a line away from the Beechey camp. Putting the glass to my eye, I followed their line to see what they were following. For the longest while I could see nothing, the bear's camouflage being so suited to this landscape, and then I saw its lumbering form moving away from the men. I estimated its height to be in excess of nine feet, but it was difficult to be exact at such a distance, and it moved with a long swaying motion, rather like a sailor who is on land for the first time after a long stretch on the water. It did not seem overly concerned by the musket fire, but moved purposefully, turning every so often to see how its pursuers were doing. I watched it for some ten minutes, by which time the men had given up the chase and the bear was becoming difficult to follow due to the ice hummocks.

Later in the day I went over to where I had seen the bear pass and found some splashes of blood, so it seems at least one ball found its mark, but to little effect. The paw prints of this beast measured a full twelve inches across. I was in two minds about its escape, on the one hand, some bear meat would have been a welcome change, but on the other such a magnificent beast with such disdain for intruders into its world deserved better than to end up on our dinner table.

March 23—Blowing hard and snowy for five days now. Temperature hovering around thirty below freezing.

This evening at supper we had a discussion about the proposed construction of a large cairn on the most notable promontory on Beechey Island, "to guide our spring exploration parties back," as Sir John put it.

"And to signal any ships which might come this way before we return to

England," Crozier added.

"Yes," Sir John agreed, "although I doubt any will come this way before our return home and, after us, I fear not many will venture to these parts."

"The cairn will also make a secure place for a record of our doing so far," Crozier went on.

"No, I think not," Sir John said. "At this early stage, although our achievements are considerable, we have not yet achieved our primary goals and any message would be inconsequential or misleading."

Of course, Crozier would not let the matter rest.

"But it is common practice in these lands for travellers to leave full records of their passing."

"I am well aware of that, thank you, Mister Crozier. But the scientific nature of our work reduces the efficacy of such procedures. We cannot, after all, leave duplicates of our entire scientific discoveries.

"However, if it pleases you, we shall, in the spring after the exploring parties return and we have something to report, place a note under the cairn."

I have not heard such open disagreement, nor such shortness of temper from Sir John. The rest of us sat in silence and Crozier merely nodded his assent. He was wrong to question Sir John so, but he does have a point. We should leave an unequivocal and detailed record of our passing this way, even if it will never be read. Fortunately, I thought of something by way of compromise based on what Le Vesconte and I constructed on our first crossing of the island.

"Perhaps for now, we could surmount the cairn, which in itself will be an eloquent statement of our passing, with a carved indicator in the shape of a pointing hand, to show the direction we plan to take. We thus give information and cannot mislead whomever comes this way in the future."

"An excellent idea Mister Fitzjames. We will commence construction of the cairn as soon as the snow eases. But now gentlemen," Sir John continued, rising from his seat, "I must to bed."

And so must I.

March 26—No sign of the snow abating and we wait impatiently to send off the exploration parties. It is early in the season yet and they are not expected to accomplish prodigious things, rather they will check our food caches and try out some of our new inventions. The party will be led by Gore and Couch and be made of stout men from the *Erebus*. How I wish I were going. I have not travelled more than two miles from the ship since Couch and I established the observatory past Cape Spencer soon after we first arrived here and my feet itch to be on the move again.

March 28—Finally the snow ceased yesterday and Gore's party set out this morning below a clear sky, heading for a weak sun. We wished them all luck and expect to see them back in no more than two weeks. Work also commenced on the cairn today.

Crozier and I sent out several hunting parties, mostly to give the men a break after being confined by the blizzard for so long and without much hope of success; however, Hodgson's party from the *Terror* came upon a musk-ox and with several well-aimed shots brought it down. It is a large male, weighing, I should guess, upwards of 800 pounds. and we all looked forward to enough meat to supply us with a change of diet for a short while.

The specimen was almost five feet high at the shoulder which forms a pronounced hump, and was covered with a coat of long, shaggy, dark brown hair which concealed another of much finer short hair which has the pronounced odour from which the beast derives its name. Its head is low slung and carries a set of heavy, curved horns. Blanky, who has seen these beasts when on Ross's expeditions, says it is unusual to find one alone, they being used to travelling in herds of twenty or thirty. Apparently, when threatened by wolves, they form a circle with their horns facing out, the old males on the outside and the young in the centre. Against this defence, there is little even a pack of wolves can accomplish and they must retreat to look for easier prey.

Supper this evening was looked on with some anticipation and the cook on *Terror* was instructed to prepare enough choice cuts for the officers of both vessels who were not engaged in other duties. Accordingly, we all congregated in our sister ship's mess looking forward to a change of fare. Only Blanky did not enter into our speculations about how wonderful the fresh meat would taste.

Well, the ox certainly fulfilled our expectations of a change, for I can honestly say that I have never tasted anything quite like it before. The meat is dark and with a rather pungent, though not unpleasant, aroma. The taste on the other hand is definitely one to be acquired, it is like very strong game but with a bitter aftertaste that is only partially helped by the consumption of bread and a heavy claret. As we ate, our conversation dwindled to silence and we all contemplated our meal in our own ways. Blanky eventually ventured that young musk-oxen have a much more palatable taste, requiring only a light Bordeaux to get down.

This comment provoked much joviality and our disappointment vanished and our humour returned. It was only the fact that it has been so long since we tasted any fresh meat that caused our plates to be cleared.

March 31—Weather continues fair with the mercury still shewing about twenty degrees of frost. I never thought that I would ever consider a temperature as cold as this warm, but in our ever strengthening sunlight, it seems positively balmy after our dark cold winter. The year is one quarter over and will be more than one half gone before we have a chance of moving from this place. I went up on Beechey today to look at our cairn which is now complete. It is of large size and should be visible from a considerable distance along the coast or out in Barrow Strait. On top we have added a large wooden replica of a human hand, fist clenched and with the index finger extended pointing across the ice to Lady Jane Sound. No-one could mistake our meaning.

The ice in Barrow Strait is densely packed and exhibits more signs of pressure than when I last looked upon it. Huge rafts of ice, ten or twelve feet thick have been hurled upwards on edge to heights which would dwarf the topmasts of our ships; we are lucky indeed to have found such a sheltered harbour for our winter sojourn, for I fear even our reinforced vessels would not fare well in those conditions.

The game continue to shew signs of increasing and we managed to bag a couple of hares on our way back. They are poor skinny beasts, pure white and with long ears, and I cannot imagine what they find to keep themselves alive in this place, except perhaps the lichens which would make a poor fare indeed. Hopefully, they will provide better fare in the form of a passable soup for our table tomorrow.

April 1—Commenced to snow this morning, light at first but heavier and with a strengthening wind later in the day. I hope it does not signal a long storm with Gore's team probably close to their maximum distance from the ship.

April 2—Not snowing today, but the wind picks up so much snow and blows it along that it is impossible to see more than five feet, yet the sky is clear above one. The temperature has dropped to fifty-seven degrees of frost. The other exploration teams are ready to leave at the first suitable weather after the return of Gore's party which may not be for a few days yet.

April 3—More snow.

April 5—Still bitterly cold. I am beginning to fear for Gore and his party, they must be struggling if they can move at all in conditions such as this.

April 7—At last the snow has stopped and the mercury risen somewhat. The wind is still there and enough to prove an inconvenience to men sled hauling in the teeth of it, but at least it is now weather to travel in. I have sent out a light party in the direction from which we can expect Gore, in the hopes of aiding them over the last stretch.

April 8—No sign of Gore or the relief party.

April 9—Still no sign although Reid keeps watch all day from the crow's nest.

April 10—Gore is back. It is not the disaster I was beginning to fear, but one man is dead and several others badly broken and frost-bitten. As I suspected they were almost at their farthest point when the storm hit. In fact they had already turned back because one man, the Marine William Braine, was much broken and could haul no more. They continued as best they could in the snow with a reduced crew, but only made two miles over rough ice on April 2. Braine could no longer even walk and had to be placed on the sled. Gore ordered camp set on the afternoon of the 2nd and the men huddled beneath the canvas. In the night, Braine began raving and coughing up blood and had to be restrained. At length he fell into a restless sleep from which no-one could arouse him. As the snow continued they did not break camp on the 3rd and late in the afternoon, without awakening, Braine died. There was some discussion about leaving him, but Gore insisted that he be brought back to our little cemetery on Beechey. I can only imagine what it was like in that cramped tent with the wind howling outside and the body of poor Braine lying there.

On the 7th the weather abated enough for them to break camp and continue. Even with their sad extra load, they made good time and met the relief party on the evening of the 9th. All were much exhausted and Stanley calculates that they will require at least a full week to recover their strength. Braine's body is frozen from the journey and Stanley has it in sick bay in preparation for an examination, although he is almost certain it is the consumption, aggravated by the heavy sled duty and, possibly, pneumonia. This is no place for sick men.

So again there is a crew digging on the island and Weekes and his assistant are banging a coffin together above. There is some urgency as Braine, although frozen for much of the journey back, shews some signs of being too long unburied. Bryant, the Marine Sergeant, is constructing a metal plaque for the coffin lid out of some copper sheathing we carry for the repair of the boats. Tomorrow we shall repeat our procession across the ice.

April 11—I visited Braine this morning and he was much in need of burying. Unlike Torrington and Hartnell, Braine was thirty-three, bearded and balding. His body shews the marks of the harsh life of a soldier, several teeth being broken and there being a large healed scar on his forehead. He was a tall man, six feet I would guess, but his body is so much wasted that there is little more than skin over his bones.

It is strange, but his death affects me less than the earlier ones, perhaps because he was older and died working, or perhaps because his death is less of an omen coming as it does amidst these hopeful, lengthening spring days. In any case, we hurriedly got him into the large, rude coffin, and proceeded with the ceremony. The lowering of the coffin was accompanied by a fusillade of musket shot from the Royal Marine contingent, and Sir John made his now familiar eulogy. Braine's headboard is as the others except for the added inscription: "Choose ye this day whom ye will serve' Joshua, ch. xxiv., 15.' His colleagues have also erected a flat slab of rock to serve as a foot board. It is strange how man, even in the most unusual and extraordinary circumstances, will attempt to recreate something familiar, in this case, the feeling of a quiet English country graveyard in the midst of this frozen wilderness. I fervently hope that our graveyard is now complete. Good night dearest.

April 12—Divine service today included a call to look forward to achievements yet to come. Sir John was at his most inspiring and I think his words helped us all put this winter behind us. The weather remains fair and the exploration parties will set out tomorrow. We are all in a frenzy of expectation, this is our real work beginning, the sleds are loaded and ready on the ice. Three will go with the express purpose of new discoveries, one to the east to extend Gore's route, one to the north along the shores of Wellington Inlet and one to the northeast to attempt to ascertain the extent of Devon in that direction. All have food caches on route and with luck should be back in five or six weeks, although they have the capacity, with the caches, to be out for considerably longer. A fourth party will attempt to cross the ice of Barrow Strait, examine the shore of Somerset and the route we propose to take down Lady Jane Sound. We are all focusing on their endeavour and looking forward to great things and new discoveries. We wish them well.

Couch has performed wonders on our sledges. They are still large and unwieldy, but he has stripped much of their unnecessary weight without weakening them unduly. I am sure his designs will become commonplace in future polar expeditions.

Our four spring sleds are each named for one of the Titans; Oceanus, Cronus, Hyperion, and Iapetus, in honour of the prodigious strengths exhibited by the haulers. Each has a banner affixed to a pole and bearing the name of the sled on one side and an inspiring legend on the other, this encourages *esprit-de-corps* and is something with which the men can identify. It also enables the young officers to have an independent command, albeit a small one. Tomorrow's sleds are commanded by Le Vesconte and Fairholme from our ship and Little and Irving from *Terror*. God Bless us all, Good night.

April 13—The sledging parties set off this morning with much cheering and many hurrahs. The weather was clear and many of the crew spent considerable time on the deck watching the tiny flags pull farther and farther away over the ice, with many a mind wishing no doubt to be with them. Later in the day, Reid came in to announce that he had seen a seagull, a good omen which to him means that "there's open water about arl right." This is hard to believe with several tens of feet of ice in the strait and six or so in our sheltered bay.

April 14—Still fair weather and the mercury hovering around zero. We were visited by an Arctic fox which came close in to the starboard side to examine us, but ran off before we could locate and load a musket. However, Gore brought down some ptarmigan on the island. They taste much like grouse and would probably benefit from hanging, but we do not indulge in that luxury and eat them as they come—out of the feathers. The crew remaining with the ships are occupied in caulking and painting, premature work considering when we can expect to be under sail again, but combating boredom is one of our prime motivations.

April 15—Light snow and a stiff breeze. This morning, Crozier, who is an excellent shot, and a party brought down five musk-oxen, including a calf. In all, the kill supplies us with almost 1,000 pounds of dressed meat, which we will, with determination, attempt to acquire a taste for.

April 16—Fine dinner this evening of musk-ox calf with canned vegetables and a Christmas pudding we neglected at our feast four months ago. This was accompanied by champagne from our private stocks in which we heartily toasted Sir John on the occasion of his sixtieth birthday. I ordered the issuing of an extra ration of beer for the crew and all congregated on deck to toast Franklin in a prolonged and loud manner. Sir John replied with a brief speech about the necessity of the roles played by everyone on board in the significant achievements behind us and those in the future. This was answered with much cheering before we retired to our supper.

Crozier and Hodgson came over for our repast, bringing with them a splendid diorama of the two ships in their current position, made by the crew of our sister ship. It is a wonder of the miniature art, complete with detailed figures going about their chores both on ice and at the land camp. Sir John is portrayed standing atop Beechey Island telescope to his eye, gazing southward to the lands we shall conquer come summer.

All concern over Franklin's age, a concern I never shared, has vanished. True, it is a senior age to be in these bleak lands, but our Commander conducts himself with the vigour of a man two decades younger. He is very much in charge, takes an interest in all activities, and sets the tenor for our whole operation. I do not think we could have accomplished half as much as we have without his leadership and direction and I cannot imagine a more happy band with a clearer purpose and a greater chance of ultimate success than ours, and with those last puffed-up thoughts I shall retire and bid you good night.

May 1—Arose this morning to find a brightly coloured doll attached to the mainmast beside where we post the day's conditions. I called to Reid, since he knows all that goes on, and asked him its significance.

"Well Mister Jems," he said, "that'll aye be a reminder of Mayday. 'Tis a holiday for the whalers and a day when a good Captain will give them arl a double ration." With that the old devil gave me as broad a wink as you like and departed. It seems it is a tradition amongst whaling men to celebrate May 1 and the doll was a reminder to their Captain on this voyage who is not a whaling man. Of course, I issued double rations.

The hunting continues to improve and there is often partridge on the table. There is considerable musk-oxen meat in a frozen state and we are beginning to take pleasure in it. Crozier bagged a reindeer two days ago, but it was late in the day and by the time a crew went out next morning to bring it in, the wolves had had their share and there was precious little left. A disappointment, I should like to try that meat.

May 11—Little's east sledging party is returned, having reached along the coast of Devon almost to Crocker Bay where the land becomes mountainous and glaciers make their way down to the waters of Lancaster Sound, a distance of 300 miles round trip. They have been lucky with the weather and the going was good along the ice close inshore, allowing them to make a respectable average of more than ten miles a day. The men are much tired but in good spirits and delighted to be the first back. They appear to have done good work and have much information on a coast which has only been observed from ship.

May 12—Fairholme came in today with the northern sledge. They have also benefited from the good travelling weather we have experienced of late, although they only covered 220 miles to Little's 300. This was because of the terrain, the going being somewhat slower inland than along the coast.

They crossed Devon, which Fairholme now believes to be a large island, in just seventy miles and continued east along the coast for fifty more. They found themselves on the shores of a wide inlet, which must be none other than Jones Sound. They could see several points of land to the north, some forty-five to fifty miles away. They eventually stopped at a wide bay full of jumbled ice which Fairholme kindly named Fitzjames Bay in my honour. On the return, they attempted to traverse some way to the west along the coast, but were held up by very rugged terrain and a deep inlet which separated them from a coast which swung back to the east and may even be joined to the landmass they saw to the north.

All on board are delighted with their achievements and the many new discoveries they can now enter onto the Chart. It seems that the land here is a series of very large islands, between which are wide, ice-filled channels. What wonders will the others find?

May 13—Little and Fairholme are lucky. It came on to blow today and the mercury is shewing very cold. I think Le Vesconte and Irving will be having a miserable time of it.

May 14—Still blowing and cold.

May 15—Weather cleared today and the wind dropped although it is still cold.

May 18—Irving is back from Somerset. All are well, but much exhausted and with one man badly frost-bitten on the feet. It is a wonder that their sled could still carry their supplies, it was so hard used and battered, one runner was split and more than half the rivets fixing the steel runners were gone.

Irving has covered nearly 200 miles at a gruelling six miles a day. The ice in Barrow Strait was a terrible test of stamina, the men continually having to pull and push the laden sled over ridges of sometimes prodigious height. On reaching the Somerset shore, the going improved and they made better time to the point at the entrance to Lady Jane Sound. They examined the coast for some miles south, climbed a prominent hill and could see the channel continuing as far as the eye could see. We take great encouragement from this for our summer endeavour.

Irving's journey back was the devils' own work, and it is a wonder they are all not in a much worse state. The worst was the storm of five days ago, which caught them on the ice of Barrow Strait and they had a most unpleasant time sitting in their tent listening to the ice move around them with much groaning and complaining. On one occasion, a pressure ridge rose with a mighty crash not fifty feet from where they were camped and would have been the end of them all had they camped any closer. Only Le Vesconte still out, but there is no cause for concern yet.

May 20—Wind has risen again and brought much blowing snow We expect Le Vesconte daily. We are all busy cataloguing and storing the specimens brought back by the three sledges and transposing the observational data onto our science books.

Couch and Sargent are occupied collecting the comments of the parties about the sleds and incorporating these into new designs. It seems the devices worked quite well, but Fairholme has suggested that future parties take additional light satellite sleds which can be used for exploring inlets and bays in detail while the main sleds take the most direct routes. The worst problem was with the men's boots, which are made of leather and freeze almost immediately when taken off, making putting them back on a severe problem. The men took to sleeping in their boots to prevent their freezing, but it seems that moccasins of sealskin, with the hair outermost, over feet wrapped in blankets, works better, although they do not have the grip on steep ice of the nailed boot soles.

May 24—Signs of spring are all around us. The game increases weekly and our hunting parties are busy and often successful. We have even attempted a couple of protected gardens of local plants on the island, one of those which might be of use to us, and another of flowering plants which grow in great abundance hereabouts. The ice in the bay is thinning rapidly and there are occasional patches of water on the surface, although I suspect these are due to pressure from below rather than surface melting. On the land, bare areas and rocks are increasing as the power of the sun waxes and overland sled travel is becoming hard. We now have many long hours of sunlight and the temperature in the direct sun is sometimes thirty-four or thirty-five. Tomorrow Le Vesconte will have been gone six weeks. Unless an accident has befallen him or he has missed the caches, he has more than enough supplies; however, I have sent an extra party of men to the Cape Spencer observatory to keep watch for him and render any assistance that might be necessary.

May 25—Overcast and cold. No sign of Le Vesconte.

May 26—Bright and sunny. We have demolished the ice walls around the ships and stowed our canvas roof Much activity amongst the ice of Barrow Strait.

May 27—Still no sign of Le Vesconte.

May 28—At last they are back and none the worse for their long prodigious journey. Le Vesconte has covered over 360 miles in forty-five days, very good going. He has explored the coast of Wellington Channel around Parry Bay, crossed a narrow neck of land to the north shore of Devon, which is now most definitely an island and worked back east to almost the point reached by Fairholme. At this point there was only a channel of some five miles width separating Devon from the landmass observed by Fairholme which we have christened Cornwall Land, but the ice blocking it was in such a tumult that Le Vesconte did not attempt a crossing. The land that we reached in the ships at the end of August is a peninsula projecting from Devon into the permanently frozen Polar Ocean which itself contains several large islands.

We have all breathed a sigh of relief at the safe return of all four parties and are delighted with their achievements. An important blank section of the Chart has been filled in. We will do no more sled travel this spring other than in support of our hunting parties, the ice being rotten and the ground being often bare. Couch, with Sargent as his assistant, has become our transportation expert and is now busy supervising the construction of some wheeled carts which we will use to supply the observatories when sled travel becomes impossible. The ice continues to thin around us and shews signs of activity in the open strait. We cannot wait to be on the move again, yet we must have many weeks here yet.

How is the spring in England? This place becomes more beautiful daily, yet how I miss the green lawns spotted with crocus and daffodil that we know so well.

I have just completed Goldsmith's *The Vicar of Wakefield*. It is a fine story, reminds me much of the England I love, and has done much to make me miss its cosy rural setting, but my situation makes it hard to comprehend the Squire's evil or the misfortunes which befall Doctor Primrose. It all seems so pointless against the overwhelming majesty and solemnity of this land which we are busy exploring. We have been away more than a full year now and, though our initial enthusiasm is still there, it has been dampened somewhat by the tragedies which are marked by the three lonely graves and by the terrible work that is necessary to accomplish anything in this climate. But I do not wish to sink into bleak retrospection. We are all still in good spirits and very much pleased with our accomplishments, and as soon as the ice loosens its grip and we are under sail or steam once more, all shadows will vanish. Good night.

June 6—I have sat long and thought hard, all the while staring at your picture, debating whether I should offend your sensibilities and tell you of the day's events. I have decided to proceed because of my promise to you, but I tell you now that you may wish to pass by this entry.

After dinner, I was wandering the decks, as is often my evening habit. It is full daylight from noon to midnight now and the press of our supplies is much reduced, making walking on deck a more pleasant possibility.

I was standing at the bow gazing out over the ice at the Beechey Island camp and pondering nothing of any great note, when I heard a sound. It was a scuffling and grunting like some large animal, and came from beneath my feet in the storage area for our anchors and chains. Knowing that no-one should be there at such a time and thinking that I might discover an illicit gaming house or some secret liquor store, I descended below decks to investigate.

I wish I had not! The forward area is most cramped because of the curve of the hull and, since it is little used, is an ideal repository for supplies and, as they are used up, our scientific specimens. I obtained a lantern from the mess and proceeded in a crouch. The anchor storage is hidden by a low door. Upon reaching it, I resolved to throw it wide in order to increase the dramatic effect on what I fully expected to be a covey of secret drinkers or gamblers.

I did so, and the light of the lantern revealed a horror I could never erase from my mind. In the small space were two men engaged in the most perverse of unnatural acts. They were so far gone, that even my sudden approach could not prevent the conclusion of their disgusting transaction.

I have seen men flogged for this very offence on sundry occasions. But this was not the satiation of some animal lust between two low products of the press gang. It was much worse, for the two men I found were the young Mates, Edward Couch and Robert Sargent.

I could think then of nothing to say and hurriedly retreated from the cramped space and returned to my cabin. There I thought over my options. By the rules of the service, they must be seriously punished, suffering demotion and the scorn of their peers in addition to the corporal elements. Their careers would be forfeit the minute we reached port.

Yet what would that serve? At the very least it would create a serious rift in the mess and undermine our sense of purpose, almost on the eve of our important summer's work, and destroy the lives of two men. Sargent I do not care too much for. He is effete and overly sensitive for our life. I expect little from him and it would not surprise me to see him leave the Navy of his own accord. But Couch is a different matter. He has improved much in the last year and his work on the sledges is of great importance. I had expectations of fine things from him.

My thoughts were interrupted by a knock and Couch entered. He was downcast and pale and I could not but admire the courage it must have taken for him to walk through my door. I did not let him speak—there was, after all, nothing he could say to alter the situation—instead I told him of my thoughts. I would not make an example of the pair, not because I sanctioned their behaviour, but because I felt it would, in our present circumstances, not be beneficial to the expedition, and the expedition is what must take precedence. I reserved the right to bring the matter up when we returned home, but in the meantime, he was to avoid all contact with Sargent except for the most minimal in the course of their work in the confined space of the ship. If there was even a suggestion of a repeat of their behaviour, I would recant my promise and both would be punished to the fullest extent of regulations. I then ordered him to get out and to repeat my orders to Sargent.

I don't know if I have done the correct thing. I feel sure that Sir John would not approve of my laxity, but I sincerely hope time will prove me correct. True pleasure is spiritual and intellectual, not physical, and it is surely through the conscious moral control of our wills that we achieve what greatness we do. If we give in to our desires and fail to control the baser instincts, where will it lead?

In any case, it is done and I will speak of it no more.

June 15—We are perhaps a month or more early, but preparations are well under way for our release from the ice. The observatories have been brought in. The men have done sterling work in them and we have mounds of invaluable information. The shore camp is still occupied with Weekes, Smith and the two Honeys busy with preparations. We continue to send hunting parties out and they continue to bring in a fair supply of fresh meat which we all enjoy and which keeps us all in good health. The rigging has been restored, the yards are crossed and the topgallants sent up. In the good weather we have dried and repaired the sails and they lie ready for use.

This is the hardest part of all the winter waiting, we see improvement in the weather and ice everyday and we are almost desperate to be on our way, yet every day we awake to the same vista and the same tasks. Reid is not much help in determining our future situation, never having wintered in the ice and all we can get out of him is, "Never mind now sirs, the ice'll let us go when it is good and ready," which is not much help. Sometimes I feel that Reid, despite his rude charm, is little solid help in determining the state of this element which directs our lives. Blanky, who has wintered in these realms, estimates that we have another four or five weeks before we are released, although many of us try to be more sanguine.

June 23—Travel has become a most terrible chore, the ground being waterlogged and spongy and the ice being rotten. Often we must wade waist deep through freezing water to cross the ice close to the shore. Everything is continually wet. Fortunately the weather is fair which helps to dry us out, but what we really need is a gale to blow some of this ice away.

June 30—One year since we crossed the Arctic Circle. Would that we cross it again before another year is out.

July 8—Still locked in our bay. It seems impossible that we cannot be released, the ice is moving and we are continually drenched by rains, yet we still remain immobile. Our frustrations are seemingly endless. We have tried to enliven things with some athletics on shore, and we have had some good sport, but everyone's mind is elsewhere. The hunting continues to improve, hardly a day passing without our store of fresh provisions being added to. One bright point is that we have had no sign of scurvy in the dark months, a fact I put down in no small part to the success we have had in procuring fresh meat. Most of our supplies are now on board from the storehouse on Beechey and our vessels are beginning to look shipshape again.

July 15—At last a good wind is setting from the north. With luck it will increase and open a channel for us to escape. I have put men on the ice to cut us free and by tomorrow we should be afloat in our own little pond.

July 16—Wind continuing to increase and a gap, some ten feet wide, has opened along the shore of Devon although our floe is still solidly attached to Beechey. In fact I went ashore today to collect some plants and climbed Beechey to get a look at the strait. It is an extraordinary confusion of ice, with floes being pushed up on each other and open water appearing and disappearing at the whim of some unseen hand. I wish to be free, and yet I do not relish being loose in such conditions. Still, the ships are sturdy and will take much punishment without complaint. A few more days and we must be under sail again. Tomorrow we will send a crew ashore to place a message below the cairn on Beechey Island, in which I shall report on our doings and discoveries up to this point, it is already written and sealed in a can. I do not expect that anyone will be this way to read it for very many years, but perhaps it will make it an interesting document for future generations.

Summer, 1846

July 17, 1846—WE ARE FREE! I was awakened just after I turned in last night by the most extraordinary cacophony of crashing and grinding. I rushed on deck and was amazed to see the very nature of the ice changing before my eyes as leads opened across the bay. I barely had time to fix us to our floe with ice anchors and re-call the few men on Beechey before we were set adrift. There was not even any need to cut leads as the entire mass of ice in our bay was being pushed out into the strait. The ice banged us about some, but we withstood well. By ten we were completely out of our bay and in a turmoil of disordered ice. Even in the midst of such chaos and bustle, I was surprised at how sad I felt as we rounded the point of Beechey. It has been our home for almost ten months, and although we have spent much of that time wishing to be on our way, the act of leaving is a wrench which brings a lump to my throat. Will we be home by next winter? Or will we have another home in a few months? If the latter, I hope it is half as secure as Beechey has been.

Unfortunately, we have lost our chance to leave a message on Beechey; perhaps Crozier was right after all, but we all assumed that we would leave our anchorage under steam or sail at a time more-or-less of our choosing. Still it is of little consequence since we shall bring our papers home in much better time. I am much more distressed about another consequence of our sudden departure. Yesterday I wetted the gloves you gave me for Christmas when scrambling about on the island collecting samples of the plants which are blooming all over now. Before returning to the ship, I carefully placed the gloves on a flat rock to dry, the palms of each weighted down with a pebble to prevent them blowing away. In our rush to leave, I forgot them, though I should probably have had no chance to retrieve them even if I had remembered. I thought of them only after we were under way, and then with much sadness. Links to home and loved ones are especially important in our isolation and those gloves were particularly important to me, being the most recent gift from you. I hope you will forgive my carelessness.

It is good to be back at work, although it is hard to keep our way in this chaos. The wind is very strong and we can make little headway against it, using our engines simply in trying to avoid heavy floes. We have taken a number of hard knocks but seem none the worse for it, these really are splendid vessels for this work. Our aim is to head southwest for Lady Jane Sound, but at present we have little say in where we go. It has been a tiring twenty-four hours and I must to bed now. Good night.

July 18—This morning the wind dropped and we managed to make way past Beechey and across the mouth of Wellington Channel. The ice is solid to the south and we can see no way through in the direction we wish to go. It is frustrating, but we are all in such a state of euphoria at being released that we do not worry about a little delay. This evening the ice is thickening around us and we have no room for manoeuvre, but it is quiet and presents no threat. The active ice of the strait presents such a different prospect from the calm ice we have been frozen in for so long. Perhaps there are dozens of words for ice as well as snow.

July 19—When the wind died, the ice flowed north again and surrounded us completely, the pressure is not great, but we are stuck fast and drifting back to the east. We have half recrossed Wellington Channel.

July 20—Back off Beechey and still being driven to the east. This is disheartening and we can only hope that the ice will break soon and allow us to make up lost ground. *Terror* is trapped some half a mile farther out in the strait and is nipped so that she has a list of some five degrees, but she seems in no danger.

July 21—Still heading east, very disheartening.

July 23—Free once more, but at a cost. Around 8 a.m. yesterday, the wind changed and the ice began to build up against the ship. We were lying with our bow pointing north and began to heel over to starboard to quite an alarming degree. At 4:30, a large block of ice was thrust up smashing one of our boats and badly scouring the side of the ship. I had made up my mind to order the men over the side to carry as much of the supplies as possible onto the ice to prepare for abandonment, not a happy prospect in these conditions, but the wind swung around to the northeast and the pressure eased. In remarkably short time, we had righted and leads were opening out in the strait. I was gratified to see *Terror* afloat in a lead and after a good night's work with the ice saws, we managed to join her by early morning. All day we worked on hauling along uncertain leads and have made some ten miles in approximately the direction we wish to go. It all shews how suddenly our fortunes can change in this place. Should we have abandoned the vessel, we would have been in a perilous position indeed, loose on moving ice with precious little in the way of supplies. In those circumstances I should be very grateful for the foresight in sending two stout ships on such an enterprise, but any hope of achieving our goals would have been dashed in but a moment, and all our preparations brought to naught.

July 24—Back off Beechey, but considerably farther out in the ice which is breaking up rapidly and presenting us with a bewildering array of possible routes. However, by a combination of musculature and steam power, we manage to make headway to the south.

July 27—Another year on your brother's age and a splendid dinner of roast partridge and wine to celebrate. Still hard going to make any headway.

July 29—At last we have worked our way into the mouth of Lady Jane Sound. It has been thirteen days since we were forced out of our winter harbour and it has taken us that long to cross the eighty miles to where we now sit. The irony is that, looking back over the almost open water behind us, we could now accomplish the same journey in a day with a fair wind. The inlet is open down the east side along the Somerset shore, and will remain so as long as we have a wind from the northeast. It is imperative that we make good time down here and reach the more open waters to the south.

I am sorry that I do not seem to have had anything of interest to tell you of late. The truth is that we are all very intent on our purpose and realize how important it is to make good progress early if we are to get home this year or find a good, well advanced winter harbour from which to complete the passage next season. The most important man on board just now is Reid who spends his entire time in the crow's nest, calling leads and ice conditions which are received below like the tablets brought down from the mount by Moses, for we are just as much in the wilderness as were the Israelites. Next in importance are the seamen who throw the lines over the side to sound the depth beneath our hull. We are in sufficient water for the moment, but our deep draughts are a concern and any sudden shallowing will be watched carefully. Goodsir enlists anyone he can find who is not actively engaged in some other occupation to man his nets over the side and collect whatever he may please for examination and study.

We finished the last of our fresh meat for supper and celebrated with several bottles of champagne. We will be back to salt beef and canned soup tomorrow. We have not used an uncommonly high proportion of our cans, despite the size of the pile abandoned on Beechey. The proportion blown or unfit for consumption is small, never-the-less, we will have some sharp words for Mister Goldner when we return. The consequences of any wastage in this land could have been serious, but we have had the good fortune to procure much fresh meat this spring and we are still well stocked with salt beef and pork. Had a chance to continue my duel with Osmer this evening, the first time for several weeks. I have not improved with the waiting. Past one now, I must to bed. Good night.

July 30—Passed the point reached by Irving on Somerset, on the north shore of a deep inlet we have named for Doctor Richardson, of whom you have heard me relate from Sir John's stories. Due west we can see the dark shape of Cape Walker and Wales Island. It is slow going down this narrow lead but we are all heartened at our progress and glad to be out of the dreadful ice of Barrow Strait.

August 2—Lady Jane Sound continues to lead us well in the right direction and we have been busy naming and plotting points of land on both the east and west sides. Compasses are now entirely useless, so near are we to the magnetic pole so well reached by James Ross, so we must rely entirely on our celestial sightings.

Today we discovered a channel leading to the east, it is narrow, between high lands, and much ice clogged, but the strong current flowing in it suggests that it links up with Prince Regent Inlet. This would make Somerset an island separate from Boothia which now lies off our port side. We have named the new discovery Crozier Strait.

To our great satisfaction, Lady Jane Sound is widening and swinging to the southwest, exactly the direction we wish to go. The ice is becoming heavier as the inlet widens and the going is slow, but we continue to make progress which is all we can ask.

August 3—Wales is indeed an island as we suspected. Today we passed the southern extremity of it and were presented with a fearsome sight. The waters to the west are a continuation of the dreaded ice river we encountered west of Cape Walker last summer. It must be pushed down a channel on the far side of Wales, the bulk of which has been protecting us until now. We still make headway close in to the shore of Boothia, although the ice is thickening and we have been out cutting a way.

Terror was aground briefly this morning, but managed to pull herself off without our assistance. I fear of late I have been only able to give you a catalogue of ice conditions which must be of scant interest. In truth, in a world apparently created of this substance alone, the nature of ice is of overwhelming interest to your dear brother since it has the power to determine how soon I shall be with you again.

I also find that I do not have the stamina I did when first we set out. I put it down to our diet and the generally confined nature of our quarters, although its continuance after the spring of ample fresh meat is surprising. Le Vesconte and the others feel much the same. In my case, it means that after a full day struggling with the ice, and after I have completed the ship's log and my official journal—which I must keep every day and which records the minutiae of daily life—I must admit to being greatly weakened, and only capable of putting quill to paper because of the strength of my promise to you. Please do not judge your overworked brother on the basis of a few entries which do not entertain you as they should, there will be ample opportunity for me to regale you with wild stories when we again meet. For now, good night.

August 15—What a struggle the last two weeks have been. We have none of us slept as much as we would like on account of the demon ice. On two occasions we were trapped by heavy ice and I feared we might be beset for the season, but the wind changed and we managed to cut a path free, on one occasion through ice over eight feet thick. It has been gruelling work with parties on the ice at all hours cutting and hauling to the nearest lead. The water was often open close inshore along Boothia, but our drafts would not allow us to take advantage of it. Perhaps Blanky was right when he claimed that our deep draughts would be a problem in these waters. We have spotted two deep inlets in the Boothia shore which we considered as possible retreats for the season, although not perfect since they open to the west and would be subject to ice blown in from the strait.

We now lie in open water some thirty miles off Cape Felix, the most northerly tip of King William Land, so named by James Ross in 1830. To the west across the desert of ice, about sixty miles off, is a point which we suspect to be a part of Victoria Land. Twenty-five miles to the east on the shore of Boothia lies the North Magnetic Pole also achieved by James Ross on June 1, 1831.

We have linked with the work of Ross, and the shores of Somerset and Boothia are now known completely on both sides. Some ten miles farther along the coast of King William Land lies Victory Point, the farthest point reached by Ross (and interestingly, but a few miles from the seen but not visited place he named Point Franklin). Sixty miles south of Victory Point is the cairn erected by Simpson and Dease a scant seven years ago at Cape Herschel. So we are at the limit of what is known from the east and but sixty miles from what is known from the west. All we need do is complete that distance and the Northwest Passage is ours. Push on you say, sixty miles is but the distance that separates Portsmouth from London Bridge and if that is all that remains of the fabled Passage and glory, press on!

Were it only so easy as a coach ride over the downs. But we shall prevail.

There is ample of the summer season left to us.

The weather is calm and this evening Crozier and Little came on board to dine and discuss our route. Sir John outlined the possibilities.

"We can attempt the west shore of King William Land down to Cape Herschel and hence along the continental coast—or we can keep close to the shore of Boothia and navigate the eastern shore of King William Island, coming through Simpson Strait to Cape Herschel and thence home. What do you think gentlemen?"

Little answered quickly. "Well, sir, the western shore has the advantage of being shorter and, in all probability, in deep water. True, the ice is heavy there at the moment, but we have dealt with heavy ice before."

"Indeed we have," I interjected, "and I would not willingly repeat the experience at Cornwallis Island where we near lost the *Terror* on the shore. I prefer the look of the eastern shore; it is ice free at present."

"Yes," said Little, "it is ice free, but I fear a difficult passage that way through shoally and unknown waters and our draughts are not the best suited to such work. There is also the possibility, expressed, if you recall, by Ross himself who called those waters Poctes Bay, that King William Land is attached south of this route to Boothia, making that way impossible."

"If we are to quote Ross," I rejoined, "then look to his description of the ice on the west coast. If I recall correctly, he talked of the heaviest masses of ice ever seen, with blocks driven onshore to a distance of half a mile. Our good ships could not survive conditions such as those."

"And we must consider the season," added Crozier who had been silent to now. "It is colder than last year and winter appears to be coming on early and fast. Even if a good lead appears down the west coast, which becomes increasingly unlikely with every passing day, there is no record of a suitable winter harbour for vessels of our size on that shore nor on the coast examined by Simpson and Dease. We have but three weeks of travel left to us this season and so must look to another winter in the ice. The eastern shore presents the most promising possibility of advancement in the short term and, if that promise should prove illusory, we have Ross's word that Poctes Bay will provide a splendid, protected harbour for winter quarters."

Crozier's bald statement of besetment for a second winter gave us all pause for thought. The possibility has certainly been lurking in the recesses of my mind, but I have pushed it to the back behind the more pressing needs of the moment. Now that it is out in the open, I see the truth of it. Sir John broke our silence.

"Well," he said, "I am at least gratified that Mister Crozier and Mister Fitzjames are finally in agreement on something. I too think the route down the western side of King William Land would lead us into besetment in open and perilous conditions at the mercy of heavy ice, and I do not relish that prospect. Another advantage to progressing down the east coast is the final answer to the riddle of whether Boothia is a peninsula or if there is a way linking Simpson's Strait to the waters of Committee Bay and Prince Regent Inlet."

So we are under steam, heading toward the Strait of James Ross and what mysteries it may hold. I hope an open way is ahead, I am not as enthusiastic about a winter in the ice as I was a year ago.

Good night.

August 16—Slow going, the waters here are shallow and we must proceed with caution. The weather remains fair although it is becoming colder by the day. Passed Ross's Beaufort Islands around noon and can see the north shore of Matty Island ahead. The water is shallow and we are cursing our deep draught.

August 17—Disaster! *Terror* is firmly aground on a shoal which seems to stretch from the north of Matty Island across to the Boothia shore. Around midnight a wind arose and we had to steam against it to prevent being blown south too rapidly in these treacherous waters. The *Terror* was ahead of us and reported touching bottom in seventeen feet of water around 8 a.m. At 8:30 the wind had strengthened and I was on deck watching the progress of our sister ship which lay some quarter mile ahead of us, when I distinctly saw her shudder. It quickly became obvious that she was firmly aground. We immediately threw out all anchors and managed to stop our movement while I sent a boat over to discover what had happened. She is wedged solidly and would not move although we spent the best part of the day attempting to pull her off. She does not appear to be damaged severely, but the wind from the north is a concern, especially if it strengthens or begins to blow ice down upon us. Unfortunately, *Terror* grounded at almost high tide, so we have little time each day in which to try to effect a rescue, and we must take care that the *Erebus* too does not become stuck. It is not in great spirits that I bid you good night today.

August 18—Still stuck fast, but thankfully, the wind has died away. Today the *Terror*'s crew launched a whaleboat and ferried some crates of tea and sugar to a nearby island to reduce her weight. They were also busy moving the deck cargo to the starboard side, she apparently being most firmly fixed on the port. At high tide this evening her boat crews attempted to pull her off but with no success. Tomorrow, we shall try with our steam engines.

August 19—Still in our sad plight. At the morning's high tide, we cast a line and attempted to haul *Terror* free. She groaned most horribly, but remained firm. The rest of the day was spent ferrying supplies over to us. We have precious little room for them, but Crozier does not want to place too much on the island in case we break free all of a sudden and have no chance to pick them up. Some concern this evening over a few small floes of ice drifting down on us from the north but the wind remains calm.

August 20—Still no success although it is not for want of trying. We are now laden and drawing so much water that we must take care and not become aground ourselves. We tried again with the steam this evening, but the cable parted without any sign that our colleagues were moving. The breeze began to freshen this evening to our great concern.

August 21—A miserable night. About midnight it came on to rain heavily and the wind increased from the NNW. It is all we can do to prevent ourselves being blown onto the reef and we had to pull off to a safer distance after we began to drag our anchors. The *Terror* is holding up well, fortunately she is stern first and not broadside to the wind, but the ice is increasing and our situation is not enviable.

August 22—Almost a tragedy today. One of the whaleboats in the charge of Helpman, while engaged in ferrying casks of flour over to the island, was nipped between two floes and crushed. Fortunately, the men were able to escape onto the floe and we have picked them up none the worse for their ordeal except that poor Helpman appears quite shaken up. He was never physically strong, being more of an intellectual bent, and of late has become thin and even more bird-like. Under normal conditions, he has no work in the sled hauling, but in a crisis such as we are presently, all must take a part. I hope he is not too down.

The *Terror* shews some signs of movement as the wind increases and blows down upon her, but whether it is just blowing her higher onto the reef is impossible to tell. I fear it will be touch-and-go whether we can get her off before she is broken up. All preparations have been made to abandon her if necessary. The ice is now quite heavy and we are having difficulty manoeuvring into position to render assistance. At tomorrow's high tide we will make another effort to free her with the combined power of our steam engines, but I fear if this does not work, she will be lost and we will be in a serious predicament.

August 23—Success! At 10 a.m. this morning we managed, with much good luck and many prayers, to haul poor *Terror* off the reef. She is much beaten about, but still seaworthy. If there is bad luck to be had on this voyage, it seems it must always come to the *Terror*. There are murmurings amongst the crew that she is an unlucky ship. Of course it is superstitious nonsense, but it is difficult to prevent such talk.

After the *Terror* was freed, we promptly retreated as fast as the ice would allow, abandoning the supplies on the island. We are now working our way back north up Sir James Ross' Strait. There is no practicable way through here, and to be trapped in these shoals without shelter and the ice being blown into our bay, would spell certain disaster. We must try our luck to the west, whatever it may offer.

Sir John offered much thanks for our release at a divine service this afternoon. His thoughts were heartily echoed by all.

August 27—Returned almost to where we were twelve days ago. The water is not as clear as it was then, but we can still make way through the leads. We anxiously scan the pack to the southwest for leads but so far to no avail. At least I can now sleep for an hour or two at a stretch, a thing I have not been able to do for some time.

August 28—Steaming back and forth along the pack searching for a way through. The ice has closed up to the north of us so retreat that way is impossible. We have little room to manoeuvre and without a way to the south shall be stuck in a very poor position.

September 1—Beset in a most unenviable position. The wind last night bore ice down upon us most rapidly—large floes of old ice crashing through the younger as if it were paper and not a twelve inch thick layer. I calculate the speed at eight to ten miles a day. Both ships were nipped this morning despite our best attempts at escape. I fear for our position in such active ice.

September 2—Turned out at three in the morning with the ship lifting and tilting most alarmingly. By the time I reached deck, we were heeled over and some two feet above the water. The noise of the ice and the protests of the poor ship's timbers were unbelievable—the ice crashed and thundered and the ship creaked and groaned so loudly that the officers of the watch had to place their mouths close by their companions' ears and shout to make themselves heard—add to that the continual ringing of the ship's bell as we are shaken and you have some idea of the utter bedlam that surrounded us. We could do nothing except make fast what we could and pray for a change in the tides or wind to release us. Fortunately our prayers were answered around noon and the ship fell back to a more normal—and quieter—situation, as if released by the giant hand that lurks beneath us. We are still held fast and drift to the southward. The hellish din has lessened but the ice still roars at a greater distance.

September 3—Our drift continues as witnessed by the changing depths revealed by dropping leads through holes cut in the ice—I estimate some four miles since yesterday.

September 4—A gale blew up from the south last night—an unusual occurrence hereabouts—and we are now both again free of the ice. That does not mean we have free choice of where to go there being much ice all around, but we are at least not in immediate danger. All were present around the mess table this evening, Sir John having expressed the desire to dine alone. A lively discussion ensued. Fairholme began it with a question.

"If the water opened to the north, would we consider a retreat?"

"Never!" the usually quiet Le Vesconte surprised us all with the strength of this exclamation. "Certainly we are all shaken by our recent bad luck, but to give up and go home—to surrender ground so hard won and admit defeat so early—surely that is unthinkable."

After his outburst he lapsed almost apologetically back into silence. Gore took up the subject.

"I think it a moot point this late in the season. There is precious little chance that Lady Jane Sound will still be open, and if it is not, that would necessitate a season hard against the coast of Boothia or one trapped within tight, ice-clogged channels—neither an enviable prospect. None-the-less, it is an interesting point. What circumstances would impose a retreat upon us?

"Obviously, if one ship is lost, as the *Erebus* almost was in Barrow Strait or the *Terror* in James Ross' Strait, then both crews must find the surest way to safety aboard the remaining vessel. But must disaster strike before we can make that decision? What if we are faced with an insurmountable circumstance, the tackling of which might well lead to that disaster? We would surely be justified in retreat, yet, having come this far, the pressure to press on would be difficult to resist and the thought of returning without at least battle scars a hard one to accept."

"And," added Fairholme, "the expectations of success we carry with us are a heavy burden to discard. I suspect that the answers we would give to Mister Gore's questions would be different from the answers given by our loved ones back home."

It was an interesting discussion and has given me much food for thought, not least since it is the first time failure has been openly mentioned, at least in my hearing. Gore's arguments put me in mind of Crozier's talk last year of blundering on unawares into situations we cannot know or understand. And the talk of home was painful. What would your advice be, dearest Elizabeth?

But I know the answer to that. Come home—no discoveries are worth lives. Perhaps. But for the moment at least we must press on and hope for a sheltered cove on King William Land or an old stable floe to make harbour in. As Fairholme said, the pressure from home is pushing us on and the lure of completing the passage is pulling forward. So with a cry of *Onward!* I bid you good night.

September 6—Still battling south. The leads are uncertain but at least we drift in the right direction when beset. There has been no repeat of the experience of the 2nd.

September 7—Winter is most definitely settling in—open leads still form, but they are soon covered by a skin of ice and by the time we reach them, we are obliged to ram to make any headway. Fortunately both ships are remarkably sturdy and are standing up well although both do look as if they have been in the wars somewhat.

September 8—Very little headway today despite prodigious efforts on the part of the crews on the ice.

September 9—We have to admit defeat for this season. This morning Sir John gave orders to cut a way to a nearby floe and make harbour in it for the winter. This is done by cutting a dock, slightly longer and slightly wider than the ship in the side of the floe. This will protect us from the random movements of the ice unless the floe itself breaks up; we are as secure as we can be in such circumstances.

September 10—Hard work cutting but we make progress.

Winter, 1846/47

September 12, 1846—Beset for another season. We are now settled in for our second winter. *Terror* is docked some 700 yards away to our starboard, but in the same floe which is in excess of three miles across.

Preparations for winter must now begin if we are to manage as well as last year. The greater distance from land will be a concern. We are still some twenty miles off Cape Felix over some very rough ice and we will not be able to establish shore camps as readily as we did at Beechey. However, we will transport some supplies to a depot at Felix in case of the necessity for sudden abandonment of the ships and to help lay out caches for our spring explorations. I will establish magnetic observatories on the ice. With luck we will manage well and our greatest enemy will be boredom.

It has been obvious for some time that we would not be home this year, but it is only with the certainty of besetment that it has truly sunk home that I will not look upon your smiling face for yet one more year. I hope that is all. I will not bore you with the details of our winter activities, you will be able to imagine them from my tales of last year, but I will mention anything of note and, begging your indulgence, I will write to you in order to charge my own spirits should I feel the need. Now I must retire, we have done much of late and there is much yet to do.

Good night.

October 6—Well organized for the winter now. Our floe is solid and stationary, having drifted one or two miles more since we tied our fortunes to it. Everything is locked solid and we feel as secure as if we were at camp on land. The decks are cleared as much as possible with supplies set out on the ice and at Cape Felix. We have raised our canvas roof, but left it open at the aft while the weather remains fair so that we may obtain as much fresh air as possible. Only one blizzard so far and that only for two days. The wind has been high, but does not seem to blow as much snow with it as was the case near land.

The journey to Cape Felix is hard, although we have cut a route through the most difficult sections. Teams of ten men pulling heavily-laden sleds sometimes take two days to complete it. We have placed three of our whaleboats at the cape in case of need and to protect the more fragile of our supplies. Gore is out now to place a cache southward on King William Land in preparation for a spring sled journey which will complete the Northwest Passage, but by whom has not yet been determined. No-one talks of it, yet I am convinced it is on all our minds. The first completion of the Passage, even on foot, will be the crowning achievement of our journey, even if our ships complete it by water afterwards. Who would not want to be known as the discoverer of the Northwest Passage?—to succeed where Drake and Frobisher failed. Will it be I? I do not know although I hope of course. I do not have the sledding experience of Gore, Little or Fairholme, yet I am the senior officer young enough for the rigours of the journey and that must count for something with Sir John. But I will not allow myself to consider the possibilities. We must all await Sir John's decision with equanimity and accept the disappointment, which must come to some, with steadfastness.

Hodgson is also out placing a cache on the east coast for other exploring parties. Sir John has relented on his decision of last year not to allow theatrical productions, and we are commencing preparations for the same. His only caveat was that we concern ourselves primarily with 'real' plays and not the low farce of which the crew are familiar. Accordingly we are planning *A Midsummer Night's Dream* for November presentation along with an offering by the crew. Weekes will be busy with the sets which will be erected on the *Erebus*'s deck.

The Cape Felix and Boothia Chronicle is also planned for publication beginning as soon as Irving and Des Voeux can get organized. The disheartenment that we all felt at our besetment has vanished now and we all look forward to a second winter in the ice with reservations but good heart. Goodsir is uncommonly hale and hearty and does much to keep the mess spirits topped up. I do not think anything could bring that man down for long, as long as he has a supply of creatures to examine, draw and describe. Reid seems happy only when in close proximity to ice and he has plenty of that at present. Some of the floes are over twenty feet thick and composed of ice which is several years old.

How do we know the age of ice you ask? Well, apart from the greater thickness of older ice, it is denser and a deeper blue colour due, I believe, to its greater compression beneath later layers. It sounds like little enough to go on, but once one has seen the difference, it is as easy to distinguish as between a glacier and the block in the icebox. To see ice tens of feet thick and to know it was forming long before we even considered coming up here to examine it, is enough to give one pause and consider the immensity of both time and space in the natural world. Even rough old Reid waxes somewhat philosophical on the topic.

"The auld ice is what we want Mister Jems," he says. "It has been hereabouts longer than us and it'll hold us safe and sound for the winter arl right." I think he is correct in that assumption.

Le Vesconte and the others are settling themselves into the routine of taking our readings. It is strange when sitting in one of our observatories, as secure and sound as if we had the chalk of the English Downs beneath us, to think that all we have is a few feet of ice and then the dark freezing waters of the Arctic Sea below. I think I shall never look on ice the same way again.

Helpman on the *Terror* is sick with the cold. He was much disturbed by his experiences with the whaleboat when the *Terror* ran aground and has not fully recovered his spirits. He has been sick for near two weeks now, but Peddie says he is shewing signs of improvement and should be up and about shortly.

We have built a series of ice and snow cairns between the two vessels and strung a rope between so that we shall have communications even in the worst weather. The sun is barely above the horizon at noon and it will not be long until that accursed, eternal darkness is upon us again. Sometimes I feel the lack of light is a greater hardship to bear than the cold. Neither of course is equal to the hardship of not seeing you, but at least I have your picture to look upon.

What are you thinking of our adventure? Do you imagine our situation in the ice? Do you wake in the mornings anticipating news of our success? So much has happened to us in the months away. You remember me as I was when I left London. In that memory, I have become like the bones of the great fossil lizards that Owen has called dinosaurs, unchanging in their beds of rock though the world moves on around them. I hope the fossil which is me sleeps in your mind but months more and not the countless millennia of Megalosaurus or Iguanodon!

Sleep well dearest sister. Good night.

October 16—Both Hodgson and Gore returned today from establishing depots on the island. We are ready now for our spring explorations and for the completion of the Passage. Each man hopes that he will be chosen for the latter honour, but we must all wait out the winter before we know who it will be.

October 19—Sad news. Helpman died suddenly last night. He had not been able to throw off that damned cold but did not seem to be seriously threatened. In fact, Peddie reported improvement just yesterday, but around 1 a.m. this morning he took a turn for the worse and was soon in a deep state of unconsciousness with a high fever, and rambling on about ledgers and bills and such. At five he quieted and at 6:30 died peacefully in his sleep. It is a shock for us all, one that I hope does not presage a sad winter. I have always been concerned with his frailty in the harsh conditions of our life here, but I shall miss him none-the-less for that. He was a colleague from the *Clio* and put much pleasant and thought provoking reading before me in the long days of last winter.

The decision has been made to bury Helpman in the ice close to the ship since the crew can then participate which would not be possible were we to transport his body to the land.

October 21—Buried Helpman today on the ice of our floe. He was prepared as carefully as the men we left on Beechey, although there was some comment that burial in the ice was not a fitting thing to do with land and the hope of a proper burial so close at hand. But we have little choice, the land being too far away to hold a proper service. Sir John of course presided and urged us all to take heart from our achievements and not let the sad deaths we have experienced be in vain.

It was a strong speech, but did not convey the certainty for the future that has marked his words till now. Le Vesconte disagreed, so it is perhaps merely my mood which has been unaccountably low of late. In lowness of mood I am not alone, there being much greater variation in mood than the uniformly optimistic feelings around the mess table of a year ago. It is not that anyone doubts our ultimate success, but Helpman's death and the prospect of a second winter put a strain on all. Goodsir and Reid remain buoyant, but Hodgson is low and talks continually and wistfully of his family.

Collins continues a hopeless prospect for an efficient officer. He seems totally incapable of completing the log to my satisfaction, regardless of the number of times I make him rewrite it, and is only content lumbering about with his picture equipment. He is the only one who expressed open joy at our second besetment as it allows him to take more of his beloved images and spend his hours inhaling his noxious chemicals. He has become more solitary by the month and cannot be persuaded to participate in any activities other than the minimal performance of his duties.

It is not an uncommon thing for us to become focused on one thing in order to satisfy our minds and keep from bleaker thoughts. Even Osmer is continually studying his supply lists and recalculating our victualling schedule although there is no cause for any concern—we are well ahead of even the most optimistic estimates at the outset. It is merely the focus he needs and it has not changed his concentration when we sit down to a game.

Gore and Des Voeux remain companionable and Gore has taken to entertaining us with his flute now that our evenings are free. Le Vesconte has become increasingly silent which I do not like. He has always had a propensity to be this way, but seemed to relax over last winter and was almost as talkative as the others. Now he has slipped back into his old ways. Of Couch and Sargent I will say nothing.

Stanley remains congenial enough although he is increasingly inclined to chippy comments, particularly at Goodsir's expense. This does not seem to bother Goodsir in the least and he always has a clever response, but it is a sign of the strain on Stanley who, I think, misses the companionship of the wider world.

Even Sir John is less talkative of late and dines more frequently alone in his cabin. None of this is serious, merely the normal processes which affect men's character and spirits on long voyages. I mention it for your interest, not to cause any concern.

On our sister ship, Crozier shows no change of mood, continuing phlegmatic and somewhat fatalistic as to our lot. Little is more of a problem, become something of a martinet and imposing rigid discipline on the men. Crozier, I think, does not approve and has spoken of it to Little.

Peddie is resorting more to the Scotsman's solace, of which he has a not inconsiderable supply. It is of no great consequence as long as it does not interfere with his duties or the temper of the mess. Thomas remains 'the Baby' and a jokester. I think some of his pranks must grate on nerves in the close confines of the mess, but they are mostly taken in good spirit. Hornby remains his constant companion despite being the foil for many of the Baby's jokes. The others I see little of and have noticed no characteristics that I have not already mentioned.

For myself, I shall endeavour to throw off this lowness of spirit. I think of you much and shall do so more to lighten my mood. Good night.

November 5—Our calculations shewed that we lost the sun today, although it was heavily overcast and we could not confirm that.

We were in the mess this evening, feeling somewhat down at the prospect of weeks of darkness when we were aroused by a cacophony outside. On turning out, we saw the strangest procession alongside. Most of the crew of the *Terror* seemed present, led by Crozier in a powdered wig and tails. They were leading a rude cart bearing the figure of a guy dressed in rags and with the most comical sad expression painted on his face. Crozier organized his entourage as well as possible and gave a short speech indicting the guy for treason and pronouncing the penalty, then without too much delay, the mercury being set at fifty-five degrees of frost, a match was lighted and the guy burned amidst a display of rockets and some wild dancing and cavorting by the crew. Then all came aboard and accepted our hospitality. It served to cheer us all up, especially when Sir John announced that this day was also his eighteenth wedding anniversary. We toasted the old man and the good Lady Jane most fervently. Now we look forward to our theatricals on November 15 if the cold permits.

November 15—Today was the day of our great play. Weekes and Watson have performed a titanic feat in creating a stage—no a complete theatre—on our deck. The stage is set for'ard of the mainmast and bedecked with such a wild assortment of flags and bunting that the effect is quite striking. Oil torches light the boards and the deck itself, which is crowded with all manner of seating arrangements. Sir John took his seat on a specially constructed throne before the mast, and all the officers not involved sat to either side, there being no boxes in our theatre. Weekes has cunningly designed the stage so that it may be easily dismantled for storage and, just as easily, reassembled when required.

Our production, which has been advertised on very professional handbills on both ships, consisted of a shortened version of *A Midsummer Night's Dream* (shortened because, although the weather is moderate, it is still more than twenty degrees of frost on our covered deck and inactivity produces much cramp and cold extremities), followed by a magic act by the Great Mystrini (actually Hodgson in a star-covered cape and a ridiculously tall, pointed wizard's hat), a musical performance by the Terrifying Arctic Ensemble, and a short farce, *Adventures of Mumford*, by the crew.

And now for the surprise; your dear brother exercised what limited thespian talents he may possess in the role of Titania, the Queen of the Fairies. The great trick I found was not in the acting, which was successful as long as the lines were delivered with gusto, but in devising a costume which did not allow one to freeze to death and yet bore some relation to the part being characterized. I think I did well packing on many woollen undergarments beneath my flowing, regal robes, but some of the attendant fairies suffered not a little.

All in all our presentation was considered a great success and was met with wild applause and great laughter throughout. Hodgson revealed talents none of us had suspected before and you would have fallen into a delirium watching him attempt to produce an Arctic hare from out of one of his dress uniform hats. The ensemble sang loudly and were greeted with great enthusiasm by the audience who accompanied every song with much clapping and stamping.

The only blot on the evening was the crewman who played Mumford and seemed to have been celebrating the success of his endeavour somewhat prematurely and had to be loudly prompted on several occasions before collapsing completely in the middle of the last act much to the amusement of his fellows. Sir John did not appear much amused, but all was put to rights with a rousing and heartfelt rendition of "God Save the Queen" to end the evening. Overall, I think the event can be counted a success and I look forward to others in the same vein, although we might be wise to more firmly restrict access to the spirits until after the performance.

Perhaps on our return we will present a 'Pageant of the Northern Lands' for the edification of the patrons of Drury Lane! We will make up for in enthusiasm what we lack in the fine art of Kean. I fully intend to retain my costume, which I manufactured myself, and to put on a one-man show for you and the family, beside the hearth. I hope you are as well as I and I wish you a most comfortable and warm good night.

November 30—St. Andrew's Day and the cause for much joviality amongst the Scotch members of the crew which put Sir John in an uncharacteristic mood. Of late he seems to have lost some of the vigour and unbridled optimism which was so notable when we set sail. I suspect that the joy of being once more at sea in command of his own expedition and away from the complexities and difficulties of politics was much to his liking and the mood remained as long as we were progressing and making new discoveries. However, if we are honest, we must admit to not having achieved as much this year as we would have liked, although we have added significant new lines to the Chart, and in the spring will assuredly complete the last section of the Passage: All this I think weighs upon Sir John.

I miss my loved ones at home sorely, and I believe this to be a characteristic which increases with age. At dinner, Sir John talked of his first wife, Eleanor Porden, of whom you may have heard since she developed a reputation of some note as a poet. It was she who gave Sir John his only child, a girl also called Eleanor.

The old man was quite nostalgic, talking of the terrible decision he had to make at the commencement of his second expedition. In February of 1825, his wife was sick and likely to die, yet the expedition had to leave if it was to make any progress that season. He was in favour of remaining behind, even if it meant the expedition leaving without him, but Eleanor was adamant that he go and perform his duty. In June, he received the sad news that Eleanor had survived his departure by just six days. Sir John stated that he considered himself blessed to have encountered two such extraordinary women as Eleanor and Jane. Both made him flags for his expeditions. Eleanor's he unfurled at the mouth of McKenzie's River on the shores of the Arctic Sea. Jane's will await our completion of the Passage.

The prospect of the dark and cold without the distraction of being hard by land weighs on us all and must have some affect on our leader, used though he is to hardship and privation in these climes. I only hope that the coming of spring and the achieving of one of our main goals, followed by our release and homeward journey, will enliven him to his former self.

December 1—Jacko, the monkey, died today, much to the dismay of the crew. Despite the fact that she was a tremendous pest, always getting where she was not wanted and stealing everything in sight that she could carry, she was looked on with great affection by all. In actual fact, she has lived much longer than any of us suspected, having been diagnosed by Stanley shortly after we sailed with a rapid consumption. She coughed almost continuously since, but remained lively until a few days ago when she fell lethargic and even refused to eat the canned carrots which have long been her favourite food. For the last couple of days she has been exhibiting the most odd behaviour, almost a dementia, screeching wildly and attacking anyone who approached. It is a sad way for her to go and I shall miss her strange and wild antics atop the hand organ in the crew's mess.

On the other hand, Old Nep, as Neptune has become known, seems only to thrive during our adventure and, in fact, seems to enjoy the periods when we are ice-bound, since, having no apparent sense of the cold, he is free to roam at will. My only concern is that he will be surprised by a bear on one of his excursions.

December 2—Buried Jacko today in the ice in a ceremony at which the entire crew was present. She was buried with full honours, dressed in one of the fine costumes made for her by the crew and enclosed in a tiny, velvet-lined casket. The ceremony included a salute of musketry more suited to the end of some famous general than a mischievous ape.

December 24—All preparations are made for tomorrow's festivities, which will much resemble last year's. Despite the passage of time, we still have ample supplies to lay on a respectable repast and do honour to the occasion. There will be no ball on the ice this year, but our theatre group is reassembling to put on a production of *Macbeth*. There was much discussion of what would be an appropriate play, and many felt that another of the comedies would do well after the success of our last effort. However, Sir John favoured something more serious and I think he is correct, given the enthusiasm with which the men are taking to the lectures on science and natural history which we are presenting on an almost weekly basis. Indeed, the classes had to be moved on deck despite the cold, since the space allocated below was of insufficient size to accommodate the audience. In any case, we will have time for a farther production before spring and are leaning toward *The Taming of the Shrew*.

I have been busy filling in my spare time reading Prescott's *History of the Conquest of Mexico*, and find it enthralling that so few men could accomplish such extraordinary deeds against such fearful odds. Perhaps one day someone will write of our happy band in such inspiring terms for the odds we have and will overcome in this barren realm. So with such dreams of fame to come echoing in my head I bid good night!

December 25—Happy Christmas dearest Elizabeth, our second apart. We dined as well as last year, not being deficient in the small luxuries which make our festivities memorable, and all appear in good spirits. Our menu was roast beef, roast goose, ham, parsnips, preserves, and gooseberry tart.

Crozier entertained us with stories of his visit to Pitcairn's Island—the home of the *Bounty* mutineers—when he was a midshipman on the Frigate *Briton* in 1814. Apparently, they were only the second ship to visit there since the *Bounty*, because the island was misplaced on the Chart. There Crozier met Fletcher Christian's son and John Adams, the only survivor of the original mutineers. Crozier related a very amusing tale of Mackay, the leader of the islanders, when they were invited aboard for breakfast. Apparently, they had only just reached the deck when the ship's dog, a small terrier of some sort, came bounding forward to greet the newcomers. Mackay, who had never seen a dog before, leapt behind an officer in a great fright and cried, "Will it bite? Will it bite?" The islanders got their own back at the meal when they all fell to their knees to say grace with such obvious fervour that the officers of the *Briton* were put to shame.

I much regret the loss of my gift from you and wish I still had the gloves to remind me of your kind giving last year. But I must accept that, has some blizzard not removed them, your gloves still lie upon the rock where I placed them, patiently awaiting my return.

I seem to recall that last year I looked forward to being with you twelve months hence and I do so again now with more confidence. According to the Chart, we are at the exact halfway point on the passage, equally far from east and west entrances. That is not to say that we are halfway in time from beginning to end since the worst is behind us and the way home, thanks in no small part to the work of our Commander, is better known. If we are released in July, as we were last year, we will need only the barest modicum of good luck in order to wend our way along through the open waters along the coast of America and arrive by September 1 in the Straits of Behring. From there we will visit the coast of Russia and thence to the Sandwich Island where we shall replenish, but not stay long. We are all in a hurry to be home and will not want to be held at the Cape by the winter storms.

It is still my hope that Sir John will grant me permission to return from Kamschatka through Siberia and the Russian lands in which case I shall most definitely be home in time for next Christmas, or so close that you will not be averse to postponing at least a small part of your celebrations until I can join you. I fear the only present I will have to give you, excepting any curios I may see on my travels, will be a piece of your very own island—who else can say as much as that? This year you must do with only my fervent thoughts for your wellbeing and happiness sped across the width of the globe.

Merry Christmas again and good night.

December 26—Today we had sports on the ice of our floe, which remains remarkably flat in the neighbourhood of our ships although it is in much turmoil at a greater distance. The usual activities were undertaken and again *Erebus* won the overall prize. These events do so much to keep up the spirits of the men in these conditions.

Weather moderate, for this part of the world. We seem to have less snow in this locality, which I put down to our distance from land. I think many of our blizzards last winter carried with them snow which had lain in gullies and ravines on the islands and was picked up by the funnelling wind and carried over us. This year there are no such deposits of snow close by and even the land closest is a flat drear place with little in the way of topography to trap snow.

December 30—The close of another year. Crozier dined with us this evening and we fell to the old topic of how we are best to survive here. He has taken to wearing the Esquimaux clothing more and more, always as outer garments over his uniform, but the impression is still strange and I am sure excites comments among the men. Sir John has said nothing but from his looks he does not approve. Unintentionally, feeling well fed and secure, I began the discussion with an offhand comment.

"It is remarkable," I said, "how extraordinarily comfortable we are with all our many fine inventions." My pomposity I put down to the wine, but Crozier is not one to let me off with such a statement.

"I think, my dear James, that we should do well not to be too arrogant. Our inventions are but poor protection against the world we have entered."

I must admit to having been somewhat put out and responded, as closely as I can remember, thus:

"How can you say we are not protected or secured by our remarkable inventions? We are thousands of miles from home in one of the most inhospitable places on the Earth. Outside the mercury is freezing, yet we sit here in light uniforms, sipping port in a temperature I would find too warm in a London house. It is surely our inventions which have created this enviable, at least to the savage inhabitants of this land, situation?"

"Indeed," Crozier returned, "we have achieved much and we are comfortable for the moment. Perhaps even more so than the natives in their ice houses, but that aside, what is it that keeps us from the elements? A few feet of seasoned oak and a small steam heater for which there is a limited supply of fuel. Our warm cocoon is but a minute spit of comfort in the midst of a vast and indifferent nature which has the power to crush us and our inventions with ease. In a few months, or years at the most, we shall be gone, but the ice will remain, cold, violent and imperishable. Our inventions are wonders and, like you, I would not willingly venture here without them. However, they are but toys which allow us only the merest glimpse of this world and it would be rank folly to think them otherwise or to assume they have the power to overcome this land."

"Mister Crozier," Sir John interjected at this point, "I fear you do not give the good Lord his due. One cannot simply regard the bounty of the Earth and our power to mould it in isolation. It is my belief, and that of many others, that the Almighty placed man on this planet to exercise his God-given power over it. The birds and the beasts and all the fruit of the land and sea were placed here for our use and convenience; and we have a bounden duty to use them to improve ourselves and to bring the light of God into the lives of the poor savage peoples of the remote corners of the world. We are here to increase our knowledge of these lands and the peoples who may live here so that the sum of it may be incorporated into our ken and used for the ends which the Lord ordained. If we take what God has given us and use it to good ends, no possible wrong can befall us."

In the face of the word of God, the discussion drew to a close and Crozier left shortly after. I do not believe that we are safe because we use our inventions for God's good work, but I cannot believe that the extraordinary power of the human mind to overcome any obstacle cannot create machines which will protect us from any and all that a malevolent nature can present. I am confident that the year dawning will see our triumph and the triumph of our industry over this place.

New Year's Day, 1847—A day in great contrast to the last, on account both of the lack of an ice ball and also the death of poor Torrington. It is good that we did not hold our sports day on this date, as some had suggested, since the weather is not co-operating, the temperature being some thirty-seven degrees below zero or sixty-nine degrees of frost. The light wind farther reduces that temperature such that exposed flesh would become frost-bitten in a matter of minutes. Any athletic endeavour under these conditions is out of the question and we have celebrated the new year with our own thoughts. The crew did organise a small entertainment, consisting of some popular songs and recitations, but it was mainly at the instigation of the Scots. Despite some intoxication, it passed off quietly. At supper we all toasted the old year and the new and raised our glasses, none higher than I, to missed loved ones back home. Each had a silent prayer in his heart that this will be our last away.

January 6—Twelfth Night, and a pleasanter one than last year. We dined well and did greater justice to Wall's cake. Irving regaled us with a most exciting tale of his ascent of Mount Etna under exceptional difficulties, the mountain being an active volcano. This led to Crozier describing the dramatic eruption of Mount Erebus, which he witnessed while with Ross in Antarctica. We also paid our respects to some bottles of Sir John's fine port and with a warm glow in the pit of my stomach, I am now to bed.

January 12—Our production of *Macbeth* went over splendidly despite my concerns on the gloomy theme. The mood was good and ranged from booing the villain and villainess and cheering for Macduff in the final battle (splendidly executed between Gore's Macbeth and Fairholme's Macduff), to raucous laughter at the drunken porter played with fervour and conviction, if a somewhat unconventional diction, by Reid. For my own part, I gave my all in the early scenes as Duncan, "What he hath lost, noble Macbeth hath won," before he is cruelly done to death. We had of course some authenticity in the English doctor (Stanley) and the Scottish doctor (Peddie), and a very fine Lady M. in Irving who has missed his vocation with Arctic exploration. Again Weekes created some magnificent sets and we were all, for an hour or so, transported to the gloomy confines of a Scottish castle. I wonder has the Thane of Cawdor ever listened to the prophecies of the witches in a stranger place than here? But it is almost 2 a.m. It seems that indeed 'Macbeth does murder sleep.' However I must put my head down and try. Good night.

February 1—The sun has returned and all are heartily grateful to see her although she is only gracing us with a small part of her delightful countenance as yet.

In discussions today, Sir John announced that Gore will have the honour of completing the passage—what an honour for the whole crew. He will set off as soon as the spring weather appears suitable, accompanied by Des Voeux and six men. His instructions are to travel as lightly as possible and make all haste to Simpson's cairn at Cape Herschel and then return. We all envy him. At the same time, Little will lead an expedition, with Thomas and eight men of the *Terror*, in the opposite direction to examine the east shore of King

William Land and ascertain whether it is indeed connected to Boothia as Ross supposed. It too is a noble undertaking, but must be a disappointment when compared to the glory that will be Gore's.

And why not the glory for your noble brother you ask. Sir John took me aside and explained that he had considered me, but that he felt I would better serve the expedition overseeing the observatories and preparing for our release from the ice. I do not mind, there will be glory enough for all on return and we must all do whatever we can to make the entire undertaking as successful as possible. But we are still a long dark way from sledging and there is much to be done.

February 7—Happy Birthday dearest sister. Again I fervently toasted your health at an appropriate hour and wished you all the things I cannot give you at the moment. Will I be back to share next year with you?

February 13—The sun has been back with us for two weeks now and is certainly welcome but can offer us no more than light—it is really most distressingly cold—sixty-five degrees below freezing last night.

February 20—A disturbing occurrence today. I was on deck when I witnessed Collins dragging his bulky picture equipment toward the rail. Since the mercury was frozen solid and there was a stiff wind, I could not believe that he was attempting to venture onto the ice for the purposes of making an image. The chemicals would freeze and he would be putting himself at risk since the process requires the removal of gloves.

"Mister Collins," I said, "I fear it is passing cold for your purposes."

At the sound of my voice he jerked his head round and looked at me. I was disturbed to see a wild glint in his eyes.

"I must," he said, "I have no image of the ship in this dock and must obtain one before we sail."

"Mister Collins, sir," I said as firmly as I could manage, "we shall be in this dock for a certain six-month span yet, ample opportunity for image taking in more clement circumstances."

Collins acted as if I had said not a word and continued to drag his equipment toward the rail. Not wishing to raise an alarm, I was relieved to see Stanley approach. Enlisting his help, we tried again to persuade Collins to retire, but to no more effect. Finally we had to physically manhandle him back to his cabin where Stanley administered a sleeping potion. Collins made no fuss, but quietly resisted our every move. He sleeps now and, according to Stanley, will do so until morn. I hope he awakes refreshed.

February 21—Collins appears recovered. At least he does not attempt the insane any more, yet he walks about as if in a daze and there is a far distant light in his eyes. Stanley hopes it is but a temporary madness and that the affliction will pass in time. I do hope so. Few have yet noticed his condition which I take as a blessing.

February 22—No change with Collins. He performs his duties to the low standard we have come to expect and responds when spoken to, but there is no spark to him. His eyes are vacant and his voice flat and monotonous. He does not even take an interest in his beloved Daguerreotype machine. I fear Stanley may be wrong and his is not a short-term affliction. If so, then it must be dealt with as people are beginning to notice his odd behaviour. But how I know not.

February 23—Sad news I fear; Henry Collins died today. He had remained the same as previous days, present yet distant. After luncheon, he was out on the ice with Fairholme and some men, exercising on the route we have laid out around the ship. Fairholme was ahead of him when he heard a gasp. He turned and saw Collins stagger and fall to the ice. He rushed over just in time to see the poor man gasp his last and expire.

It is a shock to us all by its suddenness. Even his strange madness of late had given us no suspicion that this would be the outcome. Stanley says it was failure of the heart and I am inclined to agree, although Goodsir is more in favour of some kind of sudden violent brain fit. Whatever the case it is over now.

It is difficult to think of him other than through the glass of his madness, but he was worth more than that. He was a quiet man, not much given to raucous joviality, and solitary in his ways. I have not managed, in close to a year and one half, to make an officer out of him and get the least of his duties undertaken efficiently and promptly; yet he worked at every opportunity with the Daguerreotype machine, sometimes driving us near distraction insisting that we hold some uncomfortable and 'natural' position in an howling Arctic gale while he fiddled with his equipment. He had taken upon himself to make a permanent visual record of our adventures as far as the Daguerreotype camera would allow, and a number of his images, particularly of our Beechey Island home and our situation in the ice here, are quite striking. His pictures will remain as a legacy, and I must try to remember him as his family at home undoubtedly do, untainted by madness.

This is the first casualty in our mess and the empty place weighed heavy upon us all this evening. Such cruel suddenness brings home our own mortality. I think it is a particular shock to the youngsters in the mess who feel, with the arrogance of youth, that the fates cannot touch them.

Ah, Elizabeth, we are immortal for such a short time. What is our purpose? Is it to achieve the maximum good before our thread is cut or, as the hedonists would have us believe, derive the greatest amount of pleasure from our existence? I know which answer Couch and Sargent would give, but I cannot hold with that. Surely the ends are not pleasures which will indeed turn to dust with us. We must strive to achieve an end which will live after us, even if it is only a minute improvement in mankind's lot. Collins' images will live after him as a testament, just as the scientific and geographical achievements of our voyage will live on long after we are all forgotten as individuals.

Such weighty thoughts. How I wish you were here to discuss them with me. I miss you so. Good night.

February 25—We buried poor Collins in the ice today with the ceremony which is becoming all too sadly familiar to us all. The days continue to increase in lightness, but our mood remains low.

March 1—Dull, grey weather and bitter cold. We are well catered for and live in passable comfort, yet there is a sameness to the days which weighs heavy on the soul and atrophies the senses: the eye has little to excite it in a land of black and white too often obscured by the weather; the ear can hear only the gripe of a shipmate or the howl of the wind; taste is stifled by salt beef and biscuits; smell is excited only by odours to which we would rather not be subject; and touch is continually betrayed by burning cold. How I wish for the colours of spring, the song of a nightingale (or even a lowly crow), the taste of a peach, the smell of a rose, and the touch of your hand. At this hour I would give all the glory due myself and all my shipmates for those few simple things, especially the last.

March 14—It struck me this evening that young Master Robert will be a venerable four years old today and, as he is a son of yourself and William, is most certainly a proper handful. I hope the absence of his Godfather is not weighing too heavily upon him and that he is not straying too far from the straight and narrow. I promise to attend to his needs post-haste upon my return.

March 18—Weather continues cold and blowy although the light is increasing daily and this is having a positive effect upon everyone's spirits. The old China hands fell to talking this evening of the adventures we had there and I was prevailed upon to recite from "The Voyage of the Cornwallis." I at first declined, not through modesty—you know me better than that—but from a fear that I could remember nothing of it and could not render even such little justice as it deserved. However, I was prevailed upon and managed passably well I think. As you may recall, the original was published in the *Nautical Magazine* upon our return under the title: "The Voyage of the

'Cornwallis'. A Poem in Nine Cantos Including a Complete Transcript of The Hunt at Kolongseu Recounting the Glorious Exploits of the 'Cornwallis' and her Crew in China."

The nom-de-plume, Tim Bowline, served to protect your brother's sensitive nature from both too little praise or too much ridicule. There were many gaps in the telling, but some, particularly "Canto the Sixth," recounting the storm and capture of Ching-Kiang-Foo was, I feel, dramatically presented and well received:

The great grand canal which here crosses the river,
Was said at the town to be shallow however,
Cough, Hodgson, and Loch disdaining all fears,
To come to the truth, went in head over ears—
And thus found the canal too deep to be forded,
But a bridge shewed the place where the walls might be boarded.
Captain Richards led on. And to fill up the names,
Stoddart headed the boats. With the rockets Fitzjames
From the top of the wall we went down the street,
The Chinese who opposed having beat a retreat

The guard-house on the gate was enveloped in flames
By small rockets sent from the street by Fitzjames.
A pretty sharp volley of balls down the street,
From some Tartars, secured by a small barricade,
Which accounts for the very good stand that they made.
The marines charging on, and a few rockets plied,
Fitzjames got a shot through his arm and his side.

It is, I think, a poor enough verse but it served to conjure some pictures vividly in the minds of our China hands. Myself, for one, fondly remembered the action which is in high contrast to our current helplessness and inactivity which gets on everyone's nerves.

It is surprising how memories can come flooding back sometimes and I recalled most strikingly the time at Ching-Kiang-Foo when I went over the wall, literally sword in hand since I had lost the scabbard, with head full of thoughts of Caesar crossing the Rubicon. I had the sword raised and cut a fine heroic figure when a ball took the head of the marine by my side and effectively knocked all thoughts of Caesar from mine.

The ball I received would never have been fired had the rockets intended to demolish the barricade not misfired twice (here Goodsir reminded me of Crozier's thoughts on the imperfections of man's inventions). It passed through my arm, entering the body at the armpit and, passing round my ribs, lodged at my backbone. It felt as if I had been kicked hard by a horse, but no more and there was little blood. In fact, I walked aboard the ship for attention much to the surprise of the doctors. I surprised them once more by not developing a fever which was almost universal amongst the wounded, but I told them I had used up all my fevers with Chesney in Mesopotamia. None-the-less it took a full month to recover my health and only that speedily through the help of much ale and port wine.

Perhaps the most remarkable thing I saw in China was the famed Porcelain Tower over Nankin which is a most glorious structure, beautiful in its proportions and situation and which makes an appearance in "Canto the Eighth":

From the top is obtained a most beautiful view
Of the mountains, the suburbs, the river, and through
The whole city. An abbot resides
In a house near the tower,—the old fellow prides
Himself on the neatness with which it is kept,
And made a complaint that some sailors had crept
Outside on the roof and with true English taste
Had broken the bricks, and a whole side laid waste;
This might have been true, but we tried hard to see
Where the damage was done by these men's thoughtless spree.
I really believe that some English barbarians
Did take some bricks, but these were 'tractarians'
(As parson are now called), and soldiers to boot,
And doctors all ready as sailors to loot;
Some person asserted, that taking the mean,
'Twas not soldier nor tar, but a jolly marine.
However though every one said 'who'd have thought it,'
I've got a fine brick, from the abbot—I bought it.

This solicited a good laugh and exhausted my repertoire. I seem to have spent the night in gossip and running on about long ago adventures and it is barely worth closing my eyes before I must relieve the watch. Still I must get what sleep I can, I seem to feel so constantly tired these days. Good night.

March 31—Indications of spring increase daily, but in our present situation they are not as encouraging as last year. Being so far from land, we see few signs of wildlife and the ice begins to move in a somewhat threatening manner. We have drifted with the ice but a few miles over the course of the winter, and now lie some fifteen miles from Cape Felix. But the pressure is building up around our floe. I believe it is large enough to withstand much, but many of the smaller ones have been thrust into the air like some icy Stonehenge.

Sometimes the strangest thing happens; a ridge of ice is pushed up by the pressure and then commences to move. The process is accompanied by much grinding and howling, signifying great protestation on the part of the ice, but it is to no avail. On goes the pressure ridge, occasionally at fearful speed. Obviously, it is a phenomenon of the immense pressures which can build up, but exactly how blocks of ice the size of the sailor's hospital at Greenwich can be transported hither and thither is hard to see and no-one has felt the urge to approach an active ridge closely enough to collect information. I dread to think what would happen if one of these phenomena approached one of the ships too closely, certainly we would have to look to our preparations for abandonment with alacrity, but fortunately all have so far occurred at a healthy distance.

Yesterday we presented *The Taming of the Shrew* to great effect and with much enjoyment for all concerned. I had no part in this production, but Irving made a very amusing Katherina to Le Vesconte's Petrucchio. The occasion was somewhat marred by an exhibition of drunkenness by one member of the crew of *Terror* who was in attendance. He was much abusive in language and continued even after he was severely reprimanded and will have to be flogged. He even went so far as to lay hands roughly upon Irving and was promptly taken over and put in chains in the hold. I think Crozier will organise a flogging for tomorrow as a warning. The time hangs heavy on the crews and there is some disaffection. No more than to be expected under these trying circumstances, but it must be seen to be stamped out before it spreads. It is unfortunate, I should much prefer a more lax command, but under the circumstances, discipline must be enforced. I hope soon the spring will be far enough advanced to allow more activity on shore.

April 1—James Walker was flogged today aboard the *Terror*. The man was much repentant of his behaviour, and I think his punishment has had the desired effect on the crews. At dinner it led to a spirited discussion between Sir John and Fairholme.

"It is perhaps unfortunate," Sir John began, "and too severe a punishment for some of the minor offences for which it is administered, but it is essential for the maintenance of efficiency in the service. As long as the practice of empressment fills the big ships with the dregs of humanity, it will be necessary. Harsh discipline is essential to keep almost 1,000 of the lowest men in order and without it, Nelson's fleet would have made a poor showing at Trafalgar."

"Well, there sir," Fairholme said, "you have the advantage of us youngsters who have not seen service on the big ships in wartime. I will allow that the practice of flogging has stronger arguments in its favour in time of war when the breakdown of discipline might have such dire consequences. However, is it not the case generally that cruelty begets cruelty, especially when men feel they are being punished unjustifiably? Surely, were conditions improved, then flogging would be less necessary."

"That is a growing argument, I will allow. Yet the work of a common sailor to keep an eighty-four gun vessel at sea and ready for action is so gruelling and, I will say it, degrading, that there is no way to fill a ship's complement without resorting to the dregs of the barrel. And the only way to keep them in line is with harsh discipline."

"To keep men in such degrading conditions and then ensure loyalty through brutality—such is reprehensible," Fairholme rejoined. "And, if I may be so bold, I would remind you that the ship you ran at Greece during the independence war was known far and wide as 'Franklin's Paradise,' such was the good feeling that emanated from the commander's relaxed style of command."

"Touché," Sir John responded smiling. "Perhaps you are right. Perhaps one day soon, the cry of 'Boatswain, do your duty' will not be heard on British ships. But it is hard for one of my generation to believe so."

The weather continues uncertain and cold, although the warmth of the sun can be felt and we have uncovered the aft of the upper deck to allow some air to enter. We must attend to the rats again, as they are becoming quite a nuisance. As soon as possible we will establish a camp at Cape Felix which will serve as a base for exploration and hunting parties. It has also been determined that Collins and Helpman will be moved to more permanent resting places on the land.

April 10—A large hunting party went over to Cape Felix to try their luck. They should be gone for a few days. It is early in the season, but we all feel the need of some fresh meat. We are all feeling strangely fatigued and shew little interest in goings-on around us. I have also been suffering from some annoying headaches, most uncharacteristic for me as you know. I trust it is merely a symptom of our long spell confined in such isolated circumstances.

April 16—Pulled ourselves out of our misery to celebrate Sir John's sixty-first birthday. Wall prepared a huge cake in the shape of our ice floe with the *Erebus* and *Terror* firmly set in their sugar dock. It was accurate in every detail except across the ice was written in red sugar, 'Sir John Franklin, conqueror of the Arctic Lands.' We undertook many toasts including the old man's health and the prospect of being home by next year. You were, and are, much in my thoughts.

April 17—Hunting parties have returned empty handed. They saw some tracks of fox and hares and brought down a few partridge, but saw no evidence of large game. The land near to us appears bleak and barren, I shall enjoy leaving it. Gore and his party will set out on May 24, weather permitting. It is late, but they should not have far to go and will be lightly burdened. Their cache is some thirty miles south of Cape Felix, leaving only some forty miles to Cape Herschel. Little will set off earlier, as close to May first as seems possible by the weather. How I wish I were going with them.

May 5—Little and Thomas set off today with much celebration and good wishes. They will spend the first night at the Cape Felix camp and then proceed to the east. Sir John came on deck to wish them well; he has been bedridden for two days now with a severe cold. He seems better today, although very pale, as are we all, and somewhat silent and thoughtful. The weather has been uncommonly settled this spring, although it remains very cold. It is good not to have the eternal chilling wind, but I fear its lack will delay the break-up of the ice, since wind from the right quarter and tide are the two great destroyers of packed ice.

May 6—Sir John very much recovered. We are all busy with preparations for Gore's departure and for our own release. The canvas roofing is stowed and the sun now shines uninhibited on our decks, much to Neptune's delight. The masts are almost completely rigged and the wear on the ships is being repaired. Des Voeux is like a spring chicken at the prospect of accompanying Gore. He positively dances around the ship checking the smallest detail and has already packed and re-packed his sledging weight allowance ten times. He is really little more than a boy and exhibits the same attractive light-heartedness I remember from his days on the *Cornwallis*. When I am feeling down, I only have to look at him and I remember the joy and thrill of the adventure we are on. I sometimes think your brother is becoming an old, stodgy gentleman when I see the likes of Des Voeux enjoying the world around him.

May 22—Spent the evening completing the standard forms which Gore will deposit at obvious points along his route. The paper is the standard one issued to all exploring parties and enjoins the finder to forward the same to the Admiralty or the nearest Consul. The message is repeated in six languages, none of which would be remotely understandable to any person who is likely to find these scraps, even if they could read, but we follow the rules. I have added our present position and details of where we wintered last year and the barest sketch of our route to date. I also added the composition of the party depositing the message. It just remains for

Franklin, Gore, and Des Voeux to append their signatures and for the cans to be soldered closed. Gore will have no opportunity to add to them as he progresses.

Sir John's heavy cold has returned and he has spent most of the last two days confined to his cabin attended by Stanley. We need to be on the move once more, perhaps Gore's achievement will lift his spirits.

May 23—Sir John is much worse today, so much so that I did not wish to disturb him with the added chore of signing Gore's papers, so I had them sealed without. Stanley fears Franklin's chest is infected and he must rest completely. To add to our troubles, Des Voeux fell today and sprained his leg. It does not seem too bad but any injury can be serious for one engaged in the heavy work of hauling. The sled is loaded and alongside the ship, but I fear we may have to delay a few days. The combination of Franklin's ill health and Des Voeux's injury is bad enough, but the weather appears, about to take a turn for the worse.

May 24—Snowing and blowing hard. Postponed the leaving of the sled, which I think was a relief to Des Voeux who I suspect is suffering more than he will admit. Sir John is the same and we all walk with muffled tread so as not to disturb his rest. Talked long with Gore on his objectives and prospects. He feels that, if the weather is half-way kind and the terrain is not too harsh, which does not appear to be the case from what we have seen of it, he will make good time and cover the expected 140-mile round trip in ten or twelve days. He will be aided by Couch's latest sledge modifications and by the sail which we have rigged to help them proceed when the wind is favourable. Gore is in good spirits although a little concerned with Des Voeux's accident. He is eager to be off and spends much time examining the weather.

May 25—Still blowing hard although the snow has eased. Sir John much the same. There is an air of almost palpable expectation about the ship.

May 26—No change in either the weather or Sir John's health.

May 27—Sir John much better today and was able to receive visitors for short spells in the afternoon. He seems uncharacteristically weak and his usual strong voice is considerably muted. He was thoughtful when informed of Gore's delay and asked to talk with him for a while. The weather still much the same although the snow has almost ceased and we have hopes for the morrow. Des Voeux has completely recovered, so we have at least one benefit from the delay.

May 28—Gore set off at 3:30 a.m. in glorious sunshine and made good time with a following wind filling his sail, over to the Cape Felix camp which is now only some fifteen miles off to the southeast and which he reached in early afternoon. There he paused only long enough for a rest and tea and to signal us with a flare before proceeding in the direction of Victory Point. As long as conditions remain good, the almost eternal daylight will allow him to travel whenever his crew feels strong enough and he might well make twenty or more miles on a good day. He will leave the first message at Victory Point under the cairn erected by Ross in 1830. Every man on both ships was on deck or on the ice to cheer him off, and a large party followed the sledge over the ice for a considerable distance urging the team on with shouts and exhortations. Even Sir John managed to come up from his cabin and was greeted with a prolongation of cheering which he acknowledged with a wave.

This is the moment we have awaited since we set sail from England so long ago. In but a week or two, the Northwest Passage will be ours. Despite the undeniably important scientific work we are doing, it is undertakings such as Gore's which set the blood stirring and the heart racing. How I wish I were going too, but I share that emotion with every man of the expedition.

May 29—Fairholme and I took the advantage of the continued fair weather to visit the camp at Cape Felix at midnight last night in light almost as bright as noon. This land really does compare very unfavourably with Beechey, flat, lifeless and drear with nothing to excite the eye and precious little to excite the stomach. Our camp is quite well organized, consisting of three tents and one of the wooden observatories, and the twelve or so men who inhabit it most of the time live well, eating off crockery and drinking some passable wine.

Our hunting parties are having the most abominable luck, and while scurvy will not be a problem as long as we have antiscorbutics, and our lemon juice is lasting well, we all crave some fresh meat.

King William Land progresses from the sea in a series of low beach ridges of sharp, grey, limy rock. Inland is flat to gently rolling with small streams and ponds which I imagine in summer would make travel a most trying occupation. Our camp here exhibits a much less permanent air than the one at Beechey—we only have tents which are surrounded by mounds of supplies which give the site an air of a rag-and-bone yard. There is little snow and many of the ridges are bare rock already. The easiest travelling is on the ice close to the land which tends to be flat, although in places the pressure has driven slabs of ice a considerable distance up the beach.

We visited the graves of Helpman and Collins which were moved here from the ice. They are located on a slight rise of ground some distance behind the camp. Already they seem to blend into the landscape, only the headboards stand up—were it not for these, one could almost walk over the mounds and not notice that the ground had been disturbed. We stood in silence by the graves. Fairholme appeared pensive.

"This is indeed a sorry bleak place to spend eternity," he remarked.

"Yes," I agreed, "I hope we do not leave too many sad piles of stones before we are through."

"We will not," he said with surprising firmness. "I have promised that I shall return and return I shall."

With that he turned and strode back to the camp. That is the certainty we need to complete this venture.

It is strange—when the worst of the winter is over and we but wait for the ice to break to be on our way, this seems to be the lowest time for all. The crews are sullen and the incidence of drinking to excess increases. Despite our best efforts to control it, some of the crew are so expert at either secreting liquor they brought aboard or obtaining their fellows' rations through barter or gambling, there is little we can do except punish the culprits after the event. It is unfortunately always so in the Navy and will remain that way as long as sailors are forced to turn to alcohol as the only way to numb their pain and alleviate the crushing boredom of their lives at sea.

Even we officers feel the burden of the days, months, and years as we undertake the most interesting work and have the intellectual stimulation of each other's company. Even in our mess, Goodsir has a difficult time raising our spirits.

Fairholme and I had planned to rest for a while at the camp before returning to the ships, but noticing that the weather was bearing down in a threatening manner from the northwest, we decided on a prompt return—it would not do for the Captain to be separated from his command for too long. About half way back, we were surprised by a strongish wind which was carrying some snow. We proceeded as fast as our tired legs would allow, but the weather worsened with horrible rapidity and we were very soon blanketed in white with little idea of where we were headed.

For some time we managed to follow the well-worn road to the ships, but eventually we began to stumble over ridges and into soft wet snow and it became obvious that we had lost our way. We proceeded in what we judged to be the correct direction with increasing concern. The disorientation of a blizzard is quite an extraordinary thing, the only experience I can liken it to is being in a sand-storm in the desert, although one does not attempt to travel in those as they tend to blow themselves out quite quickly. Fortunately the temperature was not excessively cold, although we were becoming wetted by the snow and the mercury was falling.

We had been stumbling about for some hours when Fairholme heard a musket shot from our left. We made for it and were soon encouraged by other shots at regular intervals. Soon we stumbled across a wooden marker post set out around our vessels for just such an occurrence as this and in less than thirty minutes, were back warm in our mess.

Le Vesconte had observed us leaving the camp through the glass and, as we had not returned when the weather turned bad, had sent out parties to look for us and fire muskets every fifteen minutes. We both thanked him most heartily for his concern. It is certainly a treacherous land we have come to visit.

But now the restorative effect of the brandy has worn off and I must retire to recover my strength. Good night dearest.

June 5—Weather remains poor, although not as heavy as the day of my adventure. It is quite possible that Gore and Little shall meet and return together if Little has had reasonable luck down the east coast. If Gore's predictions were right and if he has not met with any unforeseen circumstances, we can begin to expect his return any day now.

Sir John has returned to his bunk. He was much improved and appeared on deck, to the cheers of the men, two days ago, but he has worsened and now runs a high fever which Stanley does his best to combat with all the medicines in his arsenal. Laudanum and sulphate of quinine seem to have at least a temporary ameliorating effect, but the burning always returns. We are all concerned for the old man, his illness is too much like poor Collins', although there is no sign of the madness.

June 6—Weather improved although still overcast and dull. The snow has turned to rain. Sir John is a bit improved, his fever eased in the night. He is still very poorly and most unsettlingly weak.

June 7—Today Franklin requested Crozier and myself to attend a meeting at his bedside. The purpose was to reassert the chain of command in the event, God forbid, of his death. Crozier will, of course, take over command. Written orders state that he is to take up command on the *Erebus*, but Sir John gave him leave to remain on *Terror* if he so wishes. Such a depressing event, especially with Sir John looking so pale and thin, a shadow of the powerful man we have come to know as our leader. We all pray that he will recover.

June 8—The sun came through today and lifted our spirits somewhat. Sir John appears better and is taking some nourishment, even able to raise a glass to toast his daughter's birthday. No sign of Gore yet. It has been arranged that the camp at Cape Felix will set off rockets when he is spotted.

June 9—Franklin remains in an improved state although still very weak. No word from Cape Felix. Le Vesconte pointed out in conversation this evening that the ice has been strangely silent of late. Upon reflection this is true, by this date last year, the ice in Barrow Strait was in a turmoil of activity, moving hither and thither and subject to hidden pressures of all kinds. Yet here we sit secure, for which we are thankful, in our floe anchored into a solid, unmoving mass of ice which stretches without break in all directions. We are glad not to be suffering the worry of escaping the moving pressure ridges in addition to our other concerns, but I wonder what it bodes for our continuing the journey.

June 10—Rockets this morning from the Cape and Gore was with us by supper. In our excitement, many rushed over the ice to meet the returning party which was accompanied and helped along by some men from the shore camp. I knew from their aspect, before they even came within hailing distance that something was amiss, and sure enough Gore had both a triumph and a tragedy to report.

First, they did indeed reach Simpson's cairn and the Northwest Passage is ours. But at what a cost. Des Voeux is dead.

The distance was greater than expected, the coast of King William Land swinging westward into a wide peninsula which increased the mileage out although they cut its base on the return and saved those miles twice. At first they made good time, travelling for much of the first twenty-four hours and camping at Victory Point. On the 29th they were crossing the deep inlet which brought Ross to a halt. The ice was rough and the going slow. Des Voeux was on a line to the side of the sledge as it traversed a steep ridge when the crew lost footing. The sledge slewed round sharply before they could take the strain and caught Des Voeux a glancing blow on the leg he had injured before. Gore proposed returning, but Des Voeux would have nothing of it and made light of the pain although it must have been considerable.

They camped on the south point of the inlet where they built a cairn and sat out the blizzard which so discomfited Fairholme and myself. They made good speed on the 30th and 31st with a following wind along flat coastal ice although the coast was swinging to the west. Des Voeux was obviously in great pain although he said nothing and pulled with the rest.

On June 1, the coast swung back to the south, but around 4 p.m., Des Voeux collapsed in the traces. Gore set camp and tended to his colleague as best he could. On removing his boots, he was shocked at the state of Des Voeux's foot and lower leg. The accident had obviously caused some bone damage and the tissue was already black and very swollen. Gore said it is a wonder he walked and hauled as far as he did.

By night Des Voeux was raving. Around 6 a.m. he awoke convinced that he was back on board the *Endymion* in the China seas and began to shout in the pidgin we used to communicate with the coolies there. At eight he fell silent and died a short time afterward.

Gore is taking it very hard as Des Voeux was a favourite of his, but we all remember and miss his enthusiasm and lightheartedness. I cannot escape the images, first, of the mere boy I met on *Cornwallis* and, second, of the good-hearted, enthusiastic young man hanging over the side poking with nets to catch something to excite Goodsir. How cruel that fate should strike such a man down when he had such a zest for life and so much to accomplish.

Gore, I think influenced by Des Voeux's sacrifice, made the decision to bury him there and press on to complete his task. The crew prepared a grave as best they could and paid their last respects. The peninsula will forever be known on the Chart as Des Voeux Peninsula.

On the 3rd they continued as the coast swung east and became broken with several large bays which they cut over. On June 4, they reached Simpson's cairn and completed the Northwest Passage. They remained a day, leaving a message buried ten feet north of the cairn. With the message they buried Des Voeux's pocket-watch to honour their comrade. They started back late on the 5th, and by traversing the neck of Des Voeux Peninsula, they made good time despite the melting conditions.

In all they covered almost 200 miles at an average speed of over thirteen miles per day, very respectable work, especially considering the hard going they encountered in the melting conditions, but it has taken a lot out of them. Several of the men are in sick bay and Gore himself is much weakened and down in spirits despite his triumph. I think perhaps he feels that he could have saved Des Voeux by ordering his crew to turn back on the second day. It was a difficult decision, given the lateness of the season and the chance that he might have been able to render assistance to Little. I have told him he has no need to reproach himself, but that is easier said than done, especially when one is in a low physical condition as Gore undoubtedly is. They saw no sign of Little although they left some extra supplies for him at Cape Herschel. It is somewhat worrisome that Little has not achieved Cape Herschel before June 5 and we must organise a relief expedition soon.

Gore confessed to being shocked at Franklin's wasted appearance, but the old man was perky enough to congratulate Gore and confirm his most deserved promotion to Commander. It seems that all our achievements are gained at some cost and that we are not to be allowed any unalloyed joy. This should be the greatest day of our voyage so far, but poor Des Voeux's death, Franklin's illness, and Little's prolonged absence cast a dark pall over all. How I wish to God that we will be home soon. I can put up with unlimited physical hardship but the pain of separation is impossible to take.

June 11–midnight—I hardly know how to write this. At ten this evening Sir John Franklin died. We are all deeply shocked by this tragedy coming as it does so closely on the heels of Gore's bitter-sweet return, and I particularly, by the mocking memory of the cheery 'All well' with which I ended Gore's sealed messages. How far we are now, but two weeks later, from 'All well.'

The old man was our expedition (and how hard it is to write in the past tense) and it is difficult to see how we can succeed without him. Even if we do, it will be a hollow victory indeed. This is his triumph. Crozier is a good man and a fine Commander, but he is no Franklin.

How the wooden walls of this cabin bear in on me tonight and how I wish I were back with you, the children and William; anywhere but this bleak, God-forsaken wilderness of ice and snow and gloom. How can such hope as that with which we began this adventure prove so fragile and transient? Even the midnight brightness of the sun is a mockery of our sadness. Good God I miss you dearest. I cannot write more.

June 12—The weather is drear as fits our mood today. The men go about their work with low heads and sullen steps, unwilling to believe the disaster that has befallen us.

Sir John sank quickly after Gore's return. It was almost as if he had been keeping himself alive for that moment with an extraordinary effort of will and, having seen the Passage completed, had no strength left to continue. By morning yesterday he was in high fever and again, unconscious, apart from a few, brief moments, until the end. Stanley tried everything his wide experience suggested, but to no avail. The end was peaceful, both Crozier and I being present. Sir John just simply stopped breathing. We both noticed at the same time and each looked in frank disbelief at the other, but the unthinkable was true.

Tomorrow we will take the great man ashore for another sad funeral. We will inter him alone on a small island just off Cape Felix. There was thought of putting him with the others at the Cape, but the island will provide a more fitting resting place for such a great man where, God-willing, he will have some rest. He should lie in some quiet churchyard or in a great tomb in some cathedral, but there is perhaps some justice in him being laid to rest in this strange land he has done so much to discover.

In any case, we must complete his task, and the first thing to be done is to find Little and his crew and bring them in before the ice breaks and we can make way. On the 14th I shall set out with Le Vesconte to follow Gore's route and meet up with them. There is small chance that we shall miss each other as Gore took pains to make the fastest route back to the ship clear. Sleds are fast becoming a liability, although the ice is still firm close inshore and we can only hope it lasts long enough for us to find them. I hope fervently that no ill has befallen them, we have had enough disaster for now.

June 13—Sir John is buried. We gave him the best send-off possible, given that the entire complement cannot desert the ships for such a long journey to the shore. Every watch and mess was well represented however and the occasion passed with fitting ceremony. Gore remained behind in charge of the ships, not feeling well enough for the journey to shore and back. Crozier read a fine service—and I think I shall never forget the sight of us all standing around the open grave like hunched statues, bundled almost unrecognizably against the cold wind which seemed to wail more mournfully than usual over the ice, which itself was groaning out in sorrow. The sight of Franklin being lowered into the shallow grave, covered with the Union flag which had been prepared so lovingly by Jane to celebrate his triumph, brought back most painfully his strange recounting of Lady Franklin's unwitting use of it when he was suffering from the flu. Was it a premonition? Who can say? It is certainly easy to believe in such things in this place.

But now I must to bed for a few hours rest before I set out to find Little. I will take no journal with me but the formal log, and will inform you of our proceedings upon my return. Irving will set off to follow Little's original course as far as he can, although the ice appears more broken along the east shore of King William Land. It is late in the season for sledge travel and I can only pray that the conditions do not become so bad that they prevent us from rendering what assistance our overdue colleagues may require. I hope to be back in a week or two, by which time we should be looking for our release from this place. Until then, Good night.

June 25—Oh Elizabeth, I am back and well, but with yet more sad news to tell.

We made poor time. Three days to Victory Point over broken ice and rocks which tore boots and sled runners alike. Every day began in a drear fog which chilled us to the bone and cast our spirits always lower. On the 17th, around noon, I heard the scraping of sled runners on bare rock coming from ahead. My first thought was that I had become disoriented and was facing back toward my sled. My first glimpse of the horror emerging from the greyness convinced me that we had found the object of our search.

The six figures before me were in their last extremity, barely more than skeletons staggering against one another and falling to their knees every few steps. Their sunken eyes watched only the ground where their next agonizing steps would fall. As I stood, dumb-struck, one of the figures, whom I assumed was Little from the tattered remains of the officer's uniform he wore, looked up and pointed a ragged arm in my direction. As if at a signal, the others collapsed to the ground. These were my lost companions.

I fired my musket to bring Le Vesconte and the others and ran forward. Little embraced me and tears coursed down his blackened cheeks. In truth, I would not have recognized him but for his uniform, so changed were his features. He attempted to speak, but only unintelligible sounds issued from his broken lips.

We set up our tents and built a fire from the remains of Little's sled. We made tea and heated some soup which, with the warmth of the fire did something to revive some of the men. That afternoon it came on to snow and, most unseasonably, kept us trapped in our tents for five days.

Little died the first night, raving about home and family, and one of his men lasted but a half day longer. The survivors would hear nothing of leaving their Commander, whom they credited with their survival, and insisted that we return his body with us to the ships. I had always considered Little to be something of an inflexible martinet, but the loyalty he inspired in his sledding crew was intense.

On the 22nd the wind dropped and we broke camp and headed back for Felix. I left most of our supplies and the remains of Little's sled at the camp and sent Sargent on ahead with the news. Our sled followed with poor Little on board and two men who were not fit to walk because of frostbite. The other two survivors walked beside us. The fresh snow helped speed our journey and we arrived back on board yesterday. I was relieved to find that Irving was already returned having been thwarted by impossible ice conditions.

Last night I read Little's log of their journey and it fills me with such admiration that I can barely contain it. The cost was great, two officers and four men dead and the remainder broken in body and spirit, but they have achieved much. They have proved King William Land an island and mapped some 250 miles of previously unknown coastline. Their total journey of more than 400 miles in fifty days is unprecedented.

At first, Little's crew had good travelling conditions down the west coast and encountered only two inlets to impede their progress. They were in the habit of examining the offshore islands they encountered and it was on one of these, on June 1st, just as the coast swung west along the strait of Simpson and Dease, that tragedy struck. The weather closed in and Thomas and three men were separated from the main party. Little did all he could without endangering the rest, firing muskets regularly and lighting gunpowder flares and searching for a full day once the weather eased, but it was to no avail and the men were not seen again.

Little was now in a serious predicament, barely more than half way around the island and his crew sadly depleted. Lightening the sled as much as possible, the survivors continued along the coast, reaching Cape Herschel but a single day after Gore had left it; had they not delayed to look in vain for the bodies of their lost comrades they at least would have been saved. As it was, Gore's directions and food caches probably saved those that did return, cutting down the miles they had to haul and supplying food when theirs was almost gone. In their weakened state they had no chance of catching Gore and merely struggled on until they stumbled out of the fog toward me. It is another triumph and tragedy. What is the cost of all our achievements? Glorious though our discoveries are, I cannot help but think that the wives and sweethearts of the poor men who lie scattered over this sad land would rather they had never been made.

I am sorry my dear for such a tale of woe of late, but I must stick with my promise to tell all, both good and bad. Perhaps I will delete these pages when I return; and return I hope to do as soon as I can, if only this damned ice would set us free.

June 27—What miseries dwell in all our minds now. This should be a happy time of preparation, but tragedy upon tragedy combine to weigh us down. Sometimes I wish I had not promised to write you this letter, but then I look upon your picture and imagine you back in the safety and comfort of home and I am strengthened. More and more it is to return to you that I continue and not for the glory of our achievements which are gained at such an abominable cost. Your company is worth a hundred Northwest Passages.

But I must leave off with this groaning. I cast my mind back to the good times as a way of recharging my spirits. Do you remember the first time we met? I had just come ashore from the *Clio* and was glad to be off the leaking hulk and safe in England after five years away. I knew of you from his letters; of his precipitous fall into the trap of love, of little Elisabeth and how her arrival brought you near to death, and of the arrival of young Robert mere months before my return. In truth, as I hurried by coach to Lincoln's Inn, I was nervous at meeting such a paragon as William described and, as I tell the truth as I am committed to do, I was not a little jealous too. As you know, William and I are as close as is possible for two people to be and to have you streak into his life like a comet and capture his entire attention so fully, was difficult.

In any case, I paid off the cab at the gate, intending to walk the drive and arrive unannounced. As the house came in sight, my attention was distracted by a figure grubbing about the vegetables of the kitchen garden. My first impression from the tattered and dirty clothes was that this was a tramp come in to steal a free meal of turnip. I stepped forward and, in my best officer's voice, said something to the effect of,

"What are you doing there you scoundrel?"

When the hunched figure stood and turned, I saw it to be a maid of the house although one of uncommon beauty and uncommonly poor sartorial sense.

"Beggin' pardon," she said, "I'm only pickin' vegetables for the Missus' dinner."

"Very well," I replied haughtily, "carry on. Is the Master in?"

"Aye," the maid answered, "and the Missus too."

I strode on up to the house and was met by William on the steps.

"James!" he exclaimed. "Why did you not write to say when you would arrive? Where is your cab? Now we shall have to make a special dinner and search out some of father's finest port. I believe there is a bottle or two left. You must tell us of all your adventures."

Then turning to the butler who was hovering in the background, he continued all in the same breath, "Patrick, be so good as to fetch the Madam." And turning back to me, "Come James, into the parlour and we shall wait for Elizabeth."

So, you can imagine that I was already somewhat stunned by the time you swept into the room. You need not imagine my horror, for you saw that when the maid from the kitchen garden, transformed into the Lady of the House, stood before me. I stammered my apologies as best I could, feeling the burden of embarrassment and not a little put out at the trick you had played on me. But William's hearty laugh when you explained the circumstances put all to rights.

"There is no controlling this woman, James," he said. "I tell her we have servants to work in the garden, but she ignores me and grubs around in the dirt like a common ditch-digger. What am I to do?"

"Nothing," I replied, "but accept with good grace the luck which has placed such a creature of beauty and character in your life."

That idyllic week when I came to know you and Elisabeth and Robert I remember fondly to this day, and it is in better spirits, with the image of the ragged 'kitchen maid' crouching over the rows of turnips firmly fixed in my mind, that I now retire and bid you, Good night.

June 28—Stanley had to operate and remove the feet of one of the men of Little's party. He had been suffering from bad frostbite for some time and nothing could be done to save them. The other sailor suffering frostbite is not so bad and has only lost a few toes.

June 30—Two years today since we crossed the Arctic Circle for the first time. Last year I had hoped to have re-crossed it by now, but it was not to be. It seems sometimes that every hope I have for a speedy return is to be cruelly frustrated. When I think back to the early days and of my enthusiasm to spend some time up here, I am amazed. How could I have not known what we were undertaking? How could I have been so naive as to think one season would suffice for our journey? It was almost as if wishing would make it so, when in fact we are often merely pawns subject to the capricious whims of ice and snow. I have seen enough of this land. I want now merely to return—to sleep in a bed, to eat a decent meal, to not be plagued by dreams, to gaze upon your face once more.

Oh Elizabeth, I would gladly sacrifice all we have achieved to sit with you for but a few short hours. We would talk of simple things—the garden which I know you cherish so, the children, God bless them; and we would plan a picnic and a walk in the woods, which could only be frustrated by a summer shower that we would laugh our way through. It all seems so far away now. I look at my hand, black, gnarled, and as rough as oak bark, and I think of yours, resting, as I have seen it so often, upon some embroidery work, and I wonder at the smoothness and paleness of your skin. Is it possible that such subtle beauty can exist in the same world as this hellish place?

But here I go groaning on about my sorry self. What must you think? The frustration of waiting for release is playing on my mind, and I must also partially blame my recent reading matter. I took down Mary Shelley's *Frankenstein*, thinking that the Arctic setting might strike a chord with me. It did, but one so bleak I fear it has brought my mood low once more. The "undiscovered solitudes" of the "most northern extremity of the globe" were too fearfully described to give me quiet. And the pitiful final cry of the monster contemplating his fiery end so that he "shall no longer feel the agonies which now consume me or be the prey of feelings unsatisfied, yet unquenched," gives me no rest.

But I must stop before my black mood seduces me into saying things I must not. We shall soon be on our way again with the siren call of warmer climes and home to encourage us on. It is just a matter of waiting for the ice. Fondest regards as always. Good night.

July 7—We are now all in a fever of anticipation for the ice to break, but as yet no sign. It is a colder season than last year with snow being as likely as rain. We do not see much of the eternal sun, but when it does appear it is a welcome joy indeed and the men's spirits pick up noticeably.

The ships are well prepared for escape, being rigged and caulked as much as is possible in our position. The ice is moving somewhat and often creaks and groans loudly, but there is no sign of open water except along the shores of the island. We continue to send hunting parties out, but they have poor luck. Partridge and hare are common enough, but the larger game, of which we need a good supply to strengthen the men, is very rare. To date we have bagged only three musk-ox, barely enough to provide one good meal for all. The reindeer, which Back and Simpson talk of to the south, do not seem to frequent these parts. Seals are out on the ice in some number and we have shot several. I even attempted the meat and blubber, but found it very hard to stomach.

We have an abundance of preserved food to last us well into next year, longer if we are careful, but without fresh meat, the ravages of scurvy will be a threat. Goodsir has been experimenting in making soup out of the lichens he has been studying in the belief that they may have antiscorbutic properties. His soups are almost undrinkable, being very bitter and producing severe stomach cramps, but he hopes to concoct something more palatable. This is the *tripe de roche* of Sir John's telling and I cannot rid myself of the image of poor, weakening Hood, lying in the barren lands, unable to stomach it. I pray we do not get into such dire straits that we have need of them.

Osmer is spending much time cataloguing our supplies and working victualling schedules for all eventualities. It is becoming something of an obsession with him, perhaps an attempt to impose order and a measure of control on our essentially disordered and uncontrollable situation. We still find time for the occasional game, and I find that, obsessed or not, he is still my master.

July 8—Crozier came over and we dined in Sir John's cabin amidst Stanley's and Goodsir's specimens. We dined alone and discussed our options.

"I fear the ice will break late this year," he began. "It is not showing much sign of movement yet. This will give us but a short season for work and we must be clear on what course we will follow."

"Indeed," I agreed, "but is there a choice to continuing on our way?"

"Yes, we could retreat. This ice river we are in is a devilish thing and there is perhaps more of a chance that the ice will open to the north, allowing us to escape the way we came. We must be ready should an opportunity present itself."

"I would be loath to retreat while there is still a chance of completing our task. Defeat would be hard to accept."

"Yes," Crozier said thoughtfully, "but consider, James, if the ice ahead does not open sufficiently to allow us to escape the ice river to the coast, and even if then we do not make good progress toward Behring's Strait, then a further winter here will bring severe problems. There are many who, I feel, would not survive another winter in such a barren location, and that would be a defeat much harder to take than retreat. My thoughts are that we must be sure of reaching as far as the Coppermine River for us to venture forward. Were we to winter there, we would be certain of escape the following year and would be able to make contact with the natives of the region. There appear to be none hereabouts."

We sat in silence for a time as I thought on his comments. With a little luck, which admittedly has been in short supply of late, we could retreat through Barrow Strait and be home this year. What a joyful thought! We would have completed the Passage, but not sailed through. If we continue, it will take remarkable luck not to have a third winter on the coast. The temptation is sore. Crozier broke our silence.

"Here is my thought, James. If the ice breaks to the south and allows us reasonable passage soon, before the end of the month, we will proceed. If it shows no sign of opening ahead, but breaks up to the north, we will retreat. How think you on that?"

"That is reasonable," I said; and so we await the elements to determine our route with as much patience as we can muster. Good night dearest.

July 9—Glorious day. For once the fog and mist rolled away and we were bathed in the most delightful sunshine for full twenty-four hours. The ice glistened all around and the men went about their chores and exercises with a renewed vigour. The ice is shewing signs of movement and there is much cracking and eruption of pressure ridges although it is far off to the west. Our floe, and all the heavy ice around it, has commenced to drift to the southwest very slowly and our hopes are high that this bodes well for our freedom. Reid is optimistic and told me today, "The ice'll let us be arl right Mister Jems, sir."

Of course he has no way of knowing any more than the rest of us, his experience being exclusively of the ice in Baffin's Bay and not this cursed ice river we find ourselves in; never-the-less, his certainty is encouraging and the men look to him as an expert on all things ice-related.

Goodsir suggested at supper that we hoist sail and go home with our ice floe and all. This provoked some speculation as to the reaction should we sail up the Thames with a mile or more of twenty-foot thick ice attached to our hull. It would certainly provide an entertainment for the populace. I even felt up to pitting my skills against Osmer, but to no avail. I must now to bed although the sun is still bright.

July 10—Back to the rain and fog today, but the ice movement continues which is what we want. If only a good wind would get up from the east, I feel sure it would do much to break up the ice and release us.

July 15—The ice is still on the move, but no leads, although Reid is a permanent feature in the crow's nest, peering through the rain and mist. We are drifting very slowly, having covered about one mile in the last week—as far as I can judge from the readings of the coast I make in breaks in the weather. The constant rain is most depressing. Man needs sunshine to be in true good spirits, especially in this land.

July 18—Still drifting.

July 19—Clear breaks allowed readings today. Our movement continues, but painfully slow.

July 20—No break yet. Still rain and fog.

July 21—The same. Our spirits are low.

July 22—We approach the end of the month, yet there is no sign of release in either direction. There is still time. If only the fates would smile upon us.

July 23—Temperature dropped below freezing and the rain turned to snow. Disheartening.

July 24—Unfortunate incident today on the *Terror*. Apparently some men acquired some spirits and indulged themselves most intemperately, appearing on deck in an inebriate state and even talking back to Hodgson who tried to control them. Four men are in irons below, in all probability feeling very sorry for themselves. They must be flogged of course, discipline must be maintained for the good of all, but it is difficult not to sympathize with their desire to escape from our depressing state for an hour or two.

We are still no closer to being released, although our drift continues and the ice noises awaken us at all hours. One of my concerns is that we will drift so far to the southwest that we will lose the option of retreating to the north. At the moment it does not matter as we can see no clear water in any direction except for a narrow strip in places hard by the beach. Our shore camp has been abandoned and we restrict ourselves to observations on the ice and the occasional hunting expedition, which still have no luck. This waiting is very hard on all of us. I pray it will not go on much longer.

Summer, 1847

July 27, 1847—Another birthday in these lands and I have declared it as good a day as any to pronounce summer upon us. I had hoped to be free by now, but we must wait longer.

The mess toasted my health and Gore entertained us all with his flute. A man could wish for no better set of comrades than I have around me here. I only hope the ice will present me with a gift and release us all to continue our work.

July 31—Month's end. Our deadline for continuing according to Crozier. Yet I still hope to continue. If nothing opens to the north and we are released to the south, we must continue our chosen course rather than stay here. Nature will decide.

August 2—Release cannot be far away now. This afternoon, Reid called out a lead, some three miles to the northward. It soon closed, but it is a sign that there is hope. The pressure ridges to the west are moving closer and are now hard against the edge of our floe. With this much activity, something must happen soon.

At dinner the talk turned to what each of us will do on our return home.

"The lot of an unemployed, half-pay officer," commented Fairholme, "does not appear bad for it allows time at home, a warm fire, and an abundance of fresh food."

This was met with a chorus of agreement.

"And that will be our lot," elaborated Gore, "unless a war breaks out. Perhaps with Russia."

"That may not be a great help," added Le Vesconte. "I suspect it would not take long to dispose of the Czar's navy, such as it is. But Gore is right. We will bring so much information back with us that it will keep all the men of science and the map-makers busy for some time. I think that the Navy will not be well disposed to sending more expeditions up here. But what choice do we Navy men have?"

"None," said Gore, "but I shall move heaven and earth to acquire a warm posting; perhaps in the West Indies."

I outlined my thoughts on going to India and Fairholme agreed that it might be a pleasurable option if Gore's war was not forthcoming.

"I am lucky," piped up Goodsir. "The harder you all work here collecting specimens, the more work I shall have upon my return. I shall catalogue and publish and be as famous as Banks. What of you Stanley?"

"You may have my specimens and the glory of publication. I shall go back to surgery and open a small practice in Edinburgh, tending to the minor ailments of society ladies and drinking port by my hearth."

"But we have not heard from Reid," Goodsir proclaimed. "What will you do? Return to the whalers?"

"Naw, Mister Harry," he replied, "I've a mind to stay home and keep mysel' a few pigs." This brought some laughter from the others, but Reid held his own. "Pigs's 'as a bad reputation arl right," he continued, "but I can tell you sure, they is as clean as any London Gent, and a darn sight cleaner than most of us I daresay." Reid really is a most engaging character.

The reference to pigs was not lost on any of us. Although we are cleaner now that bathing is infrequently possible—cleaner than we were in the depths of frigid winter—we would still offend the olfactory senses of most civilised beings. I bathe whenever the weather feels warm enough and sometimes when it does not, and I have the boy Chambers wash my uniforms whenever possible too, but even boiling does not completely rid them of a lingering animal odour. It is possible to obtain only small amounts of warm water from the boilers, but never enough for a full bath and the men must wash in the cold from tubs on the ice. To that end we declare every Thursday that the weather is clement enough 'wash day.' To see the men cavort around the ship as they splash ice cold water over themselves puts me in mind of nothing so much as a herd of walrus occupying some rocky outcrop. Of course, modesty is not a necessary social grace in our isolated community; it takes a very definite second place to completing one's ablutions rapidly, especially when a wind blows from the northwest and there is a danger of extremities becoming frost-bitten.

August 3—We are completely prepared, all hunting parties are aboard and our observatories taken down. We have even, learning from our mistake on Beechey Island, left a complete record of our activities beneath a cairn on the islet where Sir John lies off Cape Felix. It is just a question of time.

August 4—The ice is howling and groaning all around. No-one gets any sleep and men can be found gazing over the rail at all hours and I have the feeling that they are willing open water to appear. The strain is very hard for all, for it is not just the waiting for release, but the possibility that the pressure will damage us before that happens—this is what weighs on minds which have been all too inactive for too long. I am concerned at the lateness of the season whichever way we are released.

August 6—Almost disaster. Around four this afternoon, I was on deck with Le Vesconte. The weather was clear and we were preparing to take readings when, all of a sudden, a huge block of ice was thrown up with a terrifying roar, not a hundred and fifty feet from the ship. We could feel the deck shudder from the pressure and the hull creaked most despairingly. As we watched the ridge, which was composed of ice about fifteen feet thick and stood up thirty or more in the air, it began to move as if powered by some pagan God of the sea.

For several hours we watched as it crept closer and I ordered supplies and boats onto the ice in preparation for the worst. Around nine this evening, the ridge was almost alongside and I was ready to order the men onto the ice, when the pressure released its hold as suddenly as it had begun. The noise, which was almost deafening us by this time, ceased abruptly and the ridge stopped. It still sits beside us, looming over the deck most threateningly, but at least we are in no immediate danger from it. I hope at least it foreshadows some break-up.

August 7—Visitors today, the first we have had in over two years. Reid, from his position in the nest, was the first to spot them, but soon we had all the crew at the rail, straining to spot the small group of black figures moving hesitantly toward us over the ice. I sent word to Crozier and went on to the ice to meet them. When I was about one hundred feet away, they stopped and stood watching me carefully. I made a great shew of placing my sword and musket on the ice and approaching with my arms spread wide to indicate that I meant no harm. One of their number came forward to meet me and, when he was within arms reach, I offered him a Navy medallion and a selection of fish hooks as a token of friendship. After examining my gift most carefully, he turned and shouted something to the others who came forward in a rush and surrounded me with much gesticulating and smiling.

There were nine in the party, four men, one of whom seemed of great age, three women and two who were little more than children. They were all dressed in loose hides which were sewn roughly into coats which reached past their knees, and wore leggings of the same material and slippers of skin with the hair turned outermost. I must admit that the smell emanating from them was not at all pleasant, but perhaps they think the same of us.

They are not tall people, being little over five feet in height and must regard someone of Le Vesconte's stature as something of a giant. Their faces are broad with high cheekbones, wide foreheads and squat noses. They are quite charming when they smile, which our group did incessantly at the prospect of the treasures they might acquire from us. They were accompanied by a long narrow sled on which was piled a collection of skins and raw meat. The sled was drawn by four skinny dogs which were continually barking and whining and straining to escape from their tethers.

At length, Crozier came up and we managed, through his words of the Esquimaux language and some imaginative signs, to communicate fairly well. The Esquimaux were from the east and had come to these parts for seals. They indicated that they thought the hunting to be very bad this year at Tununeck, which seems to be their name, as close as I can render it, for King William Land, and they were concerned that it would be a bad year with no summer.

Amazingly they knew of Crozier from his visits to Prince Regent Inlet with Parry many years before, having been in communication with the Esquimaux who had visited his ships at that time. They even knew his name, calling him Aglooka, which he had acquired from a native boy who was now called Crozar. This habit of exchanging names is quite usual amongst the Esquimaux who commonly have several names. The leader of the Esquimaux who came forward to meet me is called Oonalee. The old man is apparently a shaman of some kind, whom Oonalee calls Angatkut. He hangs back from the others a bit and is always there watching what is happening.

We invited our guests aboard the *Erebus*, it being the closest vessel, and they accepted with alacrity. Once on board they examined everything with great interest and we had to watch out to prevent the smaller items going missing. Oonalee attempted to hide a small saw behind his back. When Crozier asked for it back, the man refused and stepped back. It was an awkward moment, but Reid defused any possible tension by sneaking up behind Oonalee and deftly taking the saw from his hands. This was regarded as a great joke by our visitors who seem to regard stealing as a kind of game.

We took Oonalee and one other to Franklin's cabin where we made them gifts of knives and various trinkets. Crozier persuaded them to draw us a chart of the land hereabouts which Oonalee's companion did with great speed and good agreement with what we have discovered. Their chart shewed that, as Little found, King William Land is an island. They also shewed Simpson's Strait and Back's Fish River and seemed to be indicating that Boothia, or Netsilik as they call it, is a peninsula and that there is no passage from Simpson's Strait to Prince Regent Inlet. Here we were unfortunately disturbed by a commotion from on deck. On going up we discovered the cause to be an altercation between Angatkut and a crew member. It seems the sailor had tried to make free with one of the women and the man had taken exception. Considering the many long months the men have been without even sight of the fairer sex, it may have been a mistake to allow any on board, even ones as unappealing as our present visitors. A few of our people are of a very low class and will take what entertainment may be had without regard to taste or circumstance.

In any event, the fight amounted to little more than mutual shoving and shouting and was easily smoothed over by the removal of the offending sailor and the distribution of more gifts, but it could so easily have turned very nasty. I think the incident contributed to the Esquimaux's decision to return to the land that night. We tried to persuade them to stay, offering them food, which they wolfed down in a most disgusting manner. They offered us seal meat in return, that being all they had, but they were determined to leave and, short of violence, we could not stop them. I was sorry to see them go since I would have liked to learn more of these strange people. Their ways are certainly odd and they have habits which we find repulsive, but, as Crozier pointed out, they live the way they do for a reason, and that is the best way they have to survive in this bleak and inhospitable land.

Their visit has thrown everyone into a turmoil of emotions. It was the first contact we have had outside our closed community for so long; and, different though our visitors were, it was never-the-less human contact, and we have been too long without that, to judge by the great numbers who lined the rail to watch the figures rapidly disappear over the ice.

At supper the conversation turned to the adoption of Esquimaux ways by Europeans should they be lost in these lands. We have all heard Crozier's arguments before, but at the back of everyone's mind lurked our present predicament and what we should do if the ice does not release us this year. Consequently, the discussion was lively on the merits or otherwise of seal meat, dog sleds, and deerskin clothing. I did not say, but felt, that the adoption of native ways might succeed for a few men in a desperate position, but could not possibly be an option for over a hundred. I hope it does not come to that.

The inevitable progression of time with no commensurate weakening of the hold the ice has of our vessels encourages the most miserable thoughts. We do not speak of them, but they are there I am convinced. I know I cannot escape the horrifying idea that we will not be released this year and, if that is the case, I cannot help but wonder how many of us will be left next spring to take advantage of what it may bring. Must I be another year with only your picture to gaze upon?

But there is time yet. I must not fall into a maudlin state of mind. The ice will yet break and we shall be on our way. Good night dear sister.

August 8—Many odd dreams last night, mostly of home and pleasant days past. Do you remember the picnics we used to take at Hampstead or out on the downs? I have been particularly in mind lately of the one we took after my return from China. Do you remember? You read to me from the works of that Cockney poet Keats whom you seemed to take much pleasure in. While I could take pleasure in the sound of your voice reading the coach timetable, I must admit to not being particularly impressed and saying that I preferred less melancholy and more story to my poems. You laughed and accused me of possessing a starved soul from spending too much time by far in the company of rough sailors. There may have been some truth in that, although you would be terribly unfair to accuse Le Vesconte or Fairholme of any roughness.

In any case, this evening I took down the small volume of Mister Keats' work that you gave me in hopes of saving my soul some short time after our outing. I am ashamed to admit that I had not opened it in the meantime but, tonight it fell open by chance on some lines that seemed to strike home to me. It was the start of a poem called "The Eve of St. Agnes:"

St. Agnes' Eve—Ah, bitter chill it was!
The owl, for all his feathers, was a-cold;
The hare limp'd trembling through the frozen grass,
And silent was the flock in woolly fold.

I am sure you can see how that might appeal to one who has not been completely warm for two years, but later there was a piece that seemed to fit in an uncanny way with some thoughts I have been having of late:

Along the chapel aisle by slow degrees:
The sculptur'd dead, on each side, seem to freeze . . .
He passeth by; and his weak spirit fails
To think how they may ache in icy hoods and mails.

I have often thought how our own dead, buried in the frozen ground of this land, will stay unchanging, while we grow old, die and decay with England as an overcoat. It is a small step to think that they may retain some painful remnant of their last extremity within their frozen, unchanging form, just as the poet's statues "ache in icy hoods and mails."

It is not a happy idea and I apologize if it disturbs you, but one thinks strange thoughts up here and it will at least shew you that I have, like Keats, a streak of melancholy. Look how your brother has changed, from the simple sailor to a poetry-quoting philosopher! What will you think of me on my return?

In any case, I must now take this poor starved soul to bed and to dreams of the picnics we shall have on my return. Good night.

August 15—Still no sign of release, although our drift to the south is increasing. The ice continues to be active, but not close enough to us to be a danger and not in a way which produces any leads which we might use. Already the season is late and our situation will be worrisome if we do not make progress soon. No further sign of our visitors.

Crozier read divine service today. This is not a habit with him as it was with Sir John, despite the fact that he is from a religious family, having two brothers dedicated to the priesthood in Ireland. He feels more that the men should worship however they choose. He read today, I think, because there is considerable worry that the ice should have let us go by now and that we might have to face another winter in this locality. He read a good sermon, not with Franklin's tone or authority, but reassuring and a comfort none-the-less. His text was on Moses' wanderings in the wilderness and, though I don't think his style is suited to an Old Testament prophet, he did a good job of drawing the parallels between the Israelites trials in the desert and our own in this white world. I think he brought comfort.

August 16—Heavy rain and fog all day. The weather has been most miserable, with the exception of a few days of sunshine. Much rain and wet snow and fog almost every morning. It is depressing for the spirit and most uncomfortable for the body. Without the sun, the temperature rarely rises much above freezing and there is often a skim of ice on the fire holes in the morning even though we are at the height of summer. The strange thing is that I feel more cold now in a wet freezing rain beneath a dull grey sky than I did when it was fifty degrees colder beneath a weak sun.

Gore played his flute for us this evening and a most emotional experience it was. Poor Gore has not been in the best of health since his return, being prone to colds and fevers almost constantly. Stanley has given him laudanum and whatever other remedies seem appropriate, but has privately confided to me that he believes the root cause of his ailments is his feelings of responsibility for the death of poor Des Voeux. We have all reassured him most firmly that this is not the case and that it was Des Voeux's own stubbornness and bravery (the latter of which appears, even in the cause of the completion of the Passage, almost unbearably futile at the moment), which contributed to the tragedy. But I suspect he only half believes us.

It is odd how a man's temper can control the physical ailments which plague him. Goodsir, who is continually in good spirits, or Reid, who takes a very straightforward view of the world, never seem to fall ill; whereas Gore, who is sensitive and obviously carries his responsibilities very seriously, and is always considering the consequences of his every action, suffers all sorts of minor complaints. In any case, Gore's playing this evening was most delightful. At first he did not want to, but upon persuasion he took up his flute and played some almost unbearably sad and beautiful tunes which had the hardest-hearted of us close to tears. Gore played with such feeling that no-one could not suffer the pain of having vivid images of home and loved ones conjured up by the refrains. We all sat in complete silence while he played on, packed-in close together, but thousands of miles away in our hearts. For myself, I was with you, and found it almost unbearably sad to return when Gore finally finished. We all thanked him most sincerely and each retired to his cabin to be alone with his thoughts. I sat gazing at your picture for a full hour before I could return to the present and scribble these few lines. When will I see you once more?

August 20—A week of continuous rain and greyness. We had our first glimpse of the coast this morning for several days and I rushed to take some readings. They revealed that our rate of drift is increasing, and that we have moved some ten miles from the location of our winter besetment. And yet we are still locked in ice as far as the eye can see. There is still activity, and ridges are thrust up and cast down all around with much noise and fuss, but of open water there is no sign and without that we will go nowhere.

August 23—Saw a bear very close to the ship today. I was on deck peering off into the eternal fog, through which I could see little more than 150 yards. All of a sudden, there was a bear, completely visible, as if it had been materialized by some magician. It was probably hunting seals and was heading north at a fairly rapid pace. They really are magnificent animals, perfectly suited to their environment. This one was running with its body thrown forward and its eyes fixed on the ice before it. It had a loping, swaying sort of gait which looked somewhat ungainly but covered the ground very effectively.

I watched it with some interest, wishing all the while that I could simply jump over the side onto the ice and run with such casual efficiency until I had returned to your side. I never thought to make for a musket until a shout from the deck indicated that others had spotted the beast. There was a flurry of activity, but the bear was gone back into the fog before anything could be done. I doubt if the creature even registered our presence, so focused was it on its task. Reid says they are just as much at home in the water and that he has seen them swimming scores of miles from any land or even floating ice. I doubt if man will ever be able to truly conquer these lands until he has acquired at least some of the talents of this remarkable beast.

August 30—Continues cold and wet. We have almost given up hope of release this year and spirits are at a very low ebb. Even if the ice opens now, and there is no indication that it will do so, we cannot possibly make much headway either forward or back, before the onset of winter. It is only twelve days until the date on which we were beset last year.

We face our third winter in the ice with considerably more misgivings than the previous two. We have sufficient food to last us for probably two more years, but without large amounts of fresh meat, of which the poor hunting in these parts has been a pitiful provider, illness must break out before next summer.

Scurvy, of course, is what we fear most, it being capable of reducing a crew to the most pitiable straits in a very short time if not checked in some way. We have our lemon juice and I shall order doses increased, but the supply is not endless, and Goodsir says there are reports that it loses its efficacy as an antiscorbutic after two or three years. Perhaps we shall have to resort to the man's disgusting lichen soup after all.

I have ordered the men to go onto the ice and hunt seals, which are moderately plentiful close to the shore where there is some open water. I don't know if the meat will be edible to the men but, at the very least, we can render the fat for the cooking stoves and lamps of any parties away from the ship. I am going over to *Terror* tomorrow to discuss our situation with Crozier.

August 31—A glimpse of the sun today which did something to raise spirits a little, but not those of Crozier.

"We are trapped, James. Another winter in the ice and not even an improved location in which to spend it. Even a small progress would have raised spirits."

"Yes," I agreed, "but we have no choice. The only alternative is abandonment and walking out to Ross's supplies at Fury Beach, but the season is much too far progressed for that."

"In any case, it is not supplies that are our problem. We have sufficient food, the ships will be as secure as last winter at least, and if we can keep scurvy at bay, we will be in fair shape to sail out next season."

The thought, "If the ice releases us," was in both our minds, but neither mentioned it. Crozier continued.

"Our most pressing problem is discipline. The men's spirits are low as we are not well advanced and on our way. They look to another winter with some trepidation. There has already been a number of incidents of unruliness on the *Terror* which have resulted in flogging, and I can only imagine them increasing. As you know, I am not a great disciplinarian, much preferring a relaxed command, but in these circumstances I have no choice. I shall institute a rigorous regime of exercise and cleanliness and entertainments must have the highest priority. It will be a difficult time, and, I think, none of us look forward to it with any degree of joy, but we will manage. The first thing is to get the men busy to take their mind off the disappointment. Your seal hunts, James, are an excellent idea."

So we face a difficult time, but we must bear up. I fear it will be longer than I had hoped before I see you again my dearest sister and that is perhaps the hardest thing to face in my present predicament. Never-the-less, it shall make our eventual reunion that much sweeter. I am in mind this evening of your visit to the *Erebus* at Greenhithe. Walking on the dock amidst all the chaos of preparation, you were strangely silent. When I asked what ailed you, you tried to make light of it.

"It is nothing," you said, "just that I cannot see the point of all this effort, simply to go to a place where no-one would willingly live."

"Discovery," I said, full of the importance of our work. "We must know the world in which we live. It is our duty."

"Sometimes," you said with a sly smile, "I think you men use duty as an excuse to go off and play with all your new inventions somewhere you will not be interrupted by we ladies."

"How can you make so small of our great inventions," I asked, laughing. "Surely you would not give up all your finery and comfort to dress in filthy animal skins and sit by an open fire in a damp cave? There would be no music to soothe you nor poetry to entertain you. And I have never yet come upon a primitive with such a lovely kitchen garden as yours."

You laughed, with that delightful note that puts me in mind of tiny silver bells tumbling over a waterfall. But then you turned serious.

"James, be very careful. I do not like the assumptions that everything you do will be so easy and you will return heroes in but a few months. Do not tempt the fates so much. I want you to return."

I made light of your concerns and they were soon lost in the hustle of setting off. But now they come back to me. Perhaps we were too cocky in our expectations, but we have paid dear for it and deserve some luck. But I shall return, later than I planned, but all the more eager to see you. Good night.

September 12—One year since we were beset in this bleak place and all we can do is look forward to a second. I have not been able to bring myself to write these last few days.

We are in fact some nineteen miles from our location of last winter, still fifteen miles from the coast of King William Island, but our closest landfall is now nearer to Victory Point than Cape Felix. So that is where I shall establish my magnetic station.

September 15—Preparations for winter well underway. The men are busy taking down the yards and stowing the rigging, with heavy hearts I add, since the sails have not served us at all this season. Osmer is laying out provisions in depots on the ice so that we shall have some more space on board. He does so meticulously and is continually having the men move something from one pile to another. It is not necessary, but it keeps the men occupied.

I wish we were closer to land. Somehow being able to set foot on *terra firma*, even if it is a barren wilderness, would be reassuring. To be solely at the mercy of this ice is a trial. We will not set up the canvas yet as the weather has not become cold and we will allow the fresh air to circulate as long as possible. Our second volume of *The Cape Felix and Boothia Chronicle* is now in preparation and we are discussing our thespian activities in some detail, but it is a terrible disappointment to be still here.

September 17—The man who had to have his feet removed through frostbite died this morning. He never fully recovered his strength after his terrible ordeal and seems to simply have given up hope. His companion on the other hand, who lost four toes, is as cheerful as any and can be seen hobbling around the deck performing such duties as he can. It confirms my sense that the spirit determines physical well-being.

We will have the funeral tomorrow on the ice with the intention of moving the grave to the mainland in the spring.

September 18—Laid our poor frost-bitten sailor to rest with the usual sad ceremony. I hope he is not joined by too many more before we see our release.

Winter, 1847/48

October 1, 1847—Well, there can be no denying it is winter now. We are well settled in although we still send out the occasional hunting party. They have pitiful success, rarely returning with anything more than word of a few tracks. When they do bag a partridge or a hare or two, it is an occasion for some rejoicing, even though the soup Wall manages to concoct is often so dilute as to be almost tasteless. We took the opportunity of some settled weather yesterday to move the men onto the ice and deal with the rats which had become a problem again. This was a cause of some concern.

"They'll no' be happy," was Reid's cryptic comment.

"How so?" I asked.

"Well," he began in the slow drawl he uses when not keen on talking, "some o' the men, no' 'arl mind ye, but some o' the men is in the habit o' doin' a wee bit rat huntin', if ye catch ma meanin'."

I didn't.

"Mister Jems," he added at my confused look as if talking to a five-year-old child, "some o' the men has seen hard times on the land when the crops has failed. Ye can no' eat the seeds for the plantin' next spring, but there is always plenty rats on a farm, even in hard times. It's fer the meat that the huntin' is done, Mister Jems. A roast rat is, tae some palates, a welcome change frae salt pork. It tastes somethin' in the way o' grouse, but a wee bit mare strong.

"So ahm told," he added hurriedly.

None-the-less, the hunting on board will be poor for a while.

We have planned a theatrical entertainment for November. After much discussion we have settled on *The School for Scandal*, although Goldsmith's *She Stoops to Conquer* was a close second and may be put on in the new year. *The School for Scandal* is a complex play and we will undoubtedly not do it justice, but I hope our enthusiasm shall carry us through as it has in the past.

Irving again is cast as the belle, Maria; Crozier will be Sir Oliver Surface; Le Vesconte will be the hypocritical Joseph Surface; and I the dissolute but good-hearted Charles. All are looking forward to doing a worthwhile job of the famous 'screen scene.'

The crew's disappointment seems to be easing as we settle into the winter routine, which I shall not bother you with a third time. The temperature is now consistently below freezing and we have had a covering of snow which has served to freshen up the grubby landscape around the vessels.

I think I shall let my already irregular entries to you become even more infrequent, not because of any lack of desire to communicate with you, for if it would bring me closer to you, I would certainly write every hour that God gives; but because there is little to entertain you with in the winter months and because, like all else in our sad lot, my supply of paper is running short. Already, I am truly amazed at the number of pages I have filled. When added to the official journal, that daily account of our mundane doings, I have rivalled the output of a minor novelist. In any case, I had better close now before I write another chapter.

October 22—Gore is dead, yet I think I shall have his flute playing in my head for as long as I live. This is the hardest blow of all, he was such a strong force in our mess and now the conqueror of the Northwest Passage. He was a very stable man, very well tempered and quiet but not shy.

If I am honest, he had not been himself since Des Voeux's death, but I hardly felt his melancholy would have such consequences. He had been plagued by minor complaints all summer, but four days ago, he fell with a high fever and strong stomach cramps which progressed into a very distressing delirium yesterday. This morning, he fell quiet and died despite Stanley's and Goodsir's attentions. It must be terribly hard for Stanley, a surgeon and physician of some talent, to watch so many fine men die and be able to do so little. Our mess is sadly depleted with Gore, Des Voeux and Collins gone, and of course we still miss Sir John enormously. We will bury Gore on the ice for now. Oh Elizabeth, how long can I go on losing such good friends?

November 5—The sun bid us farewell today and we now face three months of darkness. I hope the lack of light is our most serious worry.

We are none in the best of health. All are passing tired and go about their work with hung expressions and a heavy tread. Physical ailments are vague, most have headaches, an ache of the limbs and overwhelming tiredness, but nothing Stanley or Goodsir can pin a name to. It is as if our lowness of spirits has translated into physical failings.

I almost laugh when I think back to the tiredness of spirit I complained afflicted Crozier in Greenland. How I wish we all had but that tiredness of spirit now. Despite our close physical proximity, I suspect we all feel solitary in our minds. I know I do, and often look upon my fellows as if they are hid behind smoked glass. My only sure realities are my thoughts of you.

November 19—Presented *School for Scandal* this evening. We had planned the production for a week ago, but the weather has been too cold for theatricals. This evening it was near zero and, while uncomfortable for the audience, it was not unbearable. The play went over well and there was much joviality in the crowd, some of whom had taken the precaution of fortifying themselves against the cold with some spirits. I think it has done something to lift all our spirits. I pray that it lasts. When I return, we must go up to town in the season and take in some plays. Something cheerful I think, and we will laugh at the poor attempts at acting your brother and his companions were reduced to in the Arctic lands.

December 1—The last month of another year. We all seem very tired and worn down, even Goodsir's normally irrepressible enthusiasm for all things crawling or swimming has abated and he is hardly ever to be seen at his microscope. The depression of our spirits is worrying this early in the season, but I am hoping the Christmas festivities will pick us all up. We have entertainments and athletics of all sorts planned, and there are still enough delicacies to produce a meal or two of some interest.

Now with Gore gone, Old Nep appears to have attached himself to me more than ever. Wherever I go, he is at my heels and looks out for me by my cabin door. He, at least, has been well fed from our hunting, having developed a taste for seal meat and fat and apparently thriving on it. I wonder sometimes if he knows the predicament we are in or if he simply accepts what happens without thought or question. If the latter, then I envy him more than I can say, for, all too often, it is the thought of what might happen that drags down our spirits more than the actual events. Oh to have the simple joy of being unaware of the consequences of our actions!

But I must to bed, I do not seem to have the stamina of old and need as much sleep as I can get despite not being very active during the day. Good night.

December 25—Merry Christmas yet again from the cold vastness of these Arctic realms. We managed a respectable meal for the mess, most having hoarded some small treat for just such an occasion. We all managed to lift ourselves above the winter gloom and introduced some merriment into the occasion, an exercise which was not hindered by the production of some champagne and fine old port. Reid partook a little too freely and became quite flushed, but remained civilized, the only outward sign being a propensity to launch into some ballads in his local dialect which was no more comprehensible to the rest of us than the talk of our Esquimaux visitors. Goodsir joked that he could see no reason why we went to the effort and expense of mounting expeditions to outlandish corners of the world when there was a species of man quite misunderstood and quite worthy of study right on our own doorstep. It really is remarkable how well we all still get on after such a long period in such close proximity.

I do hope you are not worrying over much about your long-lost brother. We shall escape this season, and even if we do not, there will be rescue parties launched to our aid as old John Ross promised Franklin before we sailed. Here is to us raising a glass together by the fire next Christmas. And now I must to bed, or the effects of the port will make me fit for nothing on the morrow. All my thoughts are with you dearest sister. Good night.

January 1, 1848—A new year. One I had hoped we would not see up here, but one that will surely be our last. Peddie came over from the *Terror* this afternoon, playing his pipes for all he was worth. They really are quite a rousing instrument and all came up to line the rail and listen. Like Joshua circling Jericho, Peddie and the others of his mess circled us three times before coming aboard to accept our hospitality. It is hard to look to the future with the confidence of last year, but we must and we will make the best of our situation and stick it out until our release.

January 8—Bad news. Stanley came to me this afternoon and reported our first confirmed case of scurvy. It has been suspected for some time, as I have observed the stiff-legged way some of the men ascend and descend the ladder to the ice, but seamen Best, who has been such a sterling help with the magnetic work, came to sick bay today bleeding from the mouth and complaining of severe pain in his knee and hip joints. Stanley conducted a thorough examination and reported that the man was also heavily bruised along his back and sides. The bleeding, only superficial at this early stage, is one of the strangest and most horrible aspects of this foul disease. Apparently in the final extremity, scars from wounds healed a decade ago will open and begin to bleed anew.

We called the roll and Stanley examined the crew. He found five more cases, not so far advanced, but in need of treatment and several more he suspected. I shall increase the lemon juice ration for all and feed the sick on the cress Wall has been growing in his kitchen garden (a poor imitation of the one I first saw my dear serving-girl sister in). It is little enough to do, but what else is there? The *Terror* has eight cases, two of which are quite bad. I had not thought it would be so bad so quickly, but I suppose we have all been wishing not to recognize the inevitable when we still have six or seven months before our release.

January 18—Bitterly cold, the mercury froze last night and it has not warmed up much in the day. Thankfully there is no wind, but we are all confined to the ship. Our scurvy cases get progressively worse, but Stanley has had no new ones to report. The man who first reported sick is in a very sorry state, and I fear there is not much we can do. Stanley is feeding him lemon juice, but it appears to have small effect, perhaps, as Goodsir thought, it loses its efficacy after a time.

January 31—Our first death from scurvy. The Captain's Coxswain on the *Terror*, John Wilson, died last night. He had an advanced form of the disease, but Peddie maintains that his lungs were also infected and this complication was what caused his end.

February 1—Buried Wilson in the ice. It was a solemn ceremony on a clear very cold day, and even the brief appearance of the sun again during the readings could not lift our spirits as it has in the previous years. The long days before our uncertain summer dwell too heavily on everyone's mind.

On return from our sad duties on the ice, I went to see how Best was doing. He is weak, but in good spirits. I told him he would soon be up and about and looking forward to the summer and a return to his family. He laughed out loud.

"Family," he cried, "it is them I am here to escape."

"How so?" I asked. He regarded me in silence for some time, as if deciding whether to reply.

"I thought once my family was all. My mother, father, and sister, we were the picture of a respectable family of moderate means. My father worked in commerce in Salisbury and we lived on a small estate nearby. My mother was the perfect parent, attentive and loving. My sister, Isabella, was a shy, quiet child, four years my junior, but a fine companion on our picnics and walks in the woods and with a strong interest in nature.

"Father was away much in the course of his business, travelling to Bristol and London. As I approached my sixteenth year, and was commencing to think about following my father into business or choosing a different path, we began to notice some odd behaviour from him. He appeared distant and volatile of temper, flying into rages at the least provocation. If I was honest, it had been coming on for some time, but one always makes allowances for those close to one.

"In any case, his behaviour deteriorated steadily through the course of my sixteenth summer. He became distracted, violent, and would often fall to talking incoherently to himself. In short, he showed all the signs of dementia. After one particularly violent outburst, when only my intervention prevented violence against Isabella, we had him examined by a physician. To our horror he diagnosed a late stage of the most horrible disease.

"Unbeknown to us, father, on his trips to Bristol and London, had for many years been associating himself with women of low virtue—he had syphilis. It was too late for arsenic or any other treatment and all we could expect was to watch him slide ever farther into madness.

"But that was not the end. The doctor insisted on examining mother and we soon discovered that the wretch had infected her."

Best lapsed into downcast silence.

"So that is why you gave up life on the land?" I asked. Again he laughed, the most bitter sound imaginable.

"For that? No, bad though it was, it was not all. Mother was not the only person infected by father."

For a moment I was confused. Then I realized.

"Isabella?" I asked horrified.

Best nodded. "For a time I considered killing the wretch. I did not care what happened to me. But then I thought he deserved the slower fate of a year-by-year descent into madness. I only prayed that he had moments of lucidity in which he knew what was happening to him and why.

"I left. Wishing anonymity, I joined the Navy as an Able Seaman. It was a cowardly thing to do, but I could think of no other.

"Father finally died as did mother shortly after. Isabella went to the care of an aunt. She has been lovingly cared for, but I have not seen her since.

"So," Best looked me in the eye, "I have no wish to go home."

Without something to anchor the soul one could drown in such misery. Elizabeth, I thank God every day that I have found you.

February 5—Best died this morning.

February 6—Conference today in Franklin's cabin. Myself, Crozier, Le Vesconte, Fairholme, Hodgson, and Irving present. Crozier opened.

"There is little to be done at the moment," he said, "but we must be ready with a plan when the weather improves. The final decision is mine, but I want all senior officers present to give their opinions on the matter.

"As I see it, we have two main options for the summer. One—we can await the break-up and hope we will be released this year to sail on, or—Two—we can abandon the vessels at the first opportunity and make for help overland. Both are chancy undertakings. May I have your opinions gentlemen?"

"The former," I put in, "is uncertain to say the least. We do not know if the ice ever melts from one year to the next at this location, and if we wait and it does not, then it will be too late in the season for the second option and we will be faced with another winter in the ice—one that precious few will survive."

"But overland!" Fairholme sounded horrified. "To walk to Fury Beach is 250 miles, with men as sick and weak as they will be come the month of July. It is madness. We must trust to the ice freeing us to proceed or retreat."

"But perhaps it is only varying degrees of madness that are left open to us," Le Vesconte responded in subdued tones. "We have lost all control and must set our course with whatever nature allows us."

"But Fury Beach is not our only option for walking out." This was Hodgson. "We have three possible routes; Fury Beach and John Ross's supplies; along the continental coast and down the Coppermine on the route blazed by Franklin in 1821; or south along Back's Fish River to the posts of the Hudson's Bay Company."

"Let us examine each then," said Crozier. "Fury Beach is the closest and promises us supplies . . ."

"Which I heard had been removed by whalers," interrupted Fairholme.

"That is unconfirmed," replied Crozier, "but in any case, we would be following the escape route of John Ross and we would be close to the whaling grounds and rescue. The Coppermine River is a long journey, but if we can draw longboats to the coast, Simpson and Dease proved it to be an open route in the summer and a longboat's shallow draught is much like the canoes they used."

"True," I said, "it would shorten our journey considerably, but I am in mind of Sir John's tales of the hardships they encountered passing down that river. Half of his party of only twenty perished along the way. We are a much larger group and could expect little succour from the local population. I fear that we would not much improve our position at the expense of great effort."

"Indeed," Crozier continued, "and some of the same holds true for Back's Fish River and the southern route. Back talked of arduous rapids and gruelling work, even just to transport the effects of his small party, and, as Mister Fairholme pointed out, we will not be in the peak of health."

"And that is the crux of the matter," I put in. "If we choose to walk out, even by the shortest route to Fury Beach, we will be burdened by large numbers of sick. Any destination under those conditions is a choice of one madness over another and doomed to failure. We must address the sickness before all else."

"What then do you suggest," asked Crozier.

"Perhaps a fourth option. Back mentioned the difficulties of his journey, true, but he also waxed eloquent on the abundance of game at the mouth of his Fish River. Simpson and Dease too talked of much game on the shores of Simpson Strait.

"If, at the earliest opportunity in the spring, we abandon the ships and haul to the mouth of Back's Fish River, we can expect good hunting, certainly better than we found last year hereabouts. A few weeks of fresh meat should restore the men wonderfully, and we will then be that much closer to Fury Beach should we decide on that option, or even a return to the ships if the ice is seen to be breaking."

My compromise was met with thoughtful silence. But as time progressed, heads began to nod. It is in reality our only sane chance.

So we are in agreement. Come spring, probably late April, after the worst of the winter storms but while the ice is still good enough for travel, we will head south in search of game and reserve our other options till we are restored to health.

We shall off-load the bulk of our supplies onto the land at Victory Point against a possible return or damage to the ships by the ice. It is a desperate scheme and it will be hard to leave these vessels which have been our homes for so long, but we must do something. At least we will have some comfort in taking charge of our own destiny. So we have much to do, building sledges to transport the sick, our supplies, and the boats we will need, but we will set to with a will. Wish us luck Elizabeth.

February 7—Happy birthday dearest sister. How I wish I could celebrate it with you but, as is becoming my habit, I raised a glass to your health at a time when I hoped you might be doing the same. Next year I shall give you a present to make up for all the ones I have missed. I cannot think what, for of late I find all objects from the life I used to lead equally exotic and cannot distinguish in importance between the Crown Jewels and a good dinner.

The plans were announced today to the crew who cheered and seemed glad to be given a focus for their labours. It is strange, but men will put up with the most unbearable hardships if only they feel they are working toward some worthwhile goal. Even spirits in our mess, which have been low of late, picked up and there was much talk of the practicalities of the sledge building and supply depot at Victory Point. Osmer and I even locked minds over the chess board, a thing we have not attempted for some time. Unfortunately from my point of view, the result was the same. I suspect that Osmer's skill at the game is declining. Unfortunately, I suspect that mine is also. It is so hard to concentrate for more than a few minutes and I find my mind wandering over the board. Still, in this as in all things, we must persevere.

So, it is in better spirits on this birthday, that I wish you a good night.

February 8—A second man on the *Terror*, Caulker's Mate Cornelius Hickey, has succumbed to scurvy.

March 26—I cannot believe it has been almost seven weeks since I have put pen to paper. Certainly I have been busy and preparations are well underway for our abandonment of the ships, but that is not a good enough excuse to warrant your forgiveness. Unfortunately, once I leave my cosy cabin and writing desk, my entries will, of necessity, become less frequent. However, I shall endeavour to keep you up to date with our changing situation.

Crozier read the service today, and afterwards announced a planned date for our departure. It will be April 22, Easter Saturday. Of course, the weather could upset our plans, as it did Gore's, but that is our aim. It is probably as early as we can hope to have good travelling weather and it should allow us to arrive at Back's Fish River in time for the game. There was some discussion of the wisdom of leaving at Easter, a time for worship and prayer, but Crozier turned it around nicely and asked what better time could there be than the celebration of the Resurrection of our Lord.

Couch and Sargent have been busy with the sledge designs and we have seven almost complete on the ice. Four will carry ship's boats in which will travel the sick and some supplies. The other three will be loaded entirely with supplies and our tents and sleeping equipment. We had hoped to take more, but there is even some doubt about this number, as we may not have enough fit men to pull these. At ten men for each sled, we will require seventy haulers. At present we have that number and some spare, but there are over twenty men in sick bay and the number is increasing weekly. Almost all under Stanley's and Peddie's care are suffering from scurvy and four or five are severe cases, including Hornby, the Mate on *Terror*.

Even those not in sick bay are now shewing some signs of the dread disease. For myself, I am not too bad, although I noticed blood on my lip yesterday and one of my front teeth is coming loose. My dear, how you would be frighted now were I to appear beside you in the kitchen garden all unannounced. I can hardly even stand to look at my visage in the glass, so hollow are my cheeks and sunken my eyes. My skin, where you can see it through the dirt and stubble, is pallid and in need of some sunlight. My hair has been falling out at an alarming rate and my forehead is now quite expansive and suggestive of extreme intelligence. The rest of my hair is thin enough for a phrenologist to carry out a study with no difficulty. But do not worry, I shall bathe and feed before presenting myself for your inspection.

The worst symptom is the fatigue. It takes an uncommon amount of will to do the simplest tasks. We must all continually force ourselves and the men along to complete our preparations. All my joints ache and protest most inconveniently at the least hard work.

Next week we hope to begin ferrying our supplies over to Victory Point. We will not be able to build a stone house as we did at Beechey, but if we are to return here it will be this summer, and canvas should suffice for protection from the elements until then.

I see that I even forgot to mention our thespian activities, which were directed to *She Stoops to Conquer* on February 16. As always, it was a success, although marred by some drunkenness on the part of a few crew members who had to be disciplined. Drunkenness is greatly on the increase and we have to flog regularly to try to stamp it out. I understand why the men resort to it, and I have long considered intemperance to be one of the great banes of the British Navy, but there is little that can be done to eradicate it completely.

I am sorry but I cannot give you more details of our activities since I last wrote. The effort of composing even the few words above has exhausted me and, if I am to be good for work tomorrow, I must to bed. Good night.

March 27—Another death on board *Terror*, Marine Henry Wilkes.

March 28—Sunshine today and standing in it I felt a warmth I had not felt for a long time. It has been a cold winter with, as in previous years, the mercury frozen solid on a number of occasions, but we have not had much snow and thankfully, the wind has been moderate for the most part. Daily now, the temperature is increasing and, according to the log, we are already warmer than we were at the same time last year. I hope this bodes well for an early start and for our release in the summer.

March 29—Abraham Seeley, one of our crewmen, died this morning. It is odd and distressing how these tragedies seem to cluster, almost as if the departed are seeking company on their long journey. Our small graveyard on the ice is now sadly busy and I fear we have not seen the last before we set off. I do not think we will be able to move the men to shore before we leave, all our efforts must be directed to our primary goal, that of obtaining fresh meat. Thus, when the ice does break up, our comrades will be consigned to the deep as is fitting and proper for a sailor on duty.

April 1—Well here it is at last, the month in which we shall set off. Expectations and spirits are high, although many bodies are weak. Preparations are well under way, and we shall begin transporting supplies to Victory Point soon. Couch and Sargent work like slaves preparing the sledges and ensuring that they are as light as possible yet strong enough to carry our loads. Their work is vitally important, for every pound we can save might mean the difference between life and death for some exhausted crewman. Couch is becoming quite the hero for his inventiveness and industry. The two men are still constant companions, and I have trouble in their company, but they have given me no cause for further reprimand. Oddly, they appear two of the fittest amongst us. Can it be their companionship, unnatural though it be, that fortifies them?

April 3—Crozier and Hodgson came over and greatly added to the evening by bringing several bottles of fine champagne. We all over-indulged somewhat, but as Crozier pointed out, we cannot take it with us and to leave it for the natives would not be wise.

Unfortunately, Crozier also brought some bad news. Hornby is sinking fast and is not expected to last much longer. He has taken to raving in a most unsettling manner. His death will leave *Terror* without a Mate.

But enough of that, it is a good day, and you have been much in my thoughts, as I hope I have in yours. Good night.

April 5—Hornby died today. He had been morose and most sullen since the loss of Thomas on Little's expedition.

April 7—Terrible accident today! Couch is dead. He was inspecting the underside of a sled which was being held up by the men, when the rope slipped and he was pinned to the ice. Sargent was on the scene and with the help of some crewmen, released his companion rapidly. Although in considerable pain, Couch did not outwardly appear too seriously injured. However, Stanley suspected some internal damage to vital organs and sure enough, around three this afternoon, Couch began coughing blood and weakened fast. By five he was dead. Sargent is devastated, but all shall miss him around the mess. Certainly, we shall miss the expertise he has developed in sledge design and construction.

April 8—Buried Couch today beside Hornby and the others. Crozier gave a very moving tribute, stressing how much we all owe Couch and the work he has done to make our upcoming adventure easier. Sargent broke down most embarrassingly at the graveside. I do not know if others suspect the relationship. I am glad now I did not punish the man. His behaviour was unquestionably disgusting, but it all appears so petty in these straits we find ourselves. I pity Sargent his loss.

Weather continues to warm, although less cold would be a better description. We have had several fair days and have removed our canvas coverings to allow freer circulation of air. We take the better weather this year as a good omen. Tomorrow we begin stocking the supply depot at Victory Point. I shall go over to supervise its layout and shall not be able to write for a few days.

April 15—Supply depot at Victory Point is growing. We are taking over all the materiel that might be of use in case of a return and which we do not want to lose in case an accident should befall the ships in our absence. There is a huge pile of clothing, another of instruments and tools, and another of barrels, crates and cans of food.

Stanley was somewhat concerned about leaving his medicines unattended. It is common practice to destroy anything which might be harmful to the Esquimaux. The same argument applies to our gunpowder, however, this part of the coast does not appear to be often visited by the Esquimaux and I am thinking more and more of a return to the ships after the hunt. The season is shewing all the promise of being much more open than last year and to return in the ships would be immensely preferable to walking home. Le Vesconte, on the other hand, is fixated with continuing on to Fury Beach and the whalers. Who can say which is the right course, but first we must find fresh food.

The men did well hauling the sledges over the ice. Of course, it is flat on our well-worn path to the island, but we should not have too much hard going down the coast either. We shall leave four ship's boats on the shore in case the ice is broken when we return.

Yet another man on *Erebus*, Sailmaker John Murray, is dead and the Captain of the Forecastle on the *Terror*, Reuben Male, cannot be far behind. I will be glad to leave our sad little cemetery behind even though it will mean saying good-bye to our colleagues. The 22nd cannot come soon enough.

April 17—Reuben Male died this evening.

April 21—Good Friday and we had a very moving service on deck today. Crozier does not have the force of Franklin when he speaks, but he has the gift of touching what is closest to the crew's heart.

"Our journey is not an abandonment," he intoned, "but rather a resurrection from the ice and our hope for the future. We have a goal and we must all strive to attain it. God willing, and with hard work, we will reach that goal and see no more winters in this land."

It was very uplifting and struck just the right cord on the eve of our adventure. I am coming to admire him more and more. His lowness of spirit when we sailed appears now more like a saner view of reality; and many of his prognostications, which in our naive enthusiasm were dismissed as groaning, have proved true. What if he had been in charge from the start? Would we be here now?

The weather continues to hold. It is cold, but not unbearably so and there is no wind to speak of. We leave first thing tomorrow. We will spend a few days at Victory Point organising the supplies and packing the sledges. We will take six, leaving the seventh against our return. The tension on board is almost palpable. Everyone has such mixed feelings about leaving our security to strike out into the wilderness, and yet, we have the hope of achieving our goal and being the instrument of our own salvation.

I had an interesting conversation with the cabin boy, George Chambers, this evening on deck. He has long since ceased to worship me and has turned into a fine young man. I was strolling by the rail pondering our situation and thinking of you, when I spotted his figure gazing over the side. He was so engrossed with his thoughts that I approached to within a couple of feet before he noticed my presence. He fairly jumped when he saw me, such is the imposing figure of authority your brother presents, and after mumbling a faint greeting was about to retreat below decks. I, on some unknown impulse, felt the urge to engage him in conversation.

"Stay Master Chambers. What were you pondering just now in such a concentrated way—your family?"

"Naw sir," he said, "beggin' your pardon, I has none."

"You are a foundling then?"

"Aye sir, left on the workhouse step and spent a life there until I joins the Navy and comes up here."

"Are you glad you did, Master Chambers?"

Chambers thought for a moment before replying. "Aye sir, I've seen much that I couldn't have imagined otherwise, and it is a greater adventure than living on the streets of London, that's for sure. But what I was thinking was, will I ever get home? Not that I has parents or the like to worry about me, but I should like to see England once more."

"In time you shall return," I replied. "I am confident of it. And when you do, stay with the Navy lad. It is a place where even orphans like us might make a go of it if we put ourselves to it."

"Like you sir? An orphan?"

"Yes, but not of the workhouse, there I had the luck over you to be taken in by an uncle, whose company I miss now as if he were my true father. But still, stick with it, there's many a Captain of the Foretop or Quartermaster that began as a boy like you. Now get below and warm yourself, there will be much work for us all tomorrow."

Chambers turned and hurried below, leaving me to reflect on how little we knew of each other despite being in close proximity for nigh on three years. Such are the gulfs we impose between us. As I have told you, I consider myself not of humbugging society, and yet I cannot escape its strictures, even to the degree of friendship with a cabin boy. Perhaps all should partake of a few months Arctic travel to place the world in perspective.

Unaccountably, the brief exchange with Chambers has served to uplift my outlook. Perhaps it was the glimpse of what might have been my lot had I not been so fortunate as to be taken into such a gloriously generous family as I was and to be blessed with a sister with no match in the world.

What should also have contributed to a lift in my spirits was my victory this evening over Osmer. My first, and only, in three years of play. My messmates, who have been following my series of sorry defeats over the years with some disdain and not a little pity, were jubilant. Osmer took it well initially, but, upon my refusal of a re-match, stomped off to his supply lists which have been his life of late.

We are a sorry crew that sets out tomorrow for the unknown. Franklin, Gore, Des Voeux, Couch, Collins, Little, Thomas, Hornby, Helpman, and fifteen crewmen dead and scattered over this land, and those of us left in a sad state. We must still go forward, but it is hard from this bleak perspective not to dwell on times of happiness and laughter in a world that seems impossibly carefree. Could we ever have walked on the downs or by the Thames at Greenhithe in such a jaunty manner? Or were we just deluding ourselves—imagining that the world was a simple place and all was as it should be. It is difficult to see anything as it should be now. I have taken your picture from its frame and will carry it with me through the trials to come. Wish me luck dear dear sister. Good night and God bless us all.

April 25—Victory Point. The fourth day since we deserted the ships. We have now ferried the last of our supplies to shore and are ready to set out on our journey. Tomorrow we begin the long haul south.

Try to picture your brother if you can, wrapped in every piece of wool he possesses and looking nothing like the naval officer he is, hunched over this page on a makeshift table, struggling to keep the ink from freezing, and peering against the dim light of a flickering oil lamp. Around me the tent walls flap mournfully in the bitter wind, and small jets of fine snow push in at any corner not tightly sealed. Across from me sits Crozier, busy with the official log of our journey.

About an hour ago, the tent flap was thrown open and, amidst a minor blizzard, Irving almost fell in. He was clutching the soldered can deposited in Ross's cairn by poor Gore almost one full year ago which he had struggled through the wind to retrieve from a spot four miles away. It is strange to read words that I wrote so long ago, almost a lifetime it seems, and the irony of my final cheery 'All well' echoes very hollow now, especially sitting as it does over the signatures of two of my friends who are now dead.

Rather than deposit a further message, Crozier thought it best to simply add to the margins of Gore's note. I wrote while Crozier dictated and Irving supplied a few details. The message gives but the barest outline of our endeavour to this time, our location and that of Ross's pillar, and the sad news of the death of Franklin, the eight other officers and fifteen men, leaving but 105 souls to complete this undertaking. Most are fit enough although all suffer from some exhaustion and most shew the early signs of scurvy. Some twenty are too sick to be engaged in the pulling and five are so sick as to require transport in one of the boat sledges. I pray we will find good hunting close by.

I signed the note as did Crozier as Senior Officer, and he added a postscript of our intention to leave tomorrow for Back's Fish River. I had not thought to add it, and even argued that it would be misleading to any search party, suggesting as it does that we are seeking relief across the Barren lands. But Crozier dismissed that, saying that we will, in all probability, be back here before the summer season in any case. Like me, he is now strongly of the opinion that we will return to the ships in an attempt to force passage out when the ice breaks this summer. The thought of walking hundreds of miles with our sick and weakened men, even after they have been strengthened with fresh supplies, is daunting indeed and any hope of using the vessels for escape must be followed. Irving is now outside replacing the message in a cairn.

The weather is cold, with some blowing snow, but the going appears good along the beaches and we should make good progress. We are leaving a considerable supply dump here, with food, clothes, instruments, tools, cooking utensils and stoves piled around under canvas awnings and in tents. The clothes alone form a pile over four feet in height and the area looks little like a cache of supplies by Her Majesty's Navy. It is not in such a condition as to outlast the winter storms, but, if we are to return, it will be in the summer and the canvas will provide protection until then. We have also left four boats and a sledge. Whoever returns here will be glad of this as we have tried to leave all the necessities so that any returning party need only transport fresh food. Will we see this place again? I have a feeling that we shall, but who can say for certain what the future holds. I will write more whenever I can. Good night.

May 16—Camp Plenty Bay. Our third day here and the twenty-fifth since abandonment. Gore named this place so on account of the multitude of deer tracks he observed and the large numbers of fowl he managed to bring down hereabouts.

The journey down the coast was slow, slower than we had hoped, averaging but five miles a day for the hundred we covered. The weakness of the men was one factor which led to the necessity of making detours to find the easiest route. Another cause was the need to keep such a large group together so that the fastest man travels no quicker than the slowest. We lost three men on the route, including Carpenter John Weekes, and they lie hurriedly buried along the shore. We have also a much increased sick list. We have constructed a large tent on the shore from the canvas we use to cover the ships' decks in winter. It serves as a sick bay and Stanley and Peddie are kept busy there. At present we have thirty-three souls in need of care, but we hope with some rest that will soon be reduced. Osmer found the going tough. He had no hauling to do, being in a weakened condition, but he had to be forcibly removed from the pile of supplies at Victory Point, which he insisted needed to be further catalogued and listed. I hope a few days rest and some fresh food will have an effect, but I fear his obsession is turning to madness.

The land over which we travelled was bleak in the extreme, being covered by thin snow which is sometimes blown off the ridges to expose sharp grey limy rock which cuts the men's boots up badly. We were fortunate to be able to keep to the shore ice which was mostly smooth and still solid this early in the season. The weather has been cold and we have a number of cases of frostbite, but we have been lucky to avoid any storms. We found Gore's cairns without difficulty and, when we arrived at the foot of Des Voeux Peninsula, at Cook Bay (as it was named by Gore after the great Commander from whom his namesake succeeded in the Pacific), we headed overland. This was slower going as we had to skirt bare patches of ground, but we were encouraged by increasing signs of game. Hunting parties had been out for all of our journey but had bagged only a score or so of partridge and some hare. Now we began to see deer tracks in some numbers.

On the 13th, Crozier, who is a splendid shot, brought down a large buck, and we managed a meal of fresh meat for the sick. The next day the hunting parties shot four musk oxen and we established camp here. Plenty Bay is deep and some five miles wide at its mouth. It is, of course, still frozen, but faces south and presents views of the distant mainland coast. We are at the mouth of Simpson Strait. The ice in the strait is much disturbed, but appears to be generally thinner than that around the ships. Reid took one look at it and said: "That's only one year ice, mister Jems. She'll be gone by July arl right." It was good to hear a positive prognostication delivered in that familiar rough dialect and it gave us all encouragement.

The land hereabouts presents a much better perspective than that to the north. It is still flat and mostly snow covered, but the abundance of tracks and the game we have seen and obtained give one a sense of life not enjoyed on the other side of the peninsula. It has become obvious that we must remain here for a while and hope that the game remains plentiful. Yesterday our parties bagged two deer and today only one although they spotted a moderately-sized herd to the east.

Our slow progress to this point and the deteriorating health of the men make any of our distant objectives impossible at present. I can only hope that we can obtain enough fresh food for long enough to make a difference. The needs of so many are immense and place a severe load on the hunting parties who must work all day, often with only a few fowl to shew for their exertions.

An average deer supplies fifty to sixty pounds of meat, so it will require twenty per week to supply each man with two meals a day of fresh meat. Of course this will be supplemented by hares, which can supply up to seven pounds each, and birds (one to two pounds) which we expect to see in greater abundance as the spring progresses. I don't know how long we will be able to subsist here, but at present it is an adequate refuge. Now I must close and undertake the unpleasant task of thawing my sleeping bag by forcing my fully-clothed body into it bit-by-bit. Until you have done without one for a long period, you can have no concept of how close to the pinnacle of civilized man's achievement ranks the feather bed!

Listen to this from one who lately waxed so eloquent on our chosen position in the world and the perfectibility of the wonderful inventions that will take us to an earthly paradise. Now I dream of feather beds and envy Crozier his skin suit which does not absorb moisture like our woollen clothes and then freeze as hard as Henry VIII's suit of armour. If only we had the knowledge and skill to cure the skins from the deer we have slaughtered and then turn them into clothing, more of us would have a greater degree of comfort. Good night.

May 23—Snowy and cold but at least the hunting parties could go out and had some luck, bringing back a deer, seven hares, and a dozen birds. We had been forced inside by a blizzard since the 18th and unable to hunt. I hope we do not have too much more cold and wind for it makes living in these tents almost unbearable. The cold is bad enough, but worse are the cramped conditions when the men are forced to remain inside. Each has only enough space to lie down and quickly becomes cramped. Condensation on the insides of the tent is also a serious problem, creating a fine mist of ice and snow which falls and soon soaks through everything. Cooking remains the hardship it always is away from the ships. I hope today signals an improvement.

Our camp somewhat resembles a small tent town such as might be seen surrounded by camels in the desert. Of course, if we had camels we would eat them, but I cannot help but hold the image in my mind. The large tent for the sick measures almost forty feet long and twenty wide, although it is almost full presently. The fit men sleep in six smaller tents each accommodating ten, which is the best number for a sledge-hauling crew. The six officers from the *Terror* share a tent as do the seven from *Erebus*. Crozier and I have a tent to ourselves in which we keep the instruments and a small folding table on which I am writing this. There is also a cook tent where Wall and Diggle both sleep and prepare most of the food when the weather is moderate, and there are four store tents, each guarded by a marine. So you can imagine our fourteen tents spread along the curve of the shore of this ice-filled bay near the eastern point. The large sick bay is toward the middle of the row and the cook tent a little behind. In front sit the sledges and boats, surrounded by piles of unloaded gear. We are on a low ridge about 400 yards from the bay and behind us the land rises gradually to a higher ridge which is nearly swept clear of snow by the wind. The prospect would be pleasant enough in the summer and I hope it will not be too long in coming. I must now do battle with my sleeping arrangements. Good night.

May 25—Clear and sunny to give us all hope, and the hunting was successful. Le Vesconte's party came upon a herd of twenty deer and managed to bring down four. Crozier also managed one solitary beast and all brought back some birds and hare. This part of the island is so different from the north, where there was no sign of life from one year to the next. Here we seem, by comparison, almost surrounded by nature's bounty. Of course, it may be in part due to the increased clemency of the weather this year; temperatures are considerably higher than on the same day last spring and we have, thankfully, had very few blizzards. If this trend continues, I think we stand a much better chance of releasing the ships this season.

Living in such proximity, I am beginning to get to know Crozier better. He really is a most intelligent man, not given to any harebrained schemes and, although I cannot agree with him on some points, I have a profound respect for what he says. He has been given a difficult role, replacing such a popular leader as Sir John, and his different style has led to some misunderstandings, but I firmly believe that he will do the best possible to extricate us from this dilemma—perhaps even more than Franklin could have done on account of his greater experience of these regions in which we find ourselves.

It is a full moon today, and it has been visible as a pale ghost hovering above us through many of the hours of daylight.

Looking upon it this evening, I felt some of my confidence return and ventured, "Perhaps one day far in the future, although I can see no way to do it, man's ingenuity might lead him to invent a machine capable of the immense journey to our nearest neighbour in space. What think you?"

Crozier did not immediately reply so, assuming he could not visualize such a scientific advance, I continued.

"For example, just as we cannot envisage a flying machine capable of taking a man to the moon, Drake could not possibly have envisaged the puffing and wheezing engines which now power our trains and will soon, I am fully confident, power the navies and fleets of the world." This drew a response.

"I have no trouble, James," he said, "imagining that man might one day conquer the stars themselves. On the contrary, I am almost certain that we shall, and the ocean depths and the inhospitable poles as well. My concern is that, as we rush forward to some unimaginable mechanical utopia, we will lose sight of the fact that the greatest machine is but a mere tool of the man who operates it.

"Men are imperfect and any endeavour we undertake, whether it be curing consumption or creating flying machines, must inevitably be imperfect too. Only God is perfect and only He can create perfection if He chooses.

"This is of no great consequence," he continued, "as long as we are only reaching for goals we can comprehend, such as in the exploration of our physical world. The danger is that our successful machines give us false confidence and an overweening arrogance. We come to think that we can achieve anything we wish, but as we strive for achievements outside our ken, we will be bound to fail; as we have failed."

"You think we have failed?" Such a bald statement took me by surprise. "Certainly we have had many setbacks, but we have overcome them. We have completed the Northwest Passage, even if we do not sail our ships through Behring's Strait, and collected much of great worth on this land. How can you say that we have failed?"

"James, you assume that we shall all survive and that somehow we shall return home with all our scientific results intact. That is by no means certain. But assume that we shall. To you, we have met challenges which we have overcome fully or in part. We still progress forward to some worthwhile goal. But there is another, less sanguine view. And that is—we failed before we began. That even if every man survived and we sailed in triumph, loaded with scientific data, through Behring's Strait in 1845 or 46, it would still have been a failure. A less expensive failure to be sure than the one we presently face, but a failure none-the-less.

"It is a failure because we come here in arrogance thinking that we can dominate nature. We cannot. We are at its mercy and it can snuff us out as easily as we extinguish a candle. Any attempt to defeat nature, to overcome it, is doomed. Even if nature allows us a few moments of victory, ultimately we are doomed. I have come to suspect of late that Parry and Ross and the rest are man's allowance of success in this land and that we are the price that must be paid."

This is a strange idea and gave me pause for thought. It reminded me of Le Vesconte's thought that there are places we should not venture.

"We would do better I suspect," Crozier broke into my thoughts, "to stay at home and work on improving the nature of man. Maybe then we will be more worthy of tasks such as this.

"But I am running on to no purpose. Undeniably we are here and, doomed or not, I wish to get home as much as the next man and that must be our goal. Once we achieve that there will be plenty of time to sit in comfort and discuss philosophy."

I have thought much on what he said. Certainly the struggle we are engaged in has exposed our weaknesses more than we would wish; increasing drunkenness amongst the crew, lethargy in all, unexplained illnesses, madness—man is undoubtedly imperfect. I only hope a few weeks of fresh deer meat will push the imperfection back below the surface enough to allow us an escape. I pray Crozier is wrong. Good night dearest.

May 29—Two men died today. William Bell, Quartermaster on *Erebus*, had been in a stupor for several days and his death had been expected. The other was Robert Golding, a boy on *Terror*, and his death has hit us all hard. Two days ago, he seemed no worse than many others. Yesterday at breakfast, he suddenly jumped up shouting that Stanley was poisoning him with bad food, and rushed out the door of the sick tent. It took four marines to subdue him (although he was but fourteen years old and not large) and hold him till his fit passed. After that he was tied down and remained quiet except for mumbling about the officers trying to kill him and talking of visions of monsters.

It was distressing for the other men and I am sure many were relieved when he collapsed this afternoon after a further violent rant against his comrades. He died shortly after. Golding's strange death disturbs me not least because of his youth.

The sick have been fed as much as possible on fresh meat these past two weeks and more, and many are shewing marked improvement in the outward signs of scurvy. Even those with only minor symptoms are improving, my gums no longer bleed and my loose tooth has strengthened considerably. Yet our sick tent remains busy. The men there complain of a profound weakness, pains in the stomach, an inability to draw in enough air when exercising, and all look pale and drawn. In the worse cases, they are withdrawn and cannot be brought out of themselves, some even suffering convulsions and screaming out in the night.

Stanley and Peddie, and even Goodsir with his book learning, are at a loss to explain it. They had supposed that all the illnesses were a consequence of scurvy, but now that that seems to be under some control as long as we have fresh meat, they have no way of explaining the continued sickness. The sick are fed almost exclusively on a mixture of fresh meat and the canned produce, but it has little effect. It is a mysterious circumstance and I hope we can solve this riddle soon. Goodsir is certainly trying, but has had little success.

The hunting remains good, with the animals and birds seen increasing almost daily. It is warming and there are signs of activity amongst the ice in the strait. Soon we must consider our further options for this season.

June 1—Our visitors are back. Oonalee and his family, the old man Angatkut, and several other families, twenty three souls all told. They came across the ice with dogs and sleds and seemed much surprised to see us away from the ships. Oonalee explained that they were following the deer, or tooktoo as he calls them. His group appear to have settled themselves in to join us in the hunt, since they have set up their tents about half a mile farther on around the bay.

Several of the men have expressed concern about their presence, saying that they will take away the meat which we need so desperately. But Crozier welcomes them, suggesting that they are much more experienced hunters than us, despite their primitive weapons, and that they seem perfectly happy to share what they have with us or to exchange it for trinkets; in fact, they will increase the amount of meat we take. I have no concerns about their presence, since the deer are so plentiful that there is more than enough for all. I also look forward to learning more of these people's ways.

June 2—We were awakened this morning by the most extraordinary circumstance. The first thing I heard was a clatter, not unlike dozens of sticks being knocked together. It was accompanied by a low rumbling sound. I lay awake for a few minutes trying to work out what it could be. It was 4 a.m. and fully light, and I noticed that Crozier was gone. As I began to hear voices outside, I left the tent and was met by the most extraordinary sight I have ever seen; the entire landward horizon, as far as I could see in both directions, was one solid, moving mass of living flesh. The knocking was the sound of thousands of antlers banging together in that tightly packed mass and the rumble was the hooves. I could not begin to count the beasts, but if you can picture one of the mass Chartist demonstrations magnified a hundred times, you would still not come close to the numbers. The herd was moving along the higher ridge behind our camp, fortunately, for I could imagine the havoc they would cause had we been in their path. Around me men were running to grab their weapons, and I noticed farther off, the Esquimaux cautiously approaching the herd in small groups.

It soon became evident that this bounty was not as easy to take advantage of as we had first supposed. The animals were so closely packed that it was almost impossible to hunt them, or at least to retrieve a kill, and we lost several good carcasses because of this.

Crozier I had not seen for some time, until he appeared at my shoulder. He had been off observing the Esquimaux and now had a way of hunting this mass effectively. Apparently the thing to do is approach the herd softly and low to the ground ahead of where you want to hunt. If you can approach very close, aided sometimes by the lie of the ground, then when one or two figures rise up from the ground waving their arms or some pieces of material, several deer will scare and split-off from the herd to pass the obstruction on the far side. These beasts can then be hunted and retrieved with ease.

We tried this approach with some success, but it was not until we joined with Oonalee and his men that we really began to have success. The best method seemed to be for the Esquimaux men to perform the 'cutting-out' duties and to drive small groups of deer onto the guns of one of our parties. In this way we had a great slaughter, since the deer continued to pass by us for most of the day. By evening the land for some several miles along the coast was strewn with carcasses in various stages of butchering. The dressed meat is stored in pits where it freezes solid rapidly and is thus preserved until needed.

Great bounty and not just for us. This evening we can all hear the mournful sounds of wolves circling in the distance, no doubt attracted by all the blood and fresh meat. We have men with the most scattered kills working through the night and keeping the scavengers at bay.

June 5—The last few days spent in retrieving and dressing the most distant carcasses and in bringing down a few stragglers. We now have most of our kill in pits, the digging of which is the most arduous labour in the whole process. There are many wolves around following the herd and gorging on our leavings. We have taken a few and hope to make use of the skins. However, it would appear that the wolves have exacted some revenge. Diogenes, the large Newfoundland dog from the *Terror*, has gone missing. Both dogs have been most excited with all the activity of the last few days and have been well fed on scraps. Both ran off yesterday after a lone deer which wandered past the camp but bolted before anyone could get a telling shot in. We called after them, but to no avail. Last evening Neptune returned, much cut about and quite broken in wind, but of Diogenes there was no trace. The assumption is that both were set upon by wolves and that only Neptune escaped, perhaps because of his speed. In any case, we have little hope of ever laying eyes on Diogenes again. It is hard for some of the men—they tend to form very close attachments to these beasts in their loneliness and there is as much grief over its loss as there would be over one of their comrades.

William Mark, Jacko's owner, has begun raving. It is a similar pattern to the other men who have become mad, except that Mark aims his delusions at some imaginary officer of the law whom he thinks is set upon persecuting him to the grave. Osmer too is again unwell, not with such dramatic symptoms, more a return of the exhaustion which plagued him on our arrival here, but it worries me none-the-less.

June 6—Weather continues very mild, with some light rain and a wind from the east which is not usual. The hunting continues with some success although the abundance of the 2nd has not been repeated. We have not had as much contact with the Esquimaux as we had hoped, although several of the officers, including myself, have visited their encampment and they are often around here trying to scrounge or steal anything that takes their fancy. If caught out, they burst into uproarious laughter. In some ways they are completely childlike and it is difficult to remain upset at them, although some of the men treat them with disdain and grumble that they are taking meat which is rightfully ours. I suppose it is easy to forget that the Esquimaux are largely responsible for the store of meat we have collected to this date.

Examining the Esquimaux life is a fascinating pastime. They live in small skin tents, held down by circles of rocks. When a fire is burning in the centre of one, it makes the atmosphere very oppressive, but this does not appear to bother them unduly. All live in a cheerful, improvident style, eating extraordinary amounts when it is available and seeming to have no sense of putting aside against the hard times. They will, however, cache what is physically too much for them to eat in one sitting.

An Esquimaux feast is a disgusting affair for one brought up to civilised manners, the food being all thrown together into a large skin bag and boiled using the expedient of heating rocks on a fire and then adding them to the mixture. Everyone reaches over as they please and pulls out whatever steaming morsel catches their fancy and wolfs it down, fat, grizzle and all. Their faces and clothes soon become smeared with excess fat, a fact which probably accounts for the distinctive smell which their clothing exudes.

After a feast, they will be indolent for a day or two even if game presents itself, apparently trusting that more will be forthcoming when hunger again impels them to go in search of it. They own very little and all of that is of great utility. They prize anything of wood or iron which they can fashion into a tool to their liking, even collecting our discarded wood shavings to fuel their fires.

Since we have arrived here, we have killed some forty-five deer, which have yielded slightly over 3,000 pounds of fresh dressed meat allowing for spoilage. An additional 500 pounds of meat has been obtained from hares and a small quantity from birds, mostly partridge. Allowing one pound/man/day, this will only last us five or six weeks. Of course it will be supplemented within that time with more game, particularly fish, geese and ducks when the summer arrives, but all game will vanish once more with the onset of winter in October, and once the fresh food is gone, scurvy will very rapidly begin to stalk us once more. Thus we must look to our own resources within this short season when we can, to keep the scurvy at bay. To this end, Crozier has called a meeting of all officers from both vessels for tomorrow to discuss the possibilities open to us.

June 7—Weather still clear and warm. There is much activity in the ice out in the strait and to the west where we must go if we are to sail home. All take this to presage a good season for travel, and feel it will not be too long before open water is seen. Already gulls and a few geese have been observed.

William Mark died this morning. He has been very bad and his passing is a great relief to his companions, although several other men are beginning to exhibit the distant, hunted look which seems to proceed the dementia. Osmer too is not doing well, to my great concern.

And so to the meeting, and its momentous conclusion. All surviving senior officers were present. The sickness among the men was our first topic. Stanley commenced with a description of the symptoms and the statement, of which we all knew beforehand, that because the sick were not responding to the fresh meat, the ailment was therefore not related to the scurvy, which is now much improved.

"At first," Stanley stated, "before we abandoned the ships, I was inclined to blame the dampness, confined quarters and bad air for the sickness, but such cannot be the case here. I consider now that it is a miasma of the air in these parts which spreads the sickness, much as cholera is spread in our cities at home."

"Nonsense!" Goodsir spoke quietly, but with great authority. "Were it spread in the air, cases of the disease would be equally common amongst all classes of men. It is not. I have studied the incidence of the disease amongst us, as scientifically as is possible under the circumstances, and I have found some interesting things. The disease predominates amongst the sick . . ."

"Of course it does," Stanley interrupted irritably. "You will find more sick people in a hospital. You take this scientific approach too far Harry. Allow some room for common sense."

"However," Goodsir continued unperturbed, "those in the sick tent who definitely have the disease were not admitted for that reason. They were mostly scurvy cases who only showed symptoms of the disease after they were in Mister Stanley's care."

"Are you suggesting, Sir, that I made them sick?" Stanley was on his feet.

"No. No," said Goodsir in a conciliatory tone. "I say merely that it appears, and I admit that there are occasional cases which do not fit this pattern, that the majority of cases of this mystery disease are contracted, or at least exacerbated, by something in the sick tent."

"Do you have any idea what it might be?" Crozier asked before Stanley could gather himself for a rebuttal.

"Well, the honest answer is no. But I have some theories."

"Theories," scoffed Stanley.

"I suspect that the men are suffering from some form of poisoning. The dementia is a common effect of many poisons, as are the abdominal pain and spasms that many report."

"But what could be poisoning them?" Crozier asked.

"That I do not know."

"But you have some theories no doubt," Stanley added sarcastically. "I resent the implication that I am poisoning my patients."

"No one is poisoning your patients deliberately," Goodsir continued quietly. "Not all the sick receive the same medication, so that cannot be the source. However, many do report a strange metallic taste in their mouths. This began me thinking. What metal do all the sick come in contact with?"

Goodsir paused for dramatic effect. No one ventured an answer.

"The cans containing the preserved meat and vegetable," he said at length. "We feed the sick almost exclusively on the canned produce."

"But that is our best food," Crozier interjected.

"Yes," agreed Goodsir, "under normal circumstances, but in my judgement some or all of our canned food is contaminated, either with the tiny living organisms that some now believe carry disease, or foreign, poisonous matter."

"But we have all eaten canned food," I said, expressing the thought in everyone's mind.

"True," said Goodsir, "whatever it is, a certain quantity must be absorbed by the body before any ill effects become obvious. Only the sick, and the officers, eat significant amounts of canned food."

There was a moment's silence while we absorbed this information. Stanley broke it.

"This is nonsense. Tiny creatures in the cans killing the sick. Rubbish. It is a miasma."

"Collins, Hornby, Gore," I said quietly. "Even the monkey Jacko which was fed mostly on the canned carrots. They all died raving." It is a frightful thought that there is a poison lurking in our very food. Goodsir's arguments are persuasive, but Stanley was not about to give up.

"Why then, Mister Goodsir, can you not explain the survival of the rest of us. We have all partaken of the canned food just as those who died?"

"I do not know," Goodsir answered. "All I can postulate is that the poison, whatever it might be, varies in its effects from person to person. Some are more susceptible to its work just as some men are more or less able to withstand the affects of liquor."

"Postulates!" Stanley almost shouted the word. But Goodsir had us convinced.

"For the moment," Crozier said taking over the discussion, "while we have ample supplies of fresh meat, we will reduce the consumption of the canned food by the sick. We cannot afford to discard such a proportion of our supplies on the basis of unproven theory, but we shall only use it in large quantities when all other options have been exhausted.

"And, on the subject of options, we must move on to those for the summer. Mister Stanley, whatever the cause, how many do we have on the sick roll not fit for a long journey?"

Stanley flashed Goodsir an evil look, but answered calmly enough. "Twenty-five at last count. Some could travel short distances if they do no hauling, but a journey of any great length is out of the question for them."

"So, whatever we decide," Crozier said, "a party must be left here and retrieved at a later date. This places limits on our options. What do you think gentlemen?"

"I still favour Fury Beach," Le Vesconte put in. "It is the closest rescue, and with our canned food suspect, the supplies there become doubly important."

"You have a good point, Mister Le Vesconte," Crozier said. "I think escape along the coast or down Back's Fish River and over the Barren Lands is no longer feasible with so many sick. The only other possibility is a return to the ships."

"It is a much more open season than last year," I said, "and I feel it bodes well for a release. We also now require that one of the ships at least be brought here under sail in order to pick up the sick."

"I think much the same way," Crozier added. "I do not like the thought of splitting the command, but I see no alternative. Are we agreed then that the sick and enough men to care for them and hunt shall remain here; Le Vesconte shall lead a party to Fury Beach to make contact with a whaling vessel; and the remainder shall return to the ships in the hopes of release."

There was a general silent nodding of agreement.

"I should like to request that I be assigned the task of remaining here with the sick," Stanley put in.

"Thank you Mister Stanley," said Crozier. "I will note that."

There was more talk of details, but the decision is made; the command will be split. Le Vesconte, Blanky, Sargent, Peddie, and about twenty fit men will take one boat sled and head west to Prince Regent Inlet, Fury Beach and the whalers. They will take some food, but will have to rely heavily on game killed along the way. Thus it is imperative that they leave as soon as possible while there is still much game around and while the ice is still firm along the coast. They anticipate eventually abandoning the sled when the ice opens and taking to the boat.

Crozier, myself, Fairholme, Irving, Goodsir, Macbean, Reid and about thirty men will take two boat sleds back to the ships. We will then attempt to sail the *Erebus* or the *Terror* down the coast to pick up those left at Plenty Bay.

Stanley, Hodgson, and Macdonald will remain here with the sick and enough fit men to provide game until we arrive. At that point we will take the route which offers us the best chance of success, either along the coast to Point Turnagain, back north to Lady Jane Sound or through Simpson Strait in Le Vesconte's footsteps. I don't think anyone likes the idea of splitting the command in this way but, if we are honest, our situation, despite the abundance of fresh meat around us now, will become desperate come winter. In the back of everyone's mind, I am sure, is the thought that this plan increases the chances of at least one party's survival.

It is a bleak thought, made bleaker by seeing it in bold ink on paper, but it is the truth and we must live with it. I am certain that both are good plans and that we will all find succour this year, for by now old John Ross must be as good as his word and out searching for his friend. So we have much to do if we are to succeed, but you can be certain that we will do all that is in the power of mortal men to return to our loved ones as soon as possible. Good night dearest, dearest sister.

June 9—Such sad news. Osmer succumbed this morning. He had been weakening for some time and knew what the end would be. He did not fall to the wild ravings of some of the others, but in the last hours could be heard mumbling incoherently of supplies and victualling schedules. I found it particularly hard to watch the mind that I had locked horns with so often and so unsuccessfully over the chess board reduced to such drooling impotence. What madness is it that stalks us all and, if Goodsir is correct, betrays us in the very food we eat?

June 10—Buried Osmer today on the rise behind the camp with the other three men who have perished here. It seems we are doomed to leave sad collections of graves wherever we stop.

Preparations well under way for our journeys. There is little excitement to it, but all set-to with a will, knowing that we must now save ourselves and also that we must soon be saying farewell to some dear comrades without knowing when we shall be together again.

Le Vesconte will take one boat sled and two hauling crews. This places pressure on their food supplies, but replacement teams of haulers are essential if any distance is to be made with the weakened men, and game should be easy to come by for much of the journey.

We will take two boat sleds back to the ships with thirty men to haul and one will be left here. We have twenty-eight sick at present, some of whom will be able to hunt, or at least take part in the care of the others. Six fit men have volunteered to remain as a hunting party. Most of these have relatives or close friends among the sick.

Hodgson will be in command here and I think his is perhaps the most difficult role. He would certainly much rather be with Le Vesconte instead of condemned to inactivity with the sick, but a senior officer must remain with the surgeons. Le Vesconte will be ready to leave in a couple of days and us a few days after that, The weather has turned wet, but still warm. Still snow on the ground in most places, but it will not be here for long. The ice is still good for travelling along the coast, but the water lying on the surface makes the going uncomfortable.

Ducks of all kinds and geese are now here in some profusion and supply many of our food needs. There are still deer around and the parties have reasonable luck, but there is nothing like the profusion of earlier in the month. All in all, considering our predicament, we are eating quite well for the moment. I would, however, exchange ten years of my life to sit down at a proper table with all the plate and glass, surrounded by good company, in front of a roaring hearth, to be served a banquet by livened butlers. I have been dreaming of just such an event, and it is a torture to awake every morning to warm tea, tasteless biscuits, and half-cooked deer. I will count upon you to pamper me most frightfully on my return. Good night.

June 11—One year since the death of our leader and Crozier read a fine divine service of commemoration. There is an almost palpable tenseness to the camp now as Le Vesconte is ready to set off tomorrow morning. We had a last meal together of some splendid roast duck and afterwards he and I walked along the shore. He is in good spirits and believes strongly that he is taking the correct course. In fact, I think he feels that, even if the ships are released this summer, we will end up having to sail along Simpson Strait and are only losing valuable time by returning to them. He promised to leave markers on the shore to shew us his way should we follow.

As we walked, I looked at him and wondered at the changes the past few years have wrought in him. He is still tall and imposing but his nose, never small as you recall, now absolutely dominates his rather sunken cheeks and eyes. His full mouth has thinned and there is some blackening as the result of the scurvy, which stands out against his pale skin. If we were on a London street, he would be remarked upon as a sick man, yet he is one of the fittest amongst us.

My own looks are somewhat changed, having lost the chubbiness of cheek which you used to joke about. My forehead continues to increase in length, but the greatest change is that I now support a growth of reddish beard. I do not think it suits me, but many have this now, the difficulties of keeping clean-shaven in the cold being such as they are. In fact, when I think back to my complaints about our appearance earlier, they seem petty and we were dandies then compared to now.

I remarked on this to Le Vesconte and he laughed.

"Certainly, James," he said. "There will not be many society doors open to you looking the way you do."

"On the contrary," I returned, "all doors will be open to 'The Heroes of the Northwest Passage,' regardless of how we look. Perhaps we will even begin a trend toward an unwashed, unshaven appearance."

At that he fell silent and I was afraid he was about to launch into his theory of there being parts of the world we would do well not to visit, but he merely shrugged as if casting off a weight and smiled.

"You will need to hurry to catch me, if you do not wish to return and find that all the glory given to our exploits has not already been apportioned where it is most deserved."

We both laughed and then, firmly shaking hands and wishing each the very best of luck in the coming endeavours, we parted for a few hours rest. And that is what I must try to do now. Good night.

June 12—Le Vesconte and his crew are gone. I followed for a little distance and the last I saw of them was a group of black dots making good time along the ice.

Our preparations are complete and we leave tomorrow for the ships, so I will not be able to keep much of a journal until we are securely aboard. I shall be sorry to say good-bye to Hodgson and Stanley. Theirs is not an enviable task and they are brave men.

Most of the sick seem happy to stay, confident that we will be back for them in a short while, and who can blame them when the alternative is the horror of pulling a loaded sled over swampy ground and waterlogged ice. Our loads are mostly clothing and frozen meat, for we shall rely upon the other supplies we left at Victory Point. Wish us luck my dear.

Summer, 1848

July 14, 1848—On board *Erebus*—back in my cabin beneath your picture. It has suffered somewhat on the journey, but now rests where it should, back in its frame. We have had a frightful ordeal to achieve this goal. Crossing Des Voeux Peninsula was a nightmare of hauling through wet ground, zig-zagging to take advantage of the snow cover as much as possible. We abandoned one of the boat sledges on the shores of Cook Bay, and in it Macbean and Engineer Gregory, both too sick to continue. Two others returned to the Plenty Bay camp to request assistance for these comrades.

The rest of us struggled northward at a painfully slow pace, continually being forced from the shore ice by open water and onto the beach which was often bare and hard on both the sled and the men's feet. In fact, the water was so open that we could not cross the long inlet south of Victory Point. Our supplies were almost in sight and we had to detour twenty miles which took an extra three days.

The supplies at Victory Point were in good condition, and we have been busy transferring those we need back to the ships by sled and boat. That task is almost complete, and not a moment too soon by the looks of the ice around us. Reid is back in his nest and reports much activity and some occasional glimpses of open water, but all too far off to be of use.

We have re-manned the *Erebus* since she is the sounder vessel, the *Terror* having been damaged in her grounding to the east, and hope soon to be on our way to collect our comrades at Plenty Bay. The difficulties we met with on our travels make me worry for Le Vesconte and his party. They cannot be making good time under these conditions and I can only hope that they encounter open water soon and have the opportunity to take to their boat.

Strangely, I feel as hopeful returning to the ship as I did leaving it, a fact I put down to the familiarity of surroundings. Tonight I imagined that, just as I could see your image behind the glass above my desk, that the reverse was also possible and that you were watching me; perhaps in a dream. I fear, looking as I do, that it might be a nightmare. None-the-less, I felt it most strongly and was thrilled at the possibility. This is your cabin as much as mine and I think you are happy to have returned.

Elizabeth, how I pray for a fair wind to break this damned ice and push me home to you.

July 15—Tragedy today. The wind we all wished for did indeed rise during the night and began to do as we wished and break open the ice. Unfortunately, it also made the journey across the stretches of open water between us and the shore hazardous.

One of the boats was nipped and Irving and five men cast onto the ice. They would not have been in much danger had they remained on the floe and awaited rescue, but Irving decided to try to lead them back to the shore over uncertain, moving ice. They were making fair progress until a floe they were transferring to tipped and cast Irving and Bryant, the Sergeant of Marines, into the icy water. As the story was told, Irving could have climbed out with ease, but remained immersed in order to find and rescue Bryant who had slipped beneath the ice. This he did, but the effort was so great and the cold so intense that Irving himself had no strength left and sank from view. We recovered his body soon enough, but too late to revive him. We buried him with a few personal effects beneath some stone slabs at Victory Point. His loss is sadly felt by all, especially his enthusiasm and cheerful demeanour despite the fact that he had little to be cheerful about of late. How many fine men and friends are we destined to leave behind in this place?

July 17—A lead. This morning the floe which has been home to both our ships for so long split apart with an almost deafening roar, and a lead snaked past us no more than 200 yards away. It is not wide, and heads more to the westward than I should like, but we will use it if we can and have been busy all day cutting our way through to it. We are in it now and hauling for all we are worth. It is slow work in our weakened state, but the steam engine has failed and without Gregory our best efforts to repair it are in vain. The entire ice mass appears to be on the move and despite the *Terror* still being held fast, we do not seem to be moving away from her as fast as we should.

July 18—Still in the lead and making progress, but it is painfully slow. Our reduced number, even for one vessel, means extra work for all at a time we are least able to undertake it. We are being led away from the shore and farther out into the ice stream. We can do no more than go with the lead and hope that we will be able to turn back around Des Voeux Peninsula in time.

July 20—Rain and mist for the last two days, but our lead remains open and we continue to make slow progress. The lead is so narrow that we must often try to blast the sides to widen it so we can pass, and even so, the ice often scrapes our sides with a sickening grinding sound. The work is so exhausting that men will fall to the ice and have to be carried aboard. Even for those of us who do no physical work, it is all we can do to complete our logs and crawl into our bunks for a few minutes rest, there being so few of us that we cannot afford to sleep a full watch.

Crozier is very quiet, spending much time watching the horizon and encouraging the men to greater effort. I think the responsibility of the men left at Plenty Bay weighs heavily upon him, although they should be well and the game should still be plentiful; it is Le Vesconte that I fear for.

July 21—Beset again. Around noon our lead had narrowed so much that it gave us no more than an indication of which way we should go. The weather cleared this afternoon and we could see the *Terror* still held fast, and now some fifteen miles behind us and much closer to the shore. The drift is more due south than our lead has been taking us. King William Island now lies close to thirty miles due east. On this course we shall clear Des Voeux Peninsula by a good twenty miles and I only hope we can then cut back into the entrance to Simpson Strait.

July 25—Still beset and drifting to the southwest. The ice remains noisily active and we must simply wait for another lead. The fresh meat we brought from Plenty Bay is now rationed in an attempt to hold off a return of the scurvy.

July 26—A lead within 200 feet of us today, but such a cruel fate; it leads north. It approached rapidly and appears extensive and quite wide. All watch it and wonder: *Does this connect with the open water through which we sailed with so much hope two years ago? Is this the way home?*

It appears that some diabolical power is offering us a chance to escape, but at the cost of abandoning our comrades in Plenty Bay; we have to turn our backs on it and continue to hope for open water to the south.

July 27—I am thirty-five today and a toast at dinner, but not much to celebrate. We are still held firm but the open water to the north still beckons with a hideous seduction. It is too cruel to tempt us so.

Bryant died today. Irving's brave sacrifice was for naught. Is that to be the lot of us all? We buried Bryant in the ice.

July 30—In open water again at last, although our progress is uncertain and slow. There is no general break-up of the ice mass, just occasional leads which offer little hope other than for progress of a mile or two. The northern lead closed today, so at least we no longer have that devilish temptation to contend with.

August 15—We have moved but a dozen miles since my last note to you, and that mostly by drift rather than our own efforts. The weather has been terrible, with day after day of cold driving rain and wind. These should be ideal conditions for breaking the ice since rain and wind are the ice's two greatest enemies, and the surface around us is indeed now covered with pools of water, some three or four feet deep. The problem is the wind, which is from almost due west, and is driving thick masses of old ice down upon us. The pressure is not enough to cause any danger to the hull, but it does hold us firm. We can only wait and hope.

August 17—Still drifting. There is land ahead of us, probably islands off the end of Des Voeux Peninsula. The water is shallowing and I fear we are approaching shoals like those which caused us so much discomfort in the channel to the east of King William Land. We can see the shores of Victoria Land to the west and continue to plot new points.

August 21—Spirits are very low. If the wind does not favour us soon, we will not escape from this cursed ice for another season. That will be serious enough for us, but we have still an ample supply of food, and some fresh meat and lemon juice, to see the thirty-one of us until the spring, but what of Stanley and the sick? Soon the game will be gone and their stock of supplies cannot possibly last for a full winter. It is their lot which will weigh heavily upon us if we are not able to aid them before we are irrevocably beset. From where we lie now, it is almost sixty miles to the Plenty Bay camp, and fifteen of that is across Des Voeux Peninsula where we cannot possibly draw a sled before a good carpet of snow is on the ground. All we can do is wait and pray.

Crozier is taking it hard. Although I have pointed out that we all agreed with the decision to split our company, and that we had no reasonable alternatives, he is in command and the responsibility for even the detached parties is his alone. It is a heavy load under such circumstances.

August 28—Sunshine at last and a chance to take some readings. We are some twenty-five miles WNW of the northernmost tip of Des Voeux Peninsula, but we might as well be on the moon. The ice is most severely deformed, being thrust up into all kinds of grotesque pinnacles and ridges which would make sled hauling all but impossible for anything other than a crew in the peak of health, which we are most decidedly not.

There is no sign of the *Terror*, but, if she has not sunk, she must be somewhere to the east of us, perhaps aground in Cook Bay. There is a gleam of open water to our north, but too far to take advantage of even if we were not committed to going south. Crozier spent much of the day in the crow's nest searching for a favourable lead.

August 29—Drifting with the ice.

August 30—Drifting.

August 31—A wide lead close by. We are hauling.

September 1—Still hauling to the lead. I hate to see the men suffer so, but they are determined.

September 2—Reached within fifty feet of the lead before the wind changed and the ice came together. More work for naught.

September 5—A group of seals came up through a hole in the ice no more than a mile from the ship. A hunting party managed to get within musket shot of them and dispatched seven before they could escape back into the water. We have butchered them and stored the blubber and meat in caches as we saw the Esquimaux do. There are several seals about and we will make a concerted effort to hunt as many as we can. We may yet be thankful for some fresh food in the months to come, however disgusting it may be.

Winter, 1848/49

September 15, 1848—We are solidly beset again. We will go nowhere this season, and for how many of us will it be our last? The hard fact of besetment is a blow difficult to bear. I have lost so many good friends already. Who will I lose in the months to come? What has happened at Plenty Bay? The sick have been deserted for far too long. And what of Le Vesconte and the others? Are they at Fury Beach or has yet more evil befallen them? God help us all.

September 16—My mood is somewhat better than yesterday. Our priority now must be to render aid to the men at Plenty Bay. Time is of the essence, and Crozier is busy preparing to lead a relief party. The temptation is to rush there, but we must be adequately prepared to aid them to the maximum, and the journey will have to be undertaken at a time when the weather can be a dangerous proposition.

Our own situation is that we are now in stationary ice, having drifted some five miles in the last weeks. In total we have come but sixty miles from our last wintering site off Victory Point and now lie ten miles north of a low-lying island of some size which we have named Franklin Island. Des Voeux peninsula is twenty-five or so miles to the ESE and the closest point of Victoria Land is approximately the same distance to the WNW.

September 18—Crozier is planning to leave for Plenty Bay tomorrow and has been busy loading a sled and selecting the fittest men. It is common practice for two officers to lead such an expedition, but that is a luxury we cannot afford in our depleted state. Crozier will take the Boatswain, Thomas Terry, with him in lieu of another officer. Terry seems a solid sort and we have discussed his promotion to Mate before.

This evening we discussed plans.

"There are thirty-seven men at Plenty Bay," Crozier began.

"Forty-one," I interrupted, "counting the two men who returned and Macbean and Gregory from the boat."

"True enough, James, but I think it unlikely that all will have survived. We do not know how the illness has progressed. If Goodsir was right, they may be in a serious predicament. The fresh meat would not have lasted long and I suspect the hunting will have been poor for some time now. They may have been forced to fall back on the canned food that neither ourselves or Le Vesconte could haul.

"Regardless, let us assume the best. I will use the fittest to haul what sleds we need to carry the sick back over Des Voeux Peninsula. If, as we suspect, the *Terror* has drifted and is now beached or trapped in the ice in Cook Bay, I will establish a camp there from which we can ferry the supplies and men back here."

"Hard winter will not be long in setting in," I added.

"That is why we must hurry. Our luck has been damnable at every turn, let us hope for a break in it now. But if not, and if something befalls me, you will take command."

I began to protest, but Crozier held up his hand.

"James, we all hold on to life by but a thin thread that this land can all too easily sever. If I do not return, do not risk lives in a search. There are precious few of us left, and you will need everyone for an escape next summer. Your responsibility must be to save as many as you can."

We lapsed into silence, sipping the last bottle of port thoughtfully. I know Crozier feels responsible for the situation at Plenty Bay and if things have not gone well there he will take it hard. He has no reason to feel guilty for what might have befallen them, we all had no choice in our decisions last spring, but the responsibilities of command are heavy.

"If it comes to the worst next year, James, try to make contact with the Esquimaux. I know many scoffed at my ideas and my skin suit was cause for some merriment, but it has served me well. Did you also hear the rumour of my rejected proposal to Miss Cracroft? I know it was being spoken of."

"Yes," I replied, startled at the sudden change of topic.

"Well, it is true. I proposed twice, once in Van Diemen's Land and once in London before we sailed. I am not normally one to pursue a lost cause, but I truly believed that she refused the first time out of hopes for James Ross and that, with him married, she might consider me as second best. It was not to be. Not because she did not feel kindly toward me, I think she looked upon me quite favourably, but because of my calling. She said she could not bring herself to marry someone who would be away for years at a time. The worry would be too much to bear.

"I offered to resign from the expedition, I was that smitten, but she said no. She would always feel that she had forced me into it and that I might resent her every time I saw a ship sail past.

"I asked if she would reconsider after this voyage if I planned to retire and settle down at that time, and she said she would.

"So you see, James, why I did not share your enthusiasm at the outset. To me this expedition has been but an obstacle to be overcome as rapidly as possible to enable me to return."

"And you will yet return," I interjected, "as I shall."

"Perhaps. Perhaps. In any case, I have performed my duties to the best of my ability and have honestly given my opinion on what I believed to be the best course. I hope you do not think of me any the less for my lack of enthusiasm."

"Of course not, and I have learned much of the Esquimaux ways."

"And it may yet be of use to you," he added, smiling. "But tell me apart from my philosophical ramblings on predetermined doom, why do you think we have failed?"

"Well," I said after some thought. "Certainly our machines have let us down —our steam engines have not performed as well as hoped and, if Goodsir is correct, our preserved food has betrayed us. Yet, such inventions are important. After all, the brick was an essential precursor to civilization. But perhaps progress is too seductive. I should not like to again put myself in a situation where I needed an invention to survive and could not do so without it. I would first attempt to live without it then add it to my armoury. That way its failure can be no more than an inconvenience. Is that what you were attempting with the skin suit?"

Crozier nodded. "But it has not saved me."

"No, but perhaps had we all done that we might not be sitting here groaning now. As to why we have failed, there are many reasons; too deep a draught on the ships; lack of expertise in Esquimaux ways of travel; poor ice conditions; maybe even poisoned food. But overall it is bad luck pure and simple. Arrogance may have brought us here and we may have stumbled on unawares into situations we could not know, but that is how we must advance and if we do not advance then what is the point of living. We will not be the last up here."

"No indeed. Others will come if only to discover our fate. I wonder what they shall think? Will they look on us as fools or heroes? Unfortunately, I suspect the former, bad luck does not make a good story.

"But we are not dead yet James. We have a good bottle of port to finish and work to do. You must wish me luck."

"I do Francis. I wish us all luck."

September 19—Crozier left this morning on his mercy mission. I was sorry to see him go. We have become closer than I believed possible at the beginning of this journey. I have thought much on what he said, not least on his relationship with Sophia Cracroft. So we both have someone to return to.

September 22—Fairholme is prepared to set out to examine Franklin Island with a satellite sled. He will leave tomorrow.

I am overcome with loneliness these days. How I miss your companionship. I even found myself envying Couch the other day. Can I begrudge him the comfort he took from his relationship with Sargent? At least he had his loved one with him.

September 23—Fairholme left with a satellite sledge and three men to examine Franklin Island. I expect him to be away but a few days. We must continue with our work even in these dire circumstances. It is what we are suffering for and is the reason for all this.

September 30—Fairholme back. He reached the island within a day and spent two days examining the coast. It is low lying, much like King William Island and unimpressive. It is but a few miles long and separated to the southwest from another island—Jane Franklin Island—by a narrow strait. Fairholme crossed over and states that this body of land is considerably larger, at least ten or twelve miles long from what he could see, although it does not rise more than a few tens of feet above the sea level.

From soundings he took through the ice, Fairholme maintains that to pass the islands and continue south should the ice release us next year, we must tack to the west and not attempt the shoally water between Franklin and King William. I hope this is information we can use. So we continue, even in our difficulties, to add new information to the Chart. I shall even set up a magnetic station on Franklin Island and continue our observations as we were instructed to do.

October 3—We continue to prepare the ship for winter. The yards are down and our canvas roof all but in place. It is not overly cold as yet, so we are leaving it open at the end for fresh air. There being so few of us, we have plenty of space, but every square foot reminds us of some missing shipmate. Our coal supplies are getting low, but with economy, we should have plenty to last since we removed most from the *Terror* in July.

We continue to hunt seals whenever the opportunity presents itself and now have a considerable stock of meat. Our fresh deer meat is severely rationed to last as long as possible and we have an ample stock of salt meat and other commodities. Our canned supplies are low on the ship, having left the bulk of them with the men at Plenty Bay. If Crozier returns with many men from that place the strain on our resources will be increased, but we shall manage.

I have arranged a victualling schedule for the men until the end of the year. It consists of half a pound of bread daily, and the same of meat, alternating days with frozen fresh and salt. Flour is available every third day and vegetables, mostly potatoes, carrots, oatmeal, and rice, every second. Daily I have allowed one half ounce of tea, three-quarters of chocolate, and one of sugar. Pickles will be distributed six ounces per week, and rum two thirds of a gill every day. Lemon juice we have in relative abundance, but I worry about its efficacy given the scurvy outbreak last winter. In any case, I am issuing two ounces daily.

It will be a tedious regime, and we will all miss the variety of the canned soups and vegetables, but I believe it is ample to sustain life if the scurvy can be held at bay. By year end, the fresh meat will be finished and we must resort to the preserved seal meat, a prospect which does not delight anyone. Scurvy is not rampant amongst us, probably thanks to the fresh meat in our diet, and the mysterious illness, poisoning if it is so, is no worse. We have had no new cases of raving since we arrived back at the ship. If conditions do not worsen, we shall manage I think. Of course, I do not yet know how many souls Crozier will return with. Next spring will be our fifth since leaving Greenhithe. Surely relief must be close by! Good night dearest.

October 10, 4 a.m.—Horrible dream. I hesitate to tell you of it, but I promised not to keep anything from you and I feel the need to write it down.

I was standing on the quarter deck of the old *Cornwallis*. We were in the Arctic waters but free of the ice and anchored. Crozier was with me, but I was in command. There was a ship approaching rapidly from our port side. At first I was delighted since we had been waiting for a ship to rescue us and this was undoubtedly it, but, as it neared, I began to have a terrible presentiment of doom and ordered the anchor raised. The men struggled, but the anchor was firm and could not be budged. I ordered the chain severed, but it likewise would not surrender to our efforts. All I could do was watch, like the Ancient Mariner, as the ship drew ever closer.

At length I could make out figures on deck and I was amazed to see that they were women and children. I looked closer and was delighted to see yourself amongst them. You were shouting something I couldn't make out and beckoning for me to join you. The other figures were also waving and encouraging the rest of our crew to come over. Crozier turned to me and said, quite clearly, "Look, it is Sophia."

I felt impossibly happy, at last we would be united again and, in this new vessel, sail homeward. The ship was almost alongside now and I could see you perfectly, clearly. You were wearing the blue dress you wore at the New Year's Ball before we sailed. All the crew were straining over the rail and shouting and waving to their loved ones.

All of a sudden, I noticed a hatch open behind you. Some figures were coming out. You seemed unaware of them and continued waving joyfully, but as we watched, we fell silent. Leading the figures from below was Le Vesconte and he was followed by Irving, Gore and Osmer, indeed, all our dead comrades were issuing forth onto the deck where they stood interspersed between the ladies and children and began to wave, with slow solemn gestures, also beckoning us to come over and join them.

I awoke sweating, aware that someone had cried out and that it had been me. As you know, I am not one for the supernatural or the understanding of dreams and such like, but I cannot avoid being affected by this one and will sleep no more this night. I hope it is merely a meaningless phantom of my tired mind and that I will be able to shake it off presently. We have suffered many hardships, both physical and spiritual on this voyage, but the worst has been the separation from loved ones. If there is one thing which keeps, and will keep, me struggling against whatever odds the fates may throw at me, it is my desire to look upon you again dear sister. If I am to survive, although you never left your cosy fireside, you may take full credit for it for I shall take my last step with a vision of you firmly before me. I will up on deck now and see what is to be done.

October 15—Almost a month since Crozier left. He should be back by now I am beginning to fear the worst. The weather at least has been good for travelling with little snow or wind, although it is turning steadily colder by the day and the light is waning rapidly.

Boredom is not a factor as yet since there are so few of us that we are kept busy running the ship and preparing her for winter. We will have no plays or entertainments this year. I miss my chess games with Osmer and am trying to make up for it with backgammon against Fairholme on the beautiful board presented to us by Lady Franklin. Fairholme, however, is even more my master at this pastime than Osmer was at the other and there is little pleasure to be had.

Reid has become uncharacteristically sullen and we find it difficult to encourage him into one of his rustic philosophies. The other day we were calculating the distance to the American mainland to the south where Simpson and Dease found open water for their travels. I stated that it was in the order of ninety miles which we all thought tantalisingly close.

Reid broke his silence of several days to say, "It could as likely be in Inverness for arl the good it'll do us. This ice's got us hard arl right and there'll be no getting out o' it."

With that extraordinary comment, he stumped off to his cabin. Goodsir attempted to lighten our ensuing silence by saying that that is what comes of living in such a bleak land as Scotland, but no one felt like laughing. I suspect we all think there is much to what Reid said.

Goodsir continues to be the life of our small gatherings and continues to regale us with tales of the weird creatures that inhabit these realms. He even persuaded Fairholme to bring back some lichens from the rocks of Franklin Island and he continues his experiments with soups. I am more inclined to encourage him in our present circumstances than I was last winter.

October 21—Terry is back with the news I have been beginning to dread. Crozier's worst fears have been realised. He is dead and Plenty Bay is but a place of horrors.

The going was hard over the sea ice and it took them many days to reach Des Voeux Peninsula. From there they spotted the *Terror*, hard up against the coast of Cook Bay. They discussed heading straight for her, but Crozier ordered them to continue along the coast to the point where they could cut overland for Plenty Bay.

The first sign of disaster they encountered was the boat sled we had left. The bodies of Macbean and Gregory were still in it, waiting for a rescue that never came. A few miles farther on they came upon a second boat, obviously the one from Plenty Bay. It was surrounded by bodies. They had obviously been attempting a retreat to the ships and had succumbed to exhaustion.

There were twelve bodies around the boat including Macdonald and, most pitiably, the cabin boy, George Chambers. He had elected to stay at Plenty Bay with his friend. What an end for one so young. Of Hodgson and the others there was no sign.

Terry confessed that they all wept at the sight of their comrades, none more so than Crozier. They were deciding on their next move when one of the men shouted that he saw smoke coming from the *Terror*. Making good time over the flatter ice of the bay, they soon saw a group of figures issuing from the ship and approaching them. There were five men and they were staggering and obviously in dire straits. They were led by Thomas Farr, Captain of the Maintop on *Terror*, and threw themselves with abandon on Crozier and his companions with profuse thanks for their rescue. They were the last survivors of a party of nine men who had struggled to the *Terror* from the abandoned boat on shore. Their companions, including Hodgson, were laid to rest in bunks on board the vessel.

Crozier established camp aboard his poor ship. She was holed by the ice and sat with a list of almost ten degrees which made walking on the decks troublesome, but she was aground and a secure refuge. Farr said they had been on board for several weeks, and that all left at Plenty Bay must now be dead. Only those with no strength left had remained. Stanley was fit but had refused to leave his charges.

I can imagine how Crozier must have felt; here was the last remnant of the party he had promised to rescue, a pitiful group with a sorry tale to tell. His decision now was hard, to make back for *Erebus* with the men he had found or press on to see if any were left alive at Plenty Bay. He never really had a choice. He could not return without finding if any yet needed his aid. Leaving the weakest he set out the next day for Plenty Bay.

The wait on the *Terror* lasted full two weeks and must have been a horror. Two men died raving before Crozier returned. He was strangely reticent on what he had found, but brought no survivors with him. Almost at once he retired to his cabin.

The following morning, Terry found him in his bunk. I think his heart had simply given out at the discovery of a disaster for which I know he felt totally responsible. There was a note addressed to me by his side.

Terry lingered on the *Terror* for five further days, in which time he buried Crozier and the two most recent victims on the shore, but left the other bodies frozen in their bunks on board ship. It took the party eight days to return and they were very fortunate not to encounter severe weather in that period or they would surely have been all lost and perished. They arrived back yesterday eve in a sorry state and are being cared for now by Goodsir.

And the worst is not yet told. It will be hard, but I will copy out Crozier's note in its entirety.

My Dear James,

Plenty Bay. What a horrible irony there is to that name. As we suspected, all there are dead. Most are in the sick tent, lined along both sides and frozen in their last agony. Stanley lies in the middle as if stricken in the act of tending to his patients.

Outside a few bodies lie, carefully placed in a row, for burial as we first thought. However, when we cleared the snow off the first man, we soon discovered a much darker purpose. The food had run out and some of the men, I am convinced not Stanley, had resorted to the most degrading and ghastly ultimate act. The contents of a nearby copper kettle I will not attempt to describe, suffice it to say the image will not leave me in the short time I have to live. That men, and men whom I knew and worked beside, could sink to such extremes is terrible enough, but that they succumbed so quickly and so near to us is worse.

We found no documents and were unable to bury the dead, they being frozen solidly to the ground, so we collapsed the tent over them and held it down with a few stones. It is tragic to leave our friends unburied like that, but we had no choice and had to reserve our meagre strength for the return. I beg you, scratch the name Plenty Bay from the Chart and add Stanley Bay in its place in honour of a man who, I am certain, maintained his nobility of character in the midst of such debased morality.

So, this is what we have come to, James. For all our civilisation and all our fine inventions and all our literature and poetry, we are but base animals beneath; and not far beneath at that.

I do not think I shall see you again, and of that I am sorry, but I shall not regret leaving this nightmare. I have a slight fever, but I have lost the spirit to go on. Even the vision of Sophia cannot motivate me more. If you survive, please visit her and tell her how I feel for her.

Good Luck James and God bless you.

Francis Rawdon Moira Crozier.

I cannot write more tonight, there are too many ghosts around me.

October 29—I have not told the others of the contents of Crozier's note. I suspect Farr knows more of the situation at Stanley Bay than he is willing to admit, but I understand his reticence. Those who travelled there with Crozier also know, but they too will keep silent. Why this silence? What can it possibly benefit anyone now? Perhaps it is but a last vestige of civilisation clinging to our ragged souls. Perhaps, the places we should not go are not all geographical.

So, I am in command. But in command of what? Four officers including myself, twenty-nine men, several in a broken condition, and a ship beset in the ice with little hope of escape.

What a sad remnant of such a glorious beginning, but we must go on. Our goal now is not the glory of conquering the Northwest Passage, that has long fallen by the way. Now, perhaps the most we can hope for is that someone will live to tell our tale. That would be worthwhile. We have achieved as much as any men could and have been tricked by this treacherous place which opened a way to our goal and then cruelly closed it before and behind, trapping us in this misery. I cannot help but remember Crozier's warning, given when we were too full of hope to listen, that we must not blunder unseeing into the unknown. Well that is exactly what we have done, and now Crozier and God alone know how many others are dead. We will hold on in the hopes that Le Vesconte made it safely to civilization or that Ross is out looking for us, but I do not hold much hope now for the fates dealing us a fair hand. Oh God Elizabeth, if I could only look into your eyes once more I would be a happy man. I do not think I can write more now. Good night.

November 8—James Brown, Caulker, died last night.

November 30—John Bridgens, the Steward Reid taught to cook salt fish so long ago, died today.

December 5—William Heather, Private, Royal Marines, put a musket ball in his head this morning.

December 25—Christmas again, our fourth, and we struggle to lift our spirits a little for the occasion. We took the last of the fresh meat and distributed it for a meal, so it is salt beef and seal meat from now on. Only the three deaths since October, the scurvy is being held at bay either by the fresh meat or the lemon juice. I pray it is the latter, for the only fresh meat now is seal and, even if we can learn to stomach it, we have not enough to see us through more than a few weeks.

I have attempted to write a number of times in the last weeks, but when I came to sit at my desk, all that came to mind was woe and gloom, so I have stopped myself in time. I listed our deaths not to depress you, but so that they have some memorial.

We continue to go about our work as we were instructed in the beginning. Fairholme is a Godsend and undertakes much of the scientific investigations. Without him we could do little. We now have a vast collection of papers and readings which I shall bury in a secure place at Cook Bay if we can reach there come spring. I shall also place an account of our doings since we left England beneath a cairn on Franklin Island. It is vital that whatever happens to us, our records survive.

In summer, if the ice breaks, we shall take the ship as far as possible and then follow Le Vesconte's route by whatever means seems appropriate under the circumstances. There must be expeditions out looking for us and, if we can cross to Prince Regent Inlet, I think we stand a good chance of meeting up with them, or at least a band of friendly Esquimaux. I hope we have the strength remaining.

The men have been extraordinary in this adversity and have put up, I will not say cheerfully, with conditions which would have provoked mutiny on a less well-run expedition. We are all weak but all attempt to keep spirits up as much as possible. Old Nep is still with us and is in the best condition of anyone, frolicking around the deck as if he were at home chasing rabbits amongst the green fields of England. He has been fed on a diet of offal and seal meat and is doing well. He really is a most extraordinarily adaptable creature.

Reid remains low and sullen although he gets no worse and simply sits in silence most of the time. Goodsir maintains the highest spirits of us all and is continually seeing the humour in the most unlikely situation. The other day he prepared us a meal made entirely of his plants collected from the neighbouring islands. There was a lichen consomme to begin, roast red lichen *au jus*, baked moss and saxifrage julienne. Dessert was snow ice topped with Arctic poppy.

He maintains that, given enough quantity, there is nutrition here to sustain life. It was an affair as light hearted as possible under the circumstances, but we all tried his concoctions and were as polite as possible despite the generally disgusting flavours. In fact, Fairholme, who managed to down more than any of the rest of us, was up throughout the succeeding night with the most horrible stomach cramps. Obviously there is work to be done in the culinary realm, but for the most part we bear it well and endeavour to keep each other's spirits up as much as possible.

This evening we overindulged somewhat on wine and engaged in a round of the parlour game 'Will you come up with a Limerick?' All raised themselves to respond to this childish pastime and I think it helped. Of course there were many of the old favourites, the one best received being:

There was an old man of Tobago
Who lived on rice, gruel and sago
But at last to his bliss the physician said this
'To a roast leg of mutton you may go.'

The reason for its popularity being the references to food. We all dream of food, waking and sleeping.

Fairholme managed, despite playing fast and loose with poetic rhyme, a gentle dig at Goodsir:

There was a young man of the Arctake
Who said, 'Of some lichen I'll partake
Though the soup tastes like glue some raw seal meat stew
Will be better than prime roasted beefsteak.'

My home-made contribution was equal to Fairholme's in the strain it put on poesy, but at least avoided food:

The cold in this climate is bearable
If all of your clothing is wearable
But lose just one layer where you sit on a chair
And the consequences are terrible.

Writing these words brings me the thought that this silliness will be of scant interest or humour to you, but to such pitiful depths have the high-points of your brother's life sunk of late.

Please do not think, dear sister, that just because I am not writing much this season, that you are any farther from my thoughts than you have ever been. You are with me every minute and I could not have gone on so long as

I have without your image before me and the hope of our meeting again to spur me on. And how fervently I imagine that meeting. It has filled my imaginings a million times, each more delicious than the last. Is this the burden of love, for surely I love you more than life itself, although that says not enough given the pitiful remnant of that commodity perhaps left to me.

I cannot decide whether carrying love to the far corners of the world is a blessing or a curse. Certainly Crozier's love for Sophia Cracroft brought him low on many occasions, and proved insufficient to sustain his spirit in the final extremity.

Fairholme on the other hand has drawn nothing but strength from recollections of his family awaiting his return. Love seems like a rock to which a man can anchor or be dragged down to the deep depending on his circumstances and temperament.

And how thus my feelings for you? I count myself honoured to have met you and remember our time before I sailed as the happiest of my days. And on this adventure, without you in my thoughts, I would have given in to despond long past. Yet, how I envy William and the time he can spend in your company. What would I not give for just the merest fraction of that time?

How have I got to this from the silly jests I began with? It becomes increasingly hard to maintain a focus in my thoughts and writings. I must cease for now with the wish for a most Merry and Hopeful Christmas to you dearest Elizabeth. It must be our last apart. Good night.

January 1, 1849—Another year begins, I pray our last in these realms. We have been eating seal meat for a week now. I find it not too unpalatable, but a few of the men are refusing it. I cannot force them. Fairholme, I think, is of my opinion, Goodsir claims to thoroughly enjoy it, and Reid forces his portions down with a sort of dour resignation. In any event it will not last us long and then we shall see how much effect remains with the lemon juice.

Terry brought back Crozier's Esquimaux suit and I have been trying it out lately. It is cumbersome and makes detailed work difficult but it certainly has remarkable power to retain heat while out on the ice. Were it not so pitiable I should laugh to see us all, English Navy men, dressed in whatever rags we can lay hands on and bundled so that you would hardly know how skinny are the bodies beneath. We all sport hollow eyes, sunken cheeks and skin so blackened we are barely recognisable to one another. We all have beards which, like our hair, is lank and matted with grease and all manner of unmentionable things. I doubt that we smell very pleasant but fortunately each individual's smell seems to be strong enough to mask that of one's companions.

I think, were I miraculously transported to London, a good meal would still be my first priority, but it would be followed almost immediately by a hot bath! Then, shaved and in some fresh clothes, I should feel able to present myself as your long lost brother returned. I fear, like a decent meal, the only bath I shall be getting will be in my dreams. Good night.

February 1—Sun returned today and it was clear, so we caught a glimpse of its disc. Heartened us all I think.

February 7—Happy Birthday. Toasted your health in wine of which we still have a good supply. I hope you are dining on better fare than old seal meat.

February 10—Able Seaman, John Morfin, died last night.

February 12—Able Seaman William Orren, the little old Orkneyman I allowed home to see his wife, died today. Both he and Morfin refused to eat the seal meat.

February 15—Seal meat finished today. The weather has been bitterly cold and windy, but again we have had very little snow.

March 8—Solomon Tozer, the Marine Sergeant from *Terror*, died today of scurvy. It is on the increase. All of us are shewing more symptoms and several men are in sick bay. The lemon juice does not seem to have any power left to help us. We try to grow mustard and cress in the galley, but we produce only tiny amounts and those who can stomach it force down some of Goodsir's potions.

Goodsir himself appears remarkably well and this encourages some of the rest of us to attempt to ingest some of his bitter medicines. Fairholme is the weakest of us and refuses to touch anything that Goodsir concocts. He does so in good spirit, claiming he would rather die of starvation than the horrifying cramps he experienced after our lichen meal.

March 15—Seaman Thomas McConvey, our famous Arctic sprinter, died last night.

March 23—Seaman Samuel Crispe died of scurvy today. It is becoming a race against time—can we last with enough strength to take advantage of the game which will pass this way in a few weeks?

April 10—William Rhodes, Quartermaster, and James Daly, Marine, dead of scurvy.

April 20—James Thompson, Engineer, died raving last night.

April 22—One year since we deserted the ships at Victory Point. In a week or two, Fairholme and I will lead the fittest men over to King William Island for the hunt. I am looking forward to the fresh meat.

May 12—Fairholme and I set out tomorrow with seven men. We will travel as lightly as possible and hope to come across game soon. I will not take this journal and will tell you of our doings upon my return. God bless and good night.

June 13—Back at my familiar table. Our hunting was successful and we used well what we learned last year. We now have a large cache of deer meat on Des Voeux Peninsula and are busy ferrying it across the miles to the ship. This is a slow process due to our weakness and to the state of the ice which is very active and shewing signs of breaking up soon.

Four men died on board while we were gone, both the Honeys, Joseph Andrews, Captain of the Hold, and Seaman Edwin Lawrence, but the remainder have been gorging themselves on the first of the fresh meat which I sent back with Fairholme two weeks ago.

While Fairholme returned to the ship, I remained on King William Island with three men to hunt. I attempted to find Crozier's grave at Cook Bay, but there was still snow on the ground and it proved impossible, although we did see the boats that Terry talked of. We took time and effort to bury our records as close as possible to where I suspected Crozier lay. They are not very deep, since we did not have the strength for such hard work, but hopefully they will be secure until some rescue party comes by to claim them.

June 14—Most of the men are shewing signs of improvement with the fresh meat although Armitage, the Gun-room Steward of the *Terror*, is far gone and might not survive. Fairholme is also very sick. He is much broken with the exertion of bringing back the meat, after which he returned to meet me and help establish the cache and bring even more meat over. I have ordered him to sick bay else he would still be on the ice hauling with the rest.

The weather has been wet, but there is a wind and it is warm, so we may see a break in the ice soon. Saw ducks and seagulls earlier than last spring which perked Reid up. We asked his opinion most seriously on what the meaning of it was.

"She'll be breaking up soon arl right," he replied, which is the most positive statement he has uttered all winter.

Now I must rest. There is much work for the nineteen of us who remain.

June 19—Fairholme died this afternoon. He had simply weakened progressively until there was nothing left. Of course he had scurvy and probably a host of other ailments from which we all suffer to a greater or lesser degree, but I think he was just broken with all the exertion of the last few weeks and had no reserves left. It is a great tragedy so close to what will be our bid for freedom. He will be sorely missed.

June 30—The weather is warm for these parts and there is much water lying on the ice all around. The ice is itself in continuous motion and we all look eagerly for the first sign of open water early though it is. Our problem is that, to take advantage of a lead, it must open directly beneath the ship, we not having the strength or the manpower to cut and haul our way any distance.

July 12—A lead, frustratingly close, yet all we can do is watch it and hope it will come closer.

July 15—Our lead closed without releasing us, but others are open to the west and southwest and we hope they presage a more general break-up.

Summer, 1849

July 21, 1849—Under sail again. The ice has been continually moving for the last few days and we have been pulled with it several miles to the southwest which is good since that is the direction we must take to clear Franklin and Jane Franklin Islands. Yesterday we were still firmly attached to a floe which was surrounded by open leads and this morning we placed several large charges through holes in it and succeeded in breaking it apart. Our way is slow since we do not have the use of the engines and must rely on uncertain winds, but we make progress under our own power and everyone is delighted.

All are much improved. Only Seaman Josephus Geater remains in a serious state and I fear he will not survive. Strangely, he is one of the tallest and strongest of the crew and his strength has been of inestimable help. I cannot determine why it is often the biggest and strongest who succumb first, perhaps they feel the responsibility of their strength and wear themselves out needlessly. Whatever the cause, I have seen it again and again. With more hope than I have felt for some time, I wish you good night.

July 22—We still make progress although our course is tortuous. We are now due west of Jane Franklin Island and no more than twelve or fifteen miles from Victoria Land which seems to be cut by several deep inlets. The ice is much broken ahead and we should be able to head around the southern extremity of Jane Franklin Island and head for Simpson Strait.

July 23—Off the southern point of Jane Franklin Island. The American mainland cannot be more than fifty or so miles to the south of us and the entrance to Simpson Strait about the same distance to the east. The water is much open to the east where it is protected by the islands, but we are still in relatively heavy pack and are having difficulty working our way out of it. With a full crew and our steam engines, it would not take us long, but with so few men, we are continually subject to the capricious whims of the ice, wind and currents.

July 25—Finally, this afternoon we broke free of the heavy pack into the clear waters in the shelter of the islands. We are progressing east slowly, for the ocean bottom here is most irregular and we must not risk running aground.

July 26—Continue to make progress eastward. We will soon be in Simpson Strait and can easily see the south shore of King William Island to the north, almost due south of the horrors of Stanley Bay. Adelaide Peninsula lies to the southeast. The water is deep here, but we still proceed with caution.

July 27—In the entrance to Simpson Strait. A boat is out taking soundings. The water is open ahead, but the Strait is narrowing and the bottom most irregular. We are cursing our deep draft.

Another birthday, my fifth in these climes. Elisabeth will be eight in but a few weeks and Robert is already six and—I am certain—quite the young gentleman. How I miss seeing them grow. Perhaps it is the barrenness of the places we have visited or the lack of any diversion other than our work and the tribulations we have suffered, but my loneliness—even amidst such fine friends as I have had here—has sometimes been hard to bear. How little I considered, when we first set out, the possibility that I would spend but a fraction of this time on this endeavour. However, I feel that we near the end and that one way or the other, this will be my last celebration hereabouts.

July 28—Aground briefly this morning, but were able to shake ourselves off with the rising tide. Boat still out sounding in search of a channel we can follow through. Geater died this afternoon to no one's surprise. The remaining seventeen of us are in fair condition although none would have been accepted for the start of this voyage as we are.

July 29—There is no way through Simpson Strait for the *Erebus*. We have retreated to the deep water and anchored off a small island at the entrance to the Strait. We are preparing to take to two boats and progress in that manner. We could fit our entire company in one, but our adventures to date have convinced me of the utility of having a spare vessel to render assistance.

Myself and Goodsir will take six men. Reid and Terry who is quite a fine sailor, will take the other with seven men. If we are separated we shall arrange a rendezvous at Point Ogle and if we fail to meet there, we shall each proceed to the east as well as we can. We carry the Halkett boat with us for the traverse of rivers and lakes.

I sent Goodsir over to the island in one boat to build a cairn and bury a short account of our recent doings. If Ross is looking for us, there is a line of cairns, some with messages, but all with our trademark pointing hand indicating the direction we have taken. Tomorrow we will load the boats and set off in Le Vesconte's footsteps.

We leave the *Erebus* a second time, but this time we shall not return. Her only crew now is Geater whom we left in a bunk, not having the strength to bury him ashore and feeling it more appropriate than consigning him to the deep. Both vessels are now crewed only by the dead.

I say good-bye to my desk for the last time and will write when I can. Your picture I have again close to my breast. This is the final stage. We will succeed or not, but there cannot be much more. Pray for us.

August 1—In camp Adelaide Peninsula. We are through the narrows of Simpson Strait, but the weather has turned cold and wet and we have stopped briefly to restore our strength. There is some ice hereabouts and a thick fog this morning made progress too chancy, so we pulled into a small cove.

The land hereabouts is just as described by Back, almost a desert and so flat that a hillock of eight or ten feet in height would provide a quite distant view were it not for the constant fog and almost ceaseless rain. The ground is alternately sandy and a sort of bog into which a walker sinks almost to his knees even if unladen. We will set sail again tomorrow.

August 4—A small cove on the shore of an inlet near the entrance to Back's Fish river. We are in a sorry state. On the 2nd we set sail again though the fog remained thick. The going was slow and we roped the two boats together for security. The coast is very indented and we had to proceed with some caution.

Yesterday the fog cleared, but was followed by a strong wind from the northwest. This increased all day until we were being tossed about quite severely. The almost constant rain had us soaked through and all were exhausted having not slept hardly at all for many days; the best we can manage is to huddle together for warmth in the bottom of the boat—landing and hauling the boats ashore every day takes too much of our precious reserves of strength.

In desperation, we separated the rope and tried to make for the shelter of an inlet. Our boat managed to make the lee of the point, but Reid's and Terry's boat took a wave broadside and was swamped and several of the men were thrown into the water. We put out and after a trying hour or so, managed to bring the boat to shore.

Three of her crew were drowned, two Seamen from the *Erebus*, Thomas Hartnell, whose brother lies on Beechey Island, and Thomas Tadman, and the *Terror*'s Stoker, Luke Smith. We managed to recover their bodies, but burial is out of the question. All of the others were in a very weakened state having spent some considerable time immersed. We established camp, but the rain made a fire impossible. During the night, Terry, who was one of those swept from the boat, died, and I fear several others will follow if the weather does not moderate.

August 5—Wall, our Cook, and John Cowie, Stoker, expired in the night. We lay their bodies outside by one of the beached boats. The wind is moderating somewhat and tomorrow we must set off. We will abandon Reid's boat and all continue in the other. Another sad place where we must leave the bodies of comrades.

My plan is to round Ogle Point and cross Chantrey Inlet to Back's Cape Britannia. From there, if Back was right, we shall sail through to Prince Regent Inlet. If he was wrong and Boothia is a Peninsula, we will proceed up the coast to Simpson's and Dease's cairn at Castor and Pollux River, abandon the whaleboat and strike out on foot to the east.

It is a desperate venture and the cost can already be seen, but we have no choice and at least we are early enough in the season that we stand a chance of meeting whalers if we can head north.

August 6—Another sad tale to tell. This morning we rounded what I took to be from our chart position, Point Ogle, however, we soon discovered our mistake as we ended up in sight of another point to the east. We were close to the shore of a sizeable island and had just begun to tack back out of the false inlet when Goodsir exclaimed that he could see a boat.

At first my heart leapt for I imagined John Ross's vessel sailing down to rescue us, but it was a whaleboat pulled up and overturned on the shore of the island. We landed and discovered the tragedy which had befallen Le Vesconte last year. The bodies of Sargent and seven men were huddled under the hull, seeking some meagre shelter in their last extremity.

What happened we can only guess. The party must have progressed along the south coast of King William Island and, upon encountering open water late in the season, taken to their boat. Either they were driven here by bad weather or else, like us, they were fooled into taking this blind inlet thinking it led to Back's River.

Whatever the case, they came ashore with enough strength left to turn the boat and construct a shelter of sorts. Whether these are the last remnants and Le Vesconte, Peddie, Blanky and the others lie strewn along the coast to the north, or whether these men were too weak to continue and a party continued overland, we cannot know. I favour the former idea since, why did they not continue by boat if they intended to leave this place? We will never know for certain, but it has made me think; if our small party does not survive, what will future generations make of the sad trail of bones and debris we have left scattered over this land?

At least the rain has ceased and we can have some hot food and dry some of our clothes. I presume the next point is Ogle and we will soon know how far we can sail. Good night once more dear Elizabeth.

August 7—Camp at Cape Britannia. Weather still fine. As Back suspected, the coast does trend to the east from this cape; however, it appears to swing back to the north after some ten or fifteen miles. There is no continuation of Simpson's Strait through to Prince Regent Inlet and I fear we must walk. Tomorrow we will sail to the north to Castor and Pollux and attempt to find Simpson's cairn, from which point we shall walk eastward.

August 8—Camp at Simpson's cairn to which we have added a hand pointing toward our next destination. There was some discussion as to where we should make for. Goodsir surprised us all by expressing an opinion for the first time.

"I am of the mind that Fury Beach might be a mistake," he said. Reid attacked him quickly.

"Man," he said, "what fanciful ideas are ye comm' out wi' now?"

"Just this. It will be late by the time we make Fury Beach. Perhaps too late to hope for a whaler to rescue us. Then we will be in trouble."

"Are ye no' in trouble a'ready then?" Reid asked. Goodsir ignored him.

"The food at Fury Beach is not fresh and will do nothing to stave off scurvy if we must stay there any time, and Ross did not talk of abundant game in those parts."

"Where do you suggest we head then, Harry," I asked.

"The Melville Peninsula," he said. "True, it is a greater walk than Fury Beach, but consider the argument in its favour. It is well populated with Esquimaux who have proved friendly to previous explorers and who might be prepared to guide a small party like ours through their lands to Churchill or some other trading post."

It is an intriguing possibility and put me in mind of Crozier's comments on a small party of men being able to adopt Esquimaux ways where a large group could not. The decision is ultimately mine, and I think I favour the shorter route, if only because escape this summer must be our primary goal, and relief is more likely to come by Fury Beach than Melville Peninsula. We have no sleds to drag so that should allow us to make fair progress.

So, tomorrow we set off overland, not sailors any more, but trekkers and hunters. It is a sorry remnant of a great expedition that I command now, Reid, Goodsir and eight men, but the responsibility of command is as heavy for one life as for fifty.

Oddly, of all the many deaths, including Sir John and Osmer and Crozier, it is young Torrington who remains with me the most. Perhaps because he was the first. In that at least he was lucky to have missed all that has come since.

Strange how we mourned so fervently the loss of one from so many when now we struggle to secure the survival of but one to tell our tale. Wish us luck. Good night Elizabeth.

August 12—Boothia. We are making good progress with our light loads, almost ten miles per day over some pleasant rolling land scattered with small lakes. The ground is wet and it has rained for at least a part of each day, but it is warm and we are having luck in bringing down large numbers of duck and a few geese which keep us well supplied.

Our Halkett boat has been most useful in ferrying us over two rivers; but we do not use it for lakes of any size, it being faster to walk around them than ferry our party any distance since only three can fit in the boat at one time, and that with no packs, and that means at least six trips.

At this rate I expect to be on the shore of Prince Regent Inlet in another four or five days. I expect we shall be somewhere to the south of Ross's wintering place at Felix Harbour where he abandoned his ship's engine. From there we shall be only ten days journey from Fury Beach.

August 16—On the shores of Prince Regent Inlet. The water is open, with very little ice; how I wish we had a boat of sufficient size and we should be well on our way to Lancaster Sound and rescue. We will stop here tomorrow for the hunting, there being many seabirds on the shore hereabouts.

We are camped on a slight rise looking out to the northeast over some irregularly-shaped islands. To the north, the coast swings to due east, probably a point, the base of which we shall cross to reach, I hope, Felix Harbour. To the south the coast swings to the south. This evening, I caught Goodsir looking longingly in that direction.

"You still think of escape that way?" I asked.

"Yes," he replied. "It is strange for a scientist to say, but I have the strangest feeling that that way lies our salvation. It makes no sense, your arguments for Fury Beach are as strong as mine for Melville, yet I cannot shake the idea."

"Well," I said, "perhaps science does not yet have all the answers."

I had a sense that Goodsir was about to continue, perhaps suggesting that we split our party, so I quickly added that the decision on which direction to take was mine and that we must all pull together if we are to survive this ordeal. I hope I was not too abrupt, but it is important that we have a common aim. Goodsir simply nodded and wished me good night. I pray I am right, I do not want to have the deaths of more good men on my conscience. I pray we will be rescued soon.

I fear that I have not done as good a job of entertaining you as I had hoped, but I trust you will put that down to the circumstances rather than my poor abilities. Good night.

August 17—How have circumstances changed in but a single day!

This morning we were hunting birds along the shore. I took the opportunity to climb a large rock to ascertain the farther alignment of the coast. On descending, my foot slipped on a piece of wet moss and I fell to the shore. I landed awkwardly. The sharp pain in my left leg above the ankle combined with a loud cracking sound, which told me the worst before Goodsir had a chance to examine my injury. The bone is broken some three inches above the ankle joint. Goodsir says it is a simple fracture, but it pains me considerably and walking is impossible. Goodsir has strapped it up as best he can and that relieves the pain somewhat, but the leg is badly swollen and bruised, and it is obvious that I will not be travelling anywhere for a considerable time.

There is no question in my mind that the party should remain with me as the precious days go by, so with that in mind, I called Goodsir into the tent this afternoon.

"I think you will have your chance for the Melville Peninsula," I said. "It is obvious I cannot go anywhere for some time and we must not risk the lives of all for one. You are the senior survivor, so I hand over command to you. Lead the men where you will."

"I will do so," he said after a considerable pause, "but only for one reason. Experience tells us that we will have greater chance of meeting friendly natives to the south. That being so, it presents the best opportunity to find help and return for you."

I agreed. I had a momentary concern over the inexperience of both Goodsir and Reid, but brushed it aside. We have all much more experience than we would wish and, in any case, there is no choice. Goodsir is a solid sort and has retained his spirits better than anyone through all the horrors. I must rest now.

August 18—I am writing this in my last night of human companionship for heaven knows how long.

Goodsir and the party leave first thing tomorrow for the south. They swear they will find help within a few days and return for me, we shall see. Everyone was busy today hunting in order to leave me with a good supply of game and all have given some of their personal supplies to me. I tried to dissuade them, but in reality, I am very touched and grateful for their concern.

Reid has fashioned one of the tents into a small conical structure with just enough room for me to sit and lie in, and has used the ridge pole he salvaged to manufacture a short stick. It is not a crutch, but with practice and determination, I will be able to move about a little. My leg pains me extremely with just the slightest movement and even when stationary sometimes throbs unbearably. I am too tired to write more.

August 19—Goodsir, Reid and the eight men left at first light this morning, but after all I am not completely alone. Old Nep at first went with the party, but as soon as he realised that I was not coming, he ran back and jumped around me as if encouraging me to move. Then he ran to Goodsir, looking back all the time, before running back to repeat his pantomime in front of me. He repeated this four or five times before finally settling at my feet and watching sorrowfully as the others disappeared over the horizon.

The humans exhibited no such indecision, only pausing on a distant hillock to turn and wave a last farewell. Their leaving was emotional for all concerned, several, including myself, giving way to tears.

Reid in his gruff way shook my hand and said, "We'll be back for you Mister Jems, Sir, have nae fear at arl. Mind, that's no' tae say that I'll be forgivin' you for leavin us all to yon man wi' his moss soup."

Goodsir was more formal. "With rest the leg should mend. We will find some Esquimaux and return in a week or two, certainly before the snow falls. Good luck James."

Then all crowded round and gave me three strong cheers, which I tried to reply to by wishing them well and God speed. Then they left, marching strongly to the south.

As they disappeared, I was suddenly struck by how utterly alone I was in this vast wilderness. All I have for company are an old dog, your picture, and the pages of this journal. No longer being in command, I gave the official log to Goodsir for safekeeping. I have my sleeping bag, the tent Reid fashioned for me, a cook stove and makeshift oil lantern, enough food to last for a month if I am careful, a musket, powder and shot, although they will be of little use unless my leg mends somewhat, and a few odds and ends. Even this book has but a few pages left so I must husband my thoughts. I will attempt some sleep now.

August 20—Slept poorly, and was continually awakened by the cry of wolves, but none came close. My biggest fear is that I will be set upon by a pack of these creatures or by a marauding bear. I keep my musket primed and close to hand. Even if the wolves had been silent, I doubt if my leg would have allowed much rest, since it has the uncomfortable habit of sending shooting pains up my calf if I move any part of my body in the slightest.

Managed to cook a duck this evening and so dined well on that and biscuits. Water will be my main difficulty. There is a spring-fed pond some twenty feet away from which a small rivulet runs down to the shore. I have several cans of water close at hand, but eventually I will have to pull myself over to the stream and I do not relish the prospect.

Neptune has settled now that he seems to have made his decision. Mostly he sleeps at my feet, but occasionally he gets up and wanders around. I think the wolves last night bothered him too.

August 21—Came on to rain this morning and has continued all day. It would do me good to fill up my water cans, but everything is wet through and all I can manage is cold biscuits and some of the cooked meat Goodsir left.

How I miss the companionship of the mess. Irving would be much better suited to this fate, having spent several years on his own in the wilds of Australia, but I am more used to company and conversation. I have taken to talking with Old Nep, and he listens very politely, but is not much of a storyteller himself.

It is strange that we began with such a mass of equipment and the latest inventions—and now that I am here with the simplest of necessities. I told you I was not fit for humbugging society and now I have my wish, being as far from it as is possible. I have also whittled my belongings down to the minimum, a primitive tent and stove and a musket which is useless unless I improve myself—Crozier would see humour in that. Certainly the arrogance that Crozier blamed for our doom is gone. Maybe we would have done better to begin with more humility. In any event it is done now.

August 22—Wolves sounded very close last night and Neptune and I spent much of it awake, he with his ears cocked and me with the musket across my lap, but we saw nothing. The daylight decreases daily at this time of year and the noise in the darkness does prey on one's nerves. Still raining.

August 24—Still raining. I fear I am coming down with a slight fever, probably the result of the weather. How I wish Goodsir had left some of his medicines for me.

Neptune lies and looks at me soulfully for most of the daylight hours, only taking short walks to attend to his canine needs. He has carefully marked out a perimeter, some forty feet in all directions around us. I wonder if that is what is keeping the wolves at bay?

I find I am becoming maudlin and dwelling much on things that have been. This afternoon I was back with Chesney amongst the ancient dry Mesopotamian hills. I swear I was there, I could feel the sun and the dust caked to my skin and burning my throat as I breathed, but it was merely a waking dream and I returned to this damp grey land.

I think much on the past, the happy times and boyhood pranks with William—the early days at sea with Gambier—and China with so many friends who will no more regale the world with their stories. It bothers me mightily that it was I who persuaded many of them to accompany me here to this end.

Who is left to remember me if Goodsir does not return in time? You of course, William, a few others, but you will all remember false. To you I am preserved in time as the naive enthusiast setting out on a great adventure. That person I now look upon as a fool. It is not me. But who will ever know that. I think if I am not to return, that will be a regret. I have but few others, paramount amongst them being never setting eyes on you again. I sit for hours looking at your picture, tattered and torn, yet still you, but it is poor substitute.

Elizabeth I miss you so.

August 25—Will this rain never end? My leg is getting worse rather than better.

Today it pained me so much that I removed the splint and bandages to see what the problem was. The sight was not encouraging, there appears to be an infection, which may account for the fever which I have intermittently. I fear it has also begun to smell somewhat. If Goodsir is to return, he had better do it soon.

August 26—Fever is worse. This afternoon I blacked out while boiling some water for tea and was fortunate not to have fallen on the stove and suffered a bad burn. I must be more careful.

I have decided to bury this journal. If I wrap it securely in sailcloth and canvas it should be protected from the elements and if I bury it beneath some rocks, that should keep the animals off. I doubt now whether Goodsir will be back in time, and if he arrives soon it is a small matter to retrieve my book. If he does not return then perhaps some traveller in the future will stumble across my poor camp and deliver this to you.

I fear I have broken my promise and spent this evening rereading what I have written, but although I was tempted to correct my rude descriptions at times, I refrained. I could hardly believe that the naive, enthusiastic young Captain who wondered at his first iceberg over four years ago, is the same man as this who sits in a rough shelter watching the cold grey waves wash up onto this barren, lonely shore. In those far-off, heady days, to die would have been the bitterest pill to swallow—now it is almost a consolation—a hope of rest at last.

So much has happened, so many of my dearest friends and colleagues are gone. Franklin. How, if none of us survive, will the world view him; the fool blundering in where no one should go? Or the great man laid low by cruel circumstances over which he had no control? Crozier, who always doubted the wisdom of our adventure, yet whose dedication was responsible for us achieving as much as we did. Le Vesconte, a dear, dear friend of long standing, what has become of him? Does he lie alone in some crude grave on the shores of King William Island or did he leave his boat and the sick in an attempt to ascend Back's River? Gore, the conqueror of the Northwest Passage, but destined never to enjoy his glory. Osmer, Des Voeux, Irving, Fairholme, Couch, Stanley, so many good men, all lost.

And what of Goodsir and Reid, perhaps the two most unlikely Arctic explorers of our company? How will they fare? Is fate just tempting them on to a more prolonged doom or will they, by some miracle, endure to tell our story to the world?

And what of the decisions we made on the way to here? Would others have changed anything? If, for example, we had taken the lead down Lady Jane Sound that first winter, would we have been blessed with an open season to complete our work, or would it have simply meant another winter in that bleak ice river? Who can say?

But it is near the end now. Already it is cold at nights and this morning there was a skim of ice on my spring pond. My leg is bad and the fever worsening. What a strange end. The page is done, and the book full although it is hard to stop and admit that the tale is told. Tomorrow I shall bury it and await what comes.

For myself all I can hope is that this will somehow find its way to you to give some indication of how much you have meant to me throughout this ordeal. Without your picture in my mind, I should not have persevered half so far as I have.

Elizabeth, it has come to this end, but there is one truth to be said if I am to keep my promise to you. You cannot doubt my feelings for you, I have expressed them often enough, if awkwardly, throughout this ramble. But they are not the whole truth. I think of you as sister, true, but not because I regard William as my brother, although that too is true. I call you sister to protect myself. To push into the dark recesses of my mind the thoughts no man can have of his sister—or of his cousin's wife.

I love you dear Elizabeth.

Perhaps it is best to end this way. Best that all I have are this journal to talk to and this photograph to look upon, for how could I go from day to day, only talking to you of inconsequential, safe happenings and how could I only look upon you when I crave so much more? How could I continue to look upon William as my brother when every moment he was with you I would hate him a little more?

My dearest Elizabeth, the end will come with you in my thoughts and your picture clutched in my hand. Remember me fondly. For the last time, I wish you Good Night.

Historical Note

What became of these men? Two did eventually make it home. In 1879, an overland expedition led by Lieutenant Frederick Schwatka of the 3rd United States Cavalry Regiment, discovered a grave at Victory Point. A fine silk handkerchief and fragments of blue uniform identified the remains as those of an officer, and a weathered medal also found there turned out to be the mathematics prize awarded to Lieutenant John Irving in 1830. The bones were returned to Scotland where they were buried with full military honours in Dean Cemetery, Edinburgh, on January 7, 1881.

The other skeleton was discovered by Charles Francis Hall on the south coast of King William Island in 1869. It was returned to Britain and interred below a memorial to the Franklin Expedition in the Painted Hall at Greenwich Hospital. It was assumed, based on little more than gold teeth fillings, that it was Fitzjames' friend, Lieutenant Henry Thomas Dundas Le Vesconte. When the remains were removed to a new memorial in 2009, isotope analysis of tooth enamel and facial reconstruction strongly suggested that the skeleton was in fact that of Harry Goodsir.

The graves of Leading Stoker John Torrington, Able Seaman John Hartnell, and Royal Marine Private William Braine lie on the shores of Beechey Island. Many other bones and relics have been recovered over the years, but little is known for certain of the specific fates of the other characters in this story. Fitzjames, Crozier, Franklin and the others lie somewhere in the vast Canadian Arctic.

Inuit stories mention the *Erebus* and *Terror* and led to the discovery of the wrecks of both ships in 2014 and 2016 respectively. Other tales, also since confirmed, talk of starvation, scurvy and cannibalism as the desperate survivors struggled to reach help. One intriguing collection of tales even mentions strangers as far east as the Melville Peninsula and as late as the early 1850's. These men were accompanied by a dog and heading south toward a Hudson's Bay post. They never made it, but perhaps some survivors got farther than we commonly think.

The wrecks of the *Erebus* and *Terror* are a rich source of artifacts that will undoubtedly dramatically increase our understanding of the Franklin disaster. Perhaps the journal of James Fitzjames lies in a cabin drawer on one of the ships, preserved by the chill Arctic waters.

Acknowledgments

Much, ranging from the lunatic to the scholarly, has been written over the years on Franklin's lost third expedition. In the early years, there was considerable spiritualist interest and this was followed by numerous fictional accounts. An unpublished novel of the expedition, told in high Victorian style and presenting Fitzjames as the almost too good to be true hero of the epic, resides in the Royal Geographical Society in London. The definitive work is *Sir John Franklin's Last Arctic Expedition* by Richard Cyriax. It was published in 1939 but has recently been reprinted in facsimile edition by the Arctic Press. It provides the basis for all later accounts.

Franklin and his men are served both well and badly by abbreviated accounts in countless history and general interest Arctic books, but there has been a resurgence in more detailed discussion over the last ten or fifteen years. Much of this is due to Owen Beattie's investigations into the possibility of lead poisoning from the canned food. The grizzly image of the exhumed body of John Torrington is almost universally known from Beattie's and Geiger's books *Frozen in Time* and *Buried in Ice*. David Woodman's fascinating *Unravelling the Franklin Mystery* and *Strangers Among Us* examine the Inuit testimony and speculate on what may have happened based on those stories. Russell Potter's website (http://www.ric.edu/rpotter/sjfranklin.html) also provides much information and many good links for those interested in current examinations into Franklin's fate.

To Cyriax, Beattie, Woodman and countless others, I express my heartfelt thanks for providing the skeleton upon which I could mould the flesh of Fitzjames' journal.

This work could not have been done without the generous help of the archivists and staff at the Scott Polar Institute in Cambridge, the Royal Geographic Society, the British Library, the British Museum Newspaper Library in London, and the National Archives in Ottawa. A grant from the Arts Council of British Columbia made a trip to the United Kingdom to examine the archives possible.

The Officers and Crews

H.M.S. *Erebus*

Captain—Sir John Franklin
Commander—James Fitzjames (Captain: December 31th, 1845)
Lieutenants—Graham Gore (Commander: November 9th, 1846) Henry
Thomas Dundas Le Vesconte
James Walter Fairholme
Mates—Robert Orme Sargent (Lieutenant: August 15th, 1846)
Charles Frederick Des Voeux (Lieutenant: November 9th, 1846)
Edward Couch (Lieutenant: May 24th, 1847)
Second Master—Henry Foster Collins
Surgeon—Stephen Samuel Stanley
Assistant-Surgeon (Acting)—Harry D. S. Goodsir
Paymaster and Purser—Charles Hamilton Osmer
Ice-Master (Acting)—James Reid

Warrant Officers
Boatswain—Thomas Terry
Carpenter—John Weekes
Engineer—John Gregory

Petty Officers
Boatswain's mate—Samuel Brown
Carpenter's mate—Thomas Watson
Captain of the Forecastle—Philip Reddington
Quartermasters—Daniel Arthur
William Bell
John Downing
Sailmaker—John Murray
Caulker—James W. Brown
Blacksmith—William Smith
Leading Stoker—James Hart
Cook—Richard Wall
Captain's Coxswain—James Rigden
Captain of the Maintop—John Sullivan
Captain of the Foretop—Robert Sinclair

Captain of the Hold—Joseph Andrews
Caulker's mate—Francis Dunn
Captain's Steward—Edmund Hoar
Gun-room Steward—Richard Aylmore
Paymaster and Purser's Clerk—William Fowler
Subordinate Officers' Steward—John Bridgens
Stokers—John Cowie
Thomas Plater

Able Seamen

George Thompson, Henry Lloyd, John Hartnell, Thomas Work, John Stickland, Robert Ferrier, Thomas Hartnell, Josephus Geater, William Orren, George Williams, William Closson, Thomas Tadman, Charles Coombs, Abraham Seeley, John Morfin, Francis Pocock, Charles Best, Robert Johns, Thomas McConvey, William Mark

Royal Marines

Sergeant—David Bryant
Corporal—Alexander Paterson
Privates—Robert Hopcraft, William Pilkinton, William Braine, Joseph Healey, William Reed

Boys

George Chambers
David Young

H.M.S *Terror*

Captain—Francis Rawdon Moira Crozier
Lieutenants—Edward Little (Commander: November 9th, 1846)
George Henry Hodgson
John Irving
Mates—Frederick John Hornby (Lieutenant: May 21st, 1846)
Robert Thomas (Lieutenant: April 24th, 1847)
Second Master—Gillies Alexander Macbean
Surgeon (Acting)—John Smart Peddie (Surgeon: December 2nd, 1845)
Assistant-Surgeon—Alexander Macdonald
Clerk in Charge—Edwin James Howard Helpman
Ice-Master (Acting)—Thomas Blanky

Warrant Officers
Boatswain—John Lane
Carpenter—Thomas Honey
Engineer—James Thompson

Petty Officers
Boatswain's Mate—Thomas Johnson
Carpenter's Mate—Alexander Wilson
Captain of the Forecastle—Reuben Male
Quartermasters—David Macdonald
John Kenley
William Rhodes
Caulker—Thomas Darlington
Blacksmith—Samuel Honey
Leading Stoker—John Torrington
Cook—John Diggle
Captain's Coxwain—John Wilson
Captain of the Maintop—Thomas R. Farr
Captain of the Foretop—Harry Peglar
Captain of the Hold—William Goddard
Caulker's Mate—Cornelius Hickey
Captain's Steward—Thomas Jopson
Gun-room Steward—Thomas Armitage
Subordinate Officers' Stewards—William Gibson
Edward Genge

Stokers—Luke Smith
William Johnson

Able Seamen

George J. Cann, William Strong, David Sims, John Bailey, William Jerry, Henry Sait, Alexander Berry, John Handford, John Bates, Samuel Crispe, Charles Johnson, William Shanks, David Leys, William Sinclair, George Kinnaird, Edwin Lawrence, Magnus Manson, James Walker, William Wentzall

Royal Marines

Sergeant—Solomon Tozer
Corporal—William Hedges
Privates—William Heather, Henry Wilkes, John Hammond, James Daly

Boys

Robert Golding
Thomas Evans

If you enjoyed **Fitzjames' story**, you might enjoy others of John's titles. Here's a sample of the first volume of The Heretic's Secret Trilogy

Heretic

"*...a brave book, an unsettling book, and one that is very much needed at this time.*"—The Globe and Mail

"*...astonishingly nuanced and masterfully told...*"—Quill & Quire

The Last Heretic

"Such are the heights of wickedness
to which men are driven by religion."
—Lucretius 99–55 B.C.

Villerouge-Termenès, August 24, 1321

"You will be the last to die," the black-clad priest said almost gleefully. "There are no more. Once you are dust, this land will be free from your foul heresy."

William Bélibaste forced his shattered mouth into a parody of a smile. "What you say, Master Inquisitor, may be true," he slurred, "but it has taken all the might of the Catholic Church more than one hundred years to kill a few thousand of us. Does that not show you the power of our ideas? When you examine your mind, is there not a tiny piece that says, 'Perhaps they were right?'"

The priest shook his head. "A hundred years is but a blink in God's eternity."

"And the momentary pain I face is nothing compared to the paradise to which I go. It is you I pity, facing endless repetitions of an ignorant life in the cesspit of this material world."

"We shall see what your pity is worth on the bonfire," the priest responded, angrily pushing Bélibaste forward through the archway into the bright courtyard of the castle at Villerouge-Termenès.

Bélibaste squinted in the sharp light, closed his eyes and raised his head to feel the sun's warmth on his face. He drew in a deep draft of air and caught a faint smell of lavender. It reminded him of his childhood, tending his father's flock of sheep among the limestone hills around his village. They had been happy days, before a life of loneliness, running and hiding. But he was content now, too.

If William had one regret, it was that he had not lived one hundred and fifteen years ago, before the armoured knights of the crusade and their compassionless inquisitor priests had thundered down on his people. It was difficult to imagine those wonderful days when men and women of the Elect could walk openly, meet and minister to their congregations; when they were welcomed everywhere, from the simplest village hearth to the court of the most powerful lord. It must have been as close as this evil, corrupt world had ever come to paradise. But it was a vanished world. The priest was right: William Bélibaste *was* the last of the Elect.

A push in the small of his back brought William back to the present. He opened his eyes to see the stake in front of him, surrounded by neatly tied bundles of dry logs, straw and vine cuttings. To one side, a hooded executioner stood holding a burning torch.

William stumbled on the rough cobbles, not through fear, but because his crushed left foot was twisted in at an awkward angle. Every hobbling step sent needles of pain shooting up his leg, but he would not give the priest or the watching crowd the satisfaction of showing it. He wore a coarse woollen tunic that stretched from his neck to his ankles and hid the livid scars where red-hot irons had seared his flesh. His arms were tied behind his back, but there was no need—both his shoulders had been so seriously dislocated that, even had his arms been free, he would not have had the strength to lift a spoon and feed himself. William also suspected that several of his fingers were broken.

As William approached the pyre, he was intrigued to see that the builders had thoughtfully shaped the bundles of sticks into a short staircase up to the stake.

"Do you renounce Satan and all his ways?" the priest intoned.

"Of course I do," William said, through his broken teeth. "I renounce Satan and all this worldly filth. And I renounce Satan's minion in Rome—the Pope and his corrupt Church."

A gasp ran through the watching crowd.

"So you admit, as you face an eternity of the torments of hell, that you are a Cathar Perfect, and that you have led others into this abominable heresy?"

"You call us 'Cathars' and the Elect 'Perfects', but to ourselves we are simply Good Men and Good Women, struggling to bring light into this darkness."

William found strength as he spoke. He forced himself to stand taller and look his inquisitor in the eye. "Together, we are Good Christians, preserving the old ways and offering hope. Your degenerate Church is putrid at the heart. It offers nothing but suffering and damnation."

William raised his gaze to address the men and women gathered behind his questioner. "You think you eat the body of Christ at Communion? How big was this Christ that his body can feed so many?"

The crowd shifted uncomfortably, but William heard a choked laugh and saw a few heads nod in agreement.

"You bow and scrape to priests and cardinals who drown in the filth of the material world. How can they lead you to anything but depravity? You worship idols and—"

"Enough!" The inquisitor's voice cut William off. "Enough of this evil! The Holy Inquisition is done with this verminous devil. I place him in the hands of the secular authorities to do with as they see fit."

The Mayor of Villerouge-Termenès stepped forward nervously. He would rather not do this, but he had no choice. The Inquisition could investigate, but it could not condemn. Although that decision was left to the secular authorities, it would be a brave man who refused to do the Inquisition's bidding.

"For the crimes of heresy, denying the divinity of Christ, consorting with devils, and seducing others into your evil ways, I sentence you, William Bélibaste, to death by burning."

Two men stepped forward and half led, half carried William up the pyre to the stake. There they bound him around the waist and chest so that he remained upright.

The men hurried down, leaving William alone.

"I shall pray for your misguided soul," the inquisitor intoned.

"And I yours," William replied.

The mayor nodded to the executioner, who walked around the pyre, thrusting his torch in among the dry kindling. Tiny yellow flames grasped eagerly at the straw and grew. They turned orange as they began to eat at the sticks.

William shivered. He began to recite the only prayer the Elect recognized.

Our Father who art in Heaven,

The flames gathered strength and moved toward William's feet.

Hallowed be Thy name.

His feet were burning, the skin blistering, the pain shooting up his legs.

Thy kingdom come,

The inquisitor's mouth was moving in prayer, but William heard only his own voice and the crackling of the hungry flames.

thy will be done on earth as it is in Heaven.

The pain moved higher as his robe burned. Searing, blinding pain.

Give us this day our supplementary bread,

William concentrated with all his might. The pain was transitory. It would pass. It *would* pass.

and remit our debts as we forgive our debtors.

William knew what he had to do. It had been drummed into every member of the Elect. He must wait and endure the agony as long as possible. And then, when the pain became too great, he had to breathe in the fire as deeply as he could. That would hasten the end.

And keep us from temptation

The bright flames raced hungrily up William's body.

and free us from evil.

His hair was alight.

Thine is the kingdom,

He closed his eyes and threw his head back.

the power and glory

Wait! he told himself.

William's heart was racing.

Wait!

He had stopped sweating and felt oddly cold.

Wait!

The agony engulfed him.

for ever and ever.

Wait!

Amen.

William thrust his head forward into the flames and drew them into his body with a single deep breath. The shock stopped his heart and he slumped forward. The charred ropes holding him upright gave way and his body collapsed into the roaring heart of the fire. The crusaders and the Inquisition had won—the last of the Elect was dead.

Continue **Heretic** by picking up your copy at any Amazon site

Reviews

"...this book is a true, well-crafted page-turner...If you've ever wondered how the continents and the particular slab of rock you live on came about, you will love this book. Even if you don't, you'll still love it. Highly recommended." Ghost Mountains and Vanished Continents: North America from Birth to Middle Age

- Amazon reviewer

"The extracts from the diary describe intimate wartime experiences of death and destruction in gruesomely dispassionate terms . . . it's a story of unmitigated horror, highlighting more than any textbook the futility of war . . . This unique compilation of firsthand impressions of the Great War will be a valuable resource for adults and teens with an interest in this turning point in world history." A Soldier's Sketchbook: The Illustrated First World War Diary of R. H. Rabjohn

- Kirkus Starred Review

"And in the Morning *joins other outstanding novels about the First World War —an invaluable resource for libraries and classrooms."*

- Jeffrey Canton, Quill & Quire

"Equal parts philosophical debate and historical fiction, this book... presents a compelling and thoughtful story of war that should appeal to a wide range of readers." Flames of the Tiger

- Quill & Quire

"This absorbing, well-crafted tale...is a haunting description of the tragedy and irony of war...In this vivid narrative, the awful cacophony of war comes to life...the skilled author succeeds without moralistic preaching in highlighting the harsh reality, the utter misery, and the heartbreak of war in this intricate but fascinating book." Four Steps to Death

-VOYA

For more information on John Wilson, visit:
http://www.johnwilsonauthor.com

A Selection of Books by John Wilson

Lands of Lost Content: A Memoir
Once upon a time, a shy kid from Skye almost drowned in nostalgia as he sat in the corner of a high-ceilinged room listening to fabulous tales of earthquakes, rebellion and crocodile hunting in a magical lost world. He grew up and survived his troubled teenage years in gang-ridden Paisley, field work in war-torn Rhodesia, near-death helicopter experiences in northern Canada and several encounters with bears. A mid-life crisis encouraged him to realize the importance of that childhood nostalgia and, using a life-long passion for history and his real-life adventures, he became a successful storyteller and author of fifty historical novels and non-fiction books for kids, teens and adults. He is still searching for that lost world, but this is the tale so far.

Ghost Mountains and Vanished Oceans: North America from Birth to Middle Age
This book is more than the story of how a continent formed over 4 billion years. Told in readable, entertaining prose and filled with personal and geological anecdotes, Ghost Mountains and Vanished Oceans tells the story of our world, and in doing so, it tells our story.

The Alchemist's Dream
"In this engrossing historical adventure, John Wilson paints a vivid picture of a bygone era involving Henry Hudson's fateful search for the elusive Northwest Passage, an alchemist, mysterious passengers, and enigmatic maps. The Alchemist's Dream fascinates from start to finish." (from the Governor General's Award jury). In the fall of 1669, the Nonsuch returns to London with a load of fur from Hudson Bay. It brings something else, too—the lost journal from Henry Hudson's tragic search for a passage to Cathay in 1611. In the hands of a greedy sailor, the journal is merely an object to sell. But for Robert Bylot—a once-great maritime explorer—the book is a painful reminder of a past he'd rather forget. As Bylot relives his memories of a plague-ridden city, of the mysterious alchemist John Dee, and of mutiny in the frozen wastes of Hudson Bay, an age-old mystery is both revealed and solved. Set against the thrilling backdrop of the quest for the Northwest Passage, The Alchemist's Dream is a riveting tale of exploration, ambition,

and betrayal. It is also available in significantly enlarged and more detailed version as **The Final Alchemy**.

The Third Act (soon to be a major live-action movie)
The Third Act deals with the intercultural struggles faced by Chinese students studying in North America in the present day and by an American playwright, Neil Peterson, caught up in the Nanjing Massacre of 1937. The contemporary story focuses on three Chinese friends (Tone, Pike and Theresa) who grapple in their own ways with the pressure to succeed in an unfamiliar culture. The historical tale concerns Peterson's effort to find his literary voice and save the woman he loves amidst the chaos and horror of the fall of Nanjing in the Second Sino-Japanese War. The two stories are tied together by a play that Peterson attempted to write after his return to America. The students in the present day get caught up in putting on a performance of the missing third act of Peterson's play, and in doing so they are forced to confront their cultural and personal pasts and futures.

The Ruined City: book 1 of The Golden Mask (The inspiration for the upcoming animated feature, Heroes of the Golden Mask)
Howard is a lonely, geeky tenth-grader dealing with a father who's had some kind of breakdown, a flaky, overprotective mother and frightening waking dreams. Then he meets Cate, a strange girl who convinces him that he is an Adept, which means he can communicate through dreams with other dimensions and, under certain circumstances, travel between them. Howard discovers that our world is only one of several dimensions swirling in time and space, and that one of the others, peopled by unimaginably powerful monsters, is approaching Earth for the first time in millennia. The last time the dimensions coincided, our world was saved by the breaking of a powerful golden mask in the Chinese city of Sanxingdui. Together, Howard and Cate travel through time and space, meeting other Adepts and avoiding lurking monsters, in a quest to find the three fragments of the golden mask and prevent it from falling into the wrong hands.

A Soldier's Sketchbook: The Illustrated First World War Diary of R. H. Rabjohn
A unique First World War diary, illustrated with more than a hundred stunning pencil sketches, for children learning history and also for adults interested in a new perspective on the war and authentic wartime artefacts.

Shot at Dawn
Sentenced to death for abandoning his unit, during the night before his execution, a soldier recalls the events leading up to his arrest.

Graves of Ice
The last survivor of Sir John Franklin's doomed search for the Northwest Passage remembers his hopes and fears as he sits awaiting a rescue that will never come.

And in the Morning: Somme 1916
Flames of the Tiger: Berlin 1945
Four Steps to Death: Stalingrad 1942
Lost in Spain: The Spanish Civil War 1936
Flags of War: Shiloh 1862
Battle Scars: Libby Prison 1865
Germania: The Roman Empire 9 A.D.
Where Soldiers Lie: India 1857

The Caught in Conflict Collection is an imprint of fast-paced, historically accurate, morally-complex quick reads for Adults and Teens. They can be read in any order.

Lost Cause (The SEVEN Series)
Steve travels to Spain and uncovers his late grandfather's involvement in the Spanish Civil War.

Find out more about these and other titles by John Wilson at **www.johnwilson.com**

All of John's 50 books are available through Amazon.

Made in the USA
Coppell, TX
09 September 2023

21419639R10154